ANALYTICAL GRAPHICS

BOOK SALE

ANALYTICAL GRAPHICS

GEORGE A. DINSMORE

Associate Professor of Civil Engineering
Lehigh University

D. VAN NOSTRAND COMPANY, INC.

Princeton, New Jersey   Toronto   London   Melbourne

For Mark

Van Nostrand Regional Offices: *New York, Chicago, San Francisco*

D. Van Nostrand Company, Ltd., *London*

D. Van Nostrand Company (Canada), Ltd., *Toronto*

D. Van Nostrand Australia Pty. Ltd., *Melbourne*

PRINTED IN THE UNITED STATES OF AMERICA

Preface

The title of this text reflects the fundamental objective of modern instruction in engineering graphics—to utilize the inherent simplicity of the graphical approach to develop the beginning student's capacity for analytical reasoning and thus help to prepare him to cope with the multitude of problems requiring engineering judgement which he will face throughout his educational and professional career. In light of this goal, the detailed content of a course becomes of secondary importance and is largely dictated by the types of problems which one elects to use as a teaching medium.

Along the way toward this primary objective, the nature of the subject matter and the demands of the engineering curricula make it desirable to seize the opportunity to give the students an appreciation of graphics as a systematic problem-solving tool, to enhance their ability to visualize in orthographic representation, to give them a thorough grounding in the theory of projection, and to develop good work habits.

The content of this text is entirely drawn from the traditional areas of engineering drawing and descriptive geometry, but is restricted to only those fundamental concepts which can fairly be considered a part of the common foundation for all branches of engineering. The subject matter is severely limited in scope to permit coverage in depth in a very brief course. Locus concepts previously mastered in plane geometry are taken as a point of departure. Many topics usually covered in engineering drawing courses, such as working drawings, assembly drawings, cams, fasteners and so on, are omitted entirely, as are such items as graphical statics and mathematics which have found their way into more leisurely courses in recent years. The treatment of dimensioning is rudimentary. On the other hand, the extensive coverage of projection theory, not only orthographic, but perspective, oblique, and rotational as well, contributes directly to depth of understanding of the fundamentals.

The text has been written with one central purpose in mind: To provide a tool for the successful teaching of undergraduates. It is intended to supplement but not replace the instructor. It is not designed as a reference work or a catch-all encyclopedia of drafting practice. The instructor must carry the primary responsibility for instructing the student in the techniques of instrument usage, sketching, and so on, and especially, in relating the theoretical presentation of the text to the real world of application.

The essence of the course is found in the problems. The workbook provides an economy of time in limiting the lost motion of laying out problems. The workbook problems are comparatively straight-forward in nature and should be considered to represent a minimum coverage. The more gifted students will find real challenge to their ingenuity in the problems provided in the text. These have been arranged in order of increasing difficulty at the end of each lesson. The specimen solutions in the text usually deal with general cases. The problems progress from the general case to the specific. In other words, the main idea of a lesson is fully explored before the related puzzles of the exceptional cases are encountered.

The notation adopted for the naming and orienting of auxiliary views should be viewed as a teaching device. It should be dropped when the students have mastered the process. Long experience has shown it to be an effective medium in aiding the student in visualizing the significance of the operations being performed in the construction of successive views. Similarly, the use of the datum plane in preference to folding lines merely reflects the personal preference of one accustomed to teaching by both systems.

The material has been arranged in 42 lessons suitable for the 3 credit-hour course presently offered by many universities. Topics are arranged to permit the optimum use of class time. Difficult groups of lessons are alternated with "breathers," followed by assignments requiring review of previous difficult material. Where possible the text explanations have been kept very concise to minimize out-of-class study time.

The instructional program is readily adaptable to the requirements of a one semester, 2 credit-hour course. It is suggested that Lessons 6, 10, 11, 12, 25, 27, 28, 38, and 39 be entirely omitted, and that Lessons 1 and 2, 14 and 26, 23 and 24, 29 and 30, 36 and 37, and 41 and 42 be combined, for a net of 27 lessons. This recommendation will be found to be in keeping with the stated objectives of the program.

The author wishes to acknowledge his deep appreciation of the efforts of his many colleagues at Lehigh University who contributed their suggestions and criticisms in the development of this material, and to the earlier writers in the field whose efforts contributed to the evolution of the philosophy embodied in this work.

GEORGE A. DINSMORE

Table of Contents

CONTENTS

[viii]

Introduction

The purpose of this course is to acquaint the student with the potential of graphical methods as a means of communication and analysis. It has often been said that the engineer must be capable of making himself understood in three languages: the written and spoken word, mathematics, and graphical representation. Each of the specialized branches of engineering has evolved a specific convention of practice in engineering drawing to meet its particular needs, but all of these practices are undergirded by the general theories of projection and visualization; these theories will be our main concern in the study of this text. With this foundation material under our belts, so to speak, we will find it a relatively simple matter to master the manners and methods of graphical communication employed in our own fields of specialization as the need arises.

This text has been designed first and foremost as a learning tool. The learning process requires a cooperative effort involving your instructor, the author, but—most of all— yourself. As you progress through the text, you will find that you are called upon to complete figures, provide original sketches, and answer numerous brief but leading questions. This sort of active participation on your part is the most effective form of study, and if you will faithfully assume your share of the responsibility, the experience can be very rewarding.

The format of the book allows the student to reassemble the text and illustrations in his own three-ring notebook, as he progresses through the course.

The subject matter is largely sequential in nature. It is important that one keep up to schedule and master each topic as it unfolds. The early lessons are principally concerned with visualization in multi-view orthographic projection. Visualization ability appears to be something we all are born with to a greater or lesser degree. The more fortunate of us will sail confidently through the problems, while those not so blessed will find it something of a struggle. Fortunately, however, everyone can learn to visualize, just as everybody can learn to play the piano, even if tone deaf. The so-called non-visual procedure presented in Lesson 6 provides a mechanical crutch which many students have found to be invaluable. Every teacher of graphics has seen many students struggling in seeming futility who suddenly seem to experience a flash of illumination in which everything falls into place, becoming clear and meaningful. But—make no mistake—this can come about only as the result of a sustained effort.

Students who have had previous training in mechanical drawing will have an advantage in the first several lessons, but they should be warned that this advantage is of short duration. The course progresses rapidly onto fresh ground.

The text is written in the tight, concise, and accurate style used in technical papers except that it is not nearly as impersonal. Much is implied that is not explicitly stated. The text needs not only to be read, it should be contemplated. You should go over each lesson at least three times. The first reading should be a rapid scan to get a feeling for the content. The second should be a leisurely and detailed perusal in which you analyze, probe, question, and challenge, taking nothing for granted. The final reading should follow the solution of assigned problems.

The author hopes that you will find the pride and satisfaction of solid accomplishment in this course, and that the habits of neatness, organization, accuracy, and logical thought which are among its essential elements will become inherent aspects of your professional career.

Lesson 1

Theory of Projection

All engineering drawings derive from the fundamental operation called *projection*. A picture plane or plane of projection (the terms are used interchangeably) is interposed between the observer and the object to be represented, be it point, line, plane, or solid. Sight lines or *visual rays* from the observer to the object pierce the plane to outline a *view* of the object upon it. If the sight lines are considered as converging to the eye of the observer, the image is a *perspective projection*. If the observer is assumed to be remote from the object, however, so that the rays do not converge but remain parallel, the resulting view is an *oblique projection* if the rays are inclined to the picture plane; or it is an *orthographic projection* if the rays are perpendicular to the picture plane.

Perspective and oblique views are used primarily for their pictorial effect, whereas orthographic multiview projection is the basic tool of graphical representation.

Perspective Projection

Perspective projection is illustrated in Figure 1–1. Sight lines from the observer at the *station point* (*SP*) produce a pleasing pictorial image similar to a photograph. All lines in the perspective appear foreshortened in proportion to their distances from the picture plane. This results in a convergence of the receding edges toward a *vanishing point* (*VP*) just as railroad tracks appear to converge at some distant point in the horizon of a landscape.

The inset shows the perspective view drawn in the plane of the page. The images of the surfaces parallel to the picture plane are geometrically similar to the corresponding faces of the object. All other surfaces appear distorted.

Perspective drawings are relatively difficult and time consuming to make and are quite inconvenient to dimension. They are used primarily in architectural rendering and advertising layout.

Oblique Projection

The same object is shown in an oblique projection in Figure 1–2. The direction of sight is approximately the same as for the perspective except that the observer is assumed to be infinitely distant. The image is less pleasing esthetically than the perspective, but does have the virtue that faces parallel to the picture plane appear in their true size and shape. By changing the direction of sight it is possible to obtain any desired degree of foreshortening of the receding edges and to control the angle which these edges make with the horizontal.

Oblique drawings are not particularly difficult to make and find considerable application in engineering work where a pictorial representation is required.

[3]

Orthographic Projection

The top, front, and right side orthographic views of the object are shown pictorially in Figure 1–3. They are the results of three separate and independent projections upon mutually perpendicular picture planes designated horizontal, frontal, and profile, respectively. Collectively, these are the *principal planes of projection*, and the views drawn upon them are the *principal views*. Other principal views may be drawn looking toward the bottom, rear, or left side of the object. These too would be projected upon horizontal, frontal, and profile planes. Drawn upon mutually perpendicular planes, any three of the six possible principal views are sufficient to describe completely the shape of virtually any object.

The visual rays used in developing an orthographic view are perpendicular to the plane of projection for the particular view. It follows that surfaces on the object which are parallel to the plane of projection must appear in true shape in that view, and as edges in the other two associated principal views. Such surfaces take the name of the picture plane to which they are parallel. Hence, one may refer to the *rear frontal face* of the object, or the *left profile face* and so on. Surfaces on the object which are inclined at an angle to the picture plane appear distorted in the principal views. Parallel lines on the object necessarily appear parallel in orthographic views regardless of their orientation with respect to the plane of projection.

It is helpful to think of the picture planes as being extended to intersect one another forming a transparent box enclosing the object as in Figure 1–4. The object is shown in the *normally oriented* position within the box; that is, its surfaces are parallel to the planes of projection. Obviously, if the object were rotated or tilted, the principal views would be materially altered. Such views possess pictorial qualities similar to perspective and oblique drawings, and will receive our careful attention in subsequent lessons.

In order to obtain the desired *multiview representation* in the plane of the paper showing the true shape of the three views simultaneously, the enclosing box is opened out into the frontal plane in the manner of Figure 1–5. The arrangement of views shown is that most commonly used for engineering drawings. The top view lies directly above the front view, the two sharing the dimension of width. The side view falls to the right (or left) of the front view, and with it shares the dimension of height. These common dimensions are conveyed between the adjacent views by fine-line *projectors*.

Because the depth dimension is common to the nonadjacent top and side views, it is necessary to transfer depth coordinates between these views by reference to some frontal plane selected to serve as a datum. Depth dimensions are measured perpendicular to that *datum plane* in both views. In this illustration the frontal datum plane (*FDP*) has been arbitrarily chosen through the rear face of the object. Depth measurements are made forward from the datum toward the front view.

The top and side views in the illustration are both projected from the front view and both contain the frontal datum plane perpendicular to the projectors drawn from the front view. It is natural that the top and side views be called *related views*, and that the front view be designated the *common view*.

The 45° inclined line shown in Figure 1–5 is a commonly used artificial device for conveniently transferring measurements between related principal views. Its use does not constitute legitimate projection and it is prudent to think always in terms of measurements being made from the datum plane even when it is the inclined line rather than the datum which is actually used in the construction. The datum planes in related views should always be clearly labeled as part of the final solution of classroom problems.

The solution to the illustrative problem is redrawn in Figure 1–6(a) to show the views in normal proximity. It is customary classroom practice to leave projectors and construction lines as part of the final drawing, but they should be very light so as not to detract from the outlines of the object. Hidden features are represented by dashed lines. It is desirable to select the views so as to minimize the number of hidden lines necessary. Thus, the arrangement of Figure 1–6(a) is to be preferred to that of Figure 1–6(b) for this particular object.

It is general practice to orient the object so that the width is the greatest dimension, and the depth the least. In addition, the view which conveys the most information as to overall shape description, sometimes called the *contour view*, is usually selected as the front view. These criteria frequently conflict with one another. One must exercise judgement so as to produce a drawing of the greatest possible clarity. In the present case, the several criteria were all satisfied in the original placement of the object in the transparent box and in the decision to represent the top, front, and right side views of the object in that orientation.

The *alternate position* of the principal views shown in Figure 1–6(c) finds occasional application in practice. The transparent box is visualized as opening out into the horizontal plane instead of the frontal, thus making the top view the common view, while the front and side views become the related views. Height coordinates are transferred between the related views as measurements from a horizontal datum plane (*HDP*) arbitrarily chosen, in this case, through the bottom surface of the object.

Sketching Principal Views

Figure 1–7 shows the pictorial of a block typical of the objects to be sketched in this lesson. The principal views are required. The solution is developed in the following sequence:

1. (Figure 1–7) On the pictorial sketch the smallest possible transparent rectangular box entirely enclosing the object.
2. Select the principal views to be drawn to give greatest clarity. "Block in" the faces of the enclosing box in those views.
3. Label the datum plane in the related views.
4. (Figure 1–8) Grid the visible surfaces of the enclosing box in the pictorial to show every significant dimension coordinate. Extend interior lines to the faces of the enclosing box as may be necessary to complete the grid.
5. Grid the blocked-in principal views to agree with the grid in the pictorial.
6. In the required views draw those faces of the object which lie in the surfaces of the enclosing box.
7. (Figure 1–9) Add other detail fully visible in the pictorial.
8. (Figure 1–10) Visualize hidden detail and add all hidden lines to the pictorial.
9. Add the hidden lines to the principal views.
10. Check each view to see that each surface is completely outlined, and that every grid line has been utilized. Study the principal views and visualize the pictorial from them.
11. Re-examine the original pictorial for possible alternative solutions.

After a little practice one should be able to visualize certain of the surfaces directly, and the greater portion of the grid may then be omitted.

In Figure 1–11 an alternative interpretation of the hidden portion of the object is shown. Sketch the associated principal views on the grid provided. Two additional possibilities are given in Figure 1–12. How would the principal views be modified by each of these variations? Would the principal views be subject to possible ambiguity? Visualize at least three additional possible solutions which are fully compatible with the original pictorial.

Hidden Line Technique

The rules governing the use of hidden lines are well illustrated in Figure 1–10. Dashes are about $\frac{1}{8}''$ long for a drawing of this size, and the spaces are roughly a third of that length. Examination of the views shows that:

TOP
1. A dashed line jumps a solid line.
2. A dashed line terminating at a solid line "touches out."
3. Dashed lines meet at hidden corners.

FRONT
4. A dashed line terminates with a space at a visible corner.

PICTORIAL
5. A dashed line passing behind a second dashed line jumps the second line.
6. Dashes are shortened when necessary to satisfy the above conditions.

Sketching Technique

The importance of doing neat, well-organized work cannot be overemphasized, and while the manipulative aspects of sketching are best learned in the classroom, a few general observations are in order.

A sketch should be thought of as being a close approximation of an instrument drawing. It must be entirely clear and legible beyond question. Linework should be dense, uniform, and cleancut. Viewed from a distance of several feet, important lines should stand out as forcefully as those in the printed illustrations for this lesson. Construction lines and projectors should not be erased, but should be very faint so as not to detract from the pictorial quality of the drawing. The proportions (if not the scale) of the original object or pictorial should be carefully maintained, and, although the views should be made as large as practicable, suitable margins and clearance between views should be maintained.

Engineering Lettering

The simplified block form of the upper-case alphabet illustrated in workbook Plate 3–1 is entirely satisfactory in most engineering applications. Spacing of the letters and words is largely a matter of common sense. Very light horizontal guide lines should always be used both above and below the lettering as suggested by Plate 4–1.

The order of stroking indicated on Plate 3–1 is suggested for pencil work only.

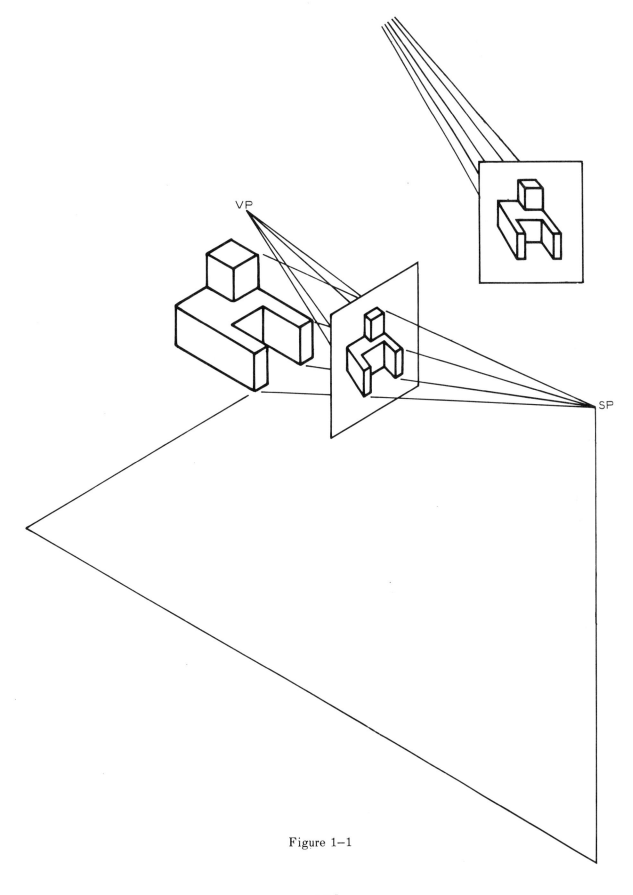

Figure 1–1

FIGURE 1–1

SUPPLEMENTARY NOTES

SUPPLEMENTARY NOTES

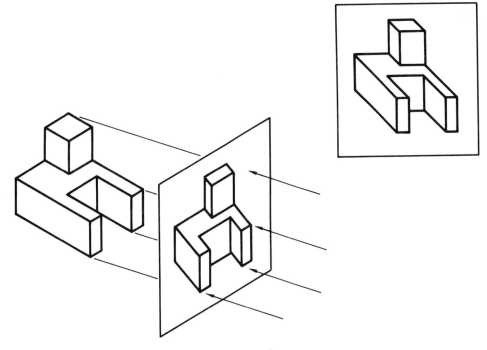

Figure 1–2

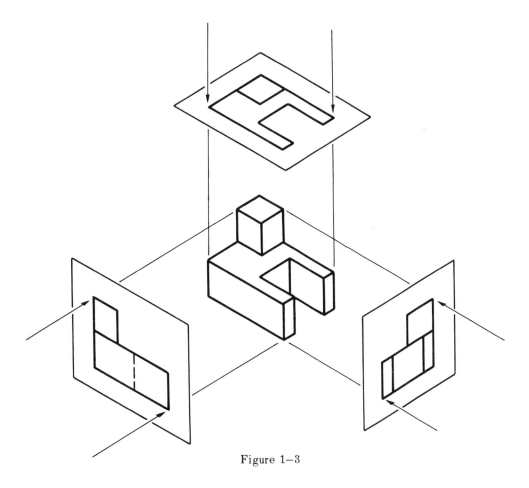

Figure 1–3

SUPPLEMENTARY NOTES

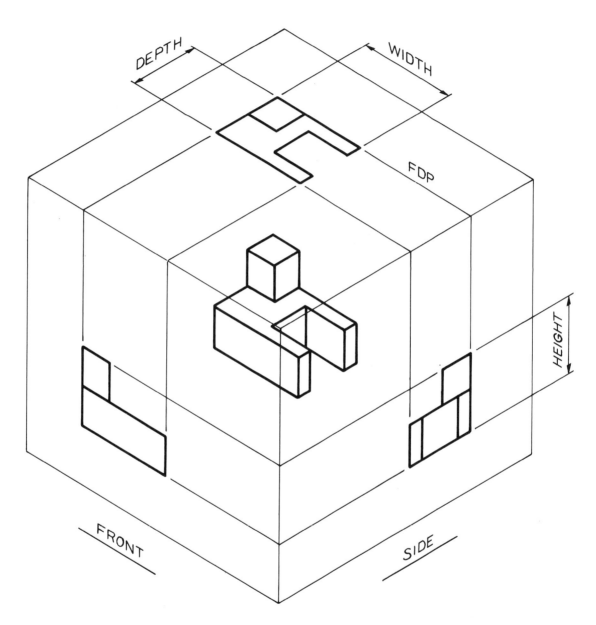

Figure 1–4

SUPPLEMENTARY NOTES

SUPPLEMENTARY NOTES

LESSON 1

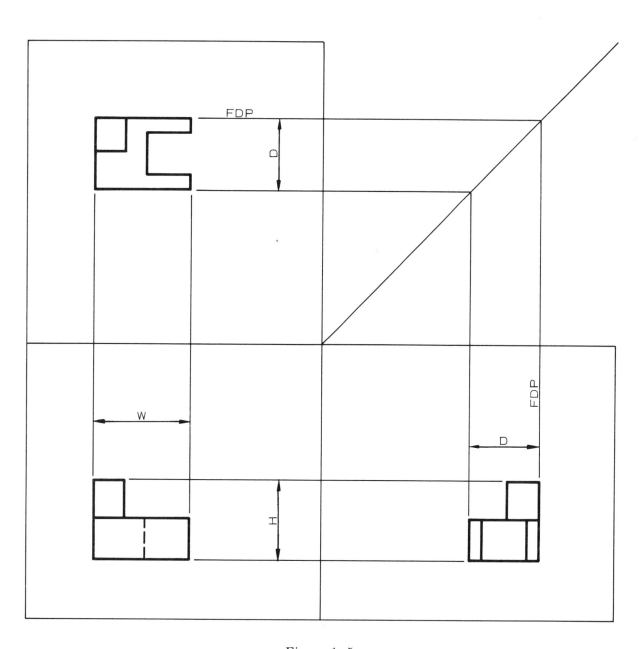

Figure 1–5

[13]

SUPPLEMENTARY NOTES

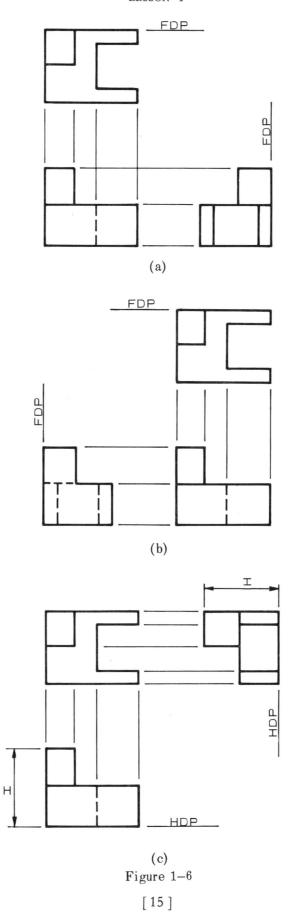

(a)

(b)

(c)

Figure 1–6

SUPPLEMENTARY NOTES

SUPPLEMENTARY NOTES

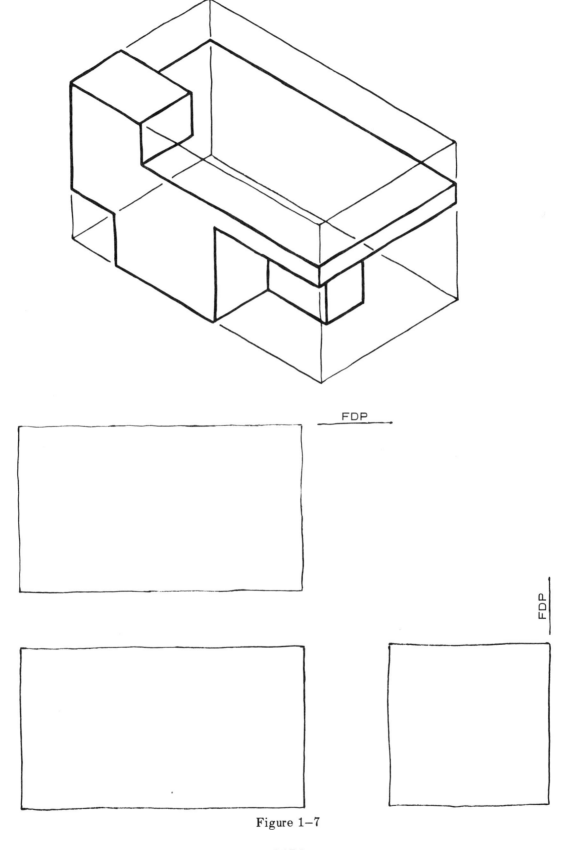

FDP

FDP

Figure 1–7

SUPPLEMENTARY NOTES

SUPPLEMENTARY NOTES

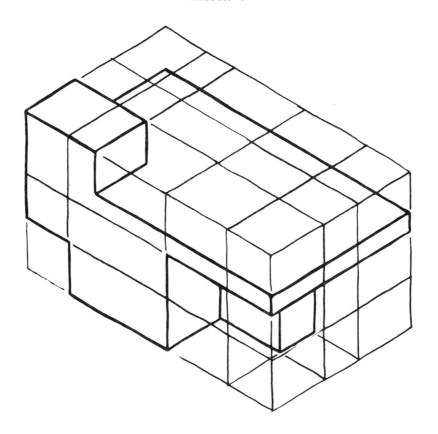

FDP

FDP

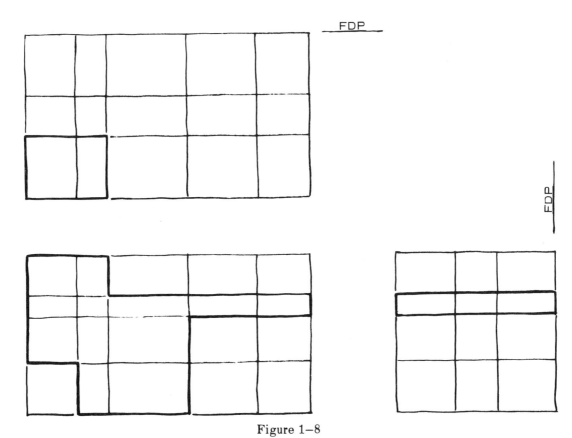

Figure 1–8

SUPPLEMENTARY NOTES

SUPPLEMENTARY NOTES

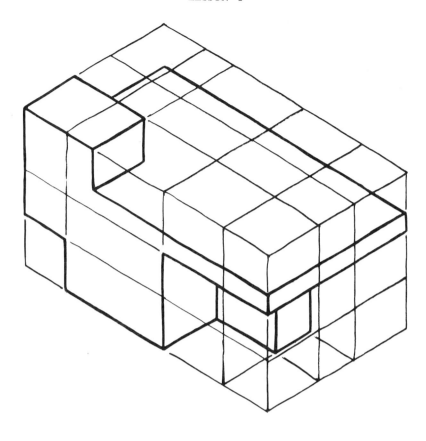

FDP

FDP

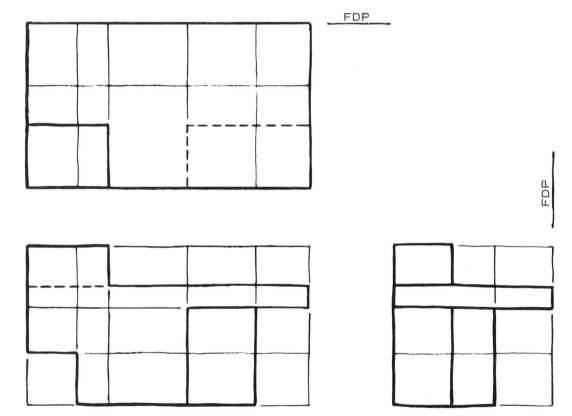

Figure 1-9

SUPPLEMENTARY NOTES

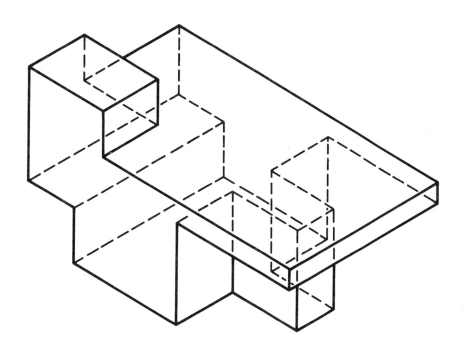

FDP

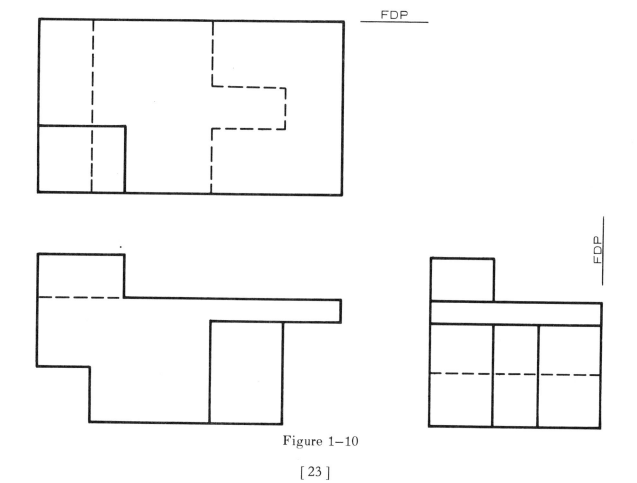

FDP

Figure 1–10

SUPPLEMENTARY NOTES

SUPPLEMENTARY NOTES

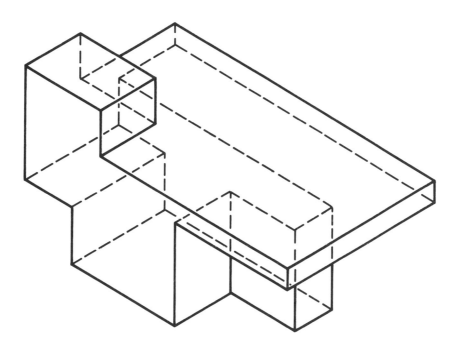

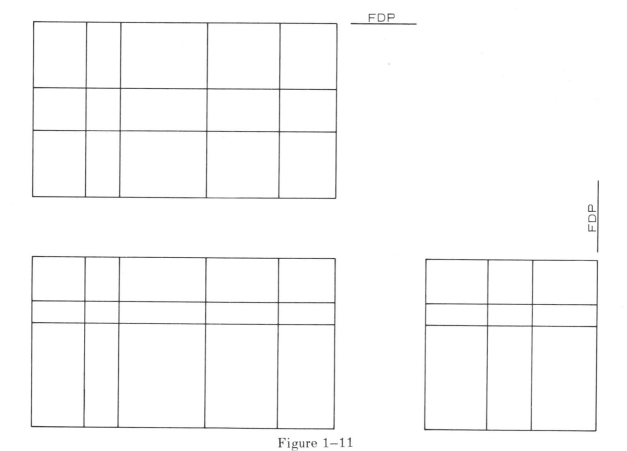

Figure 1–11

SUPPLEMENTARY NOTES

SUPPLEMENTARY NOTES

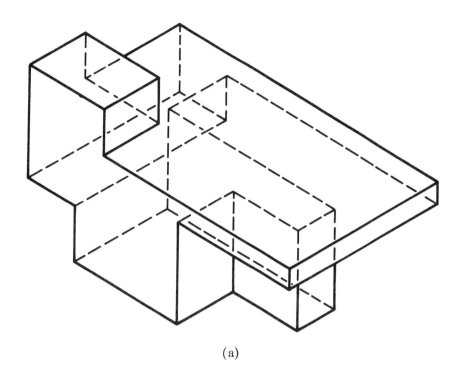

(a)

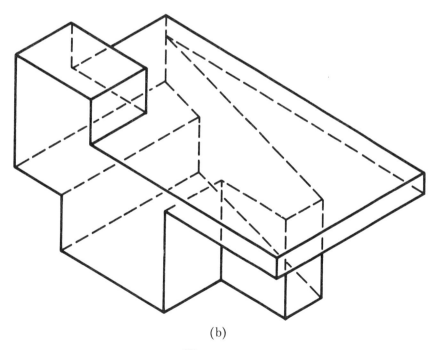

(b)

Figure 1–12

SUPPLEMENTARY NOTES

Exercises

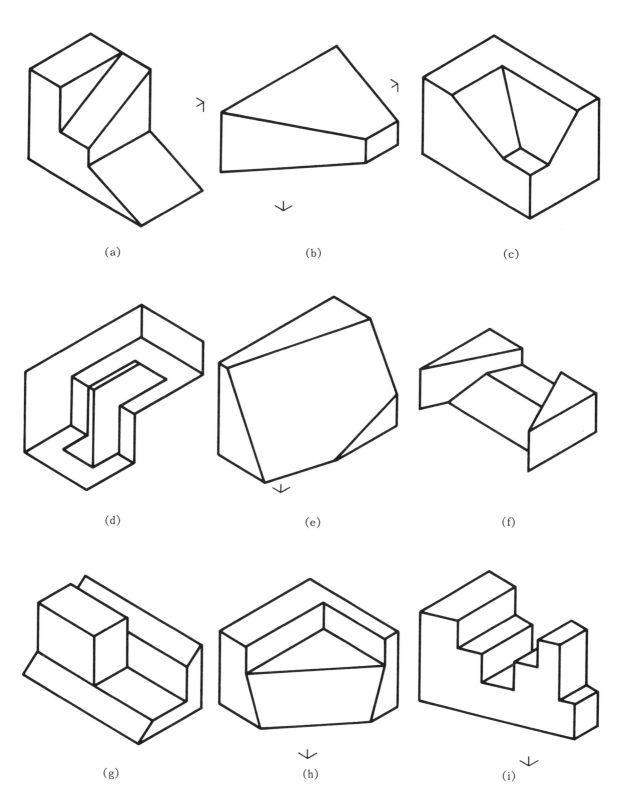

(a)

(b)

(c)

(d)

(e)

(f)

(g)

(h)

(i)

Ex. 1.1 Sketch the principal views of the blocks pictured. Use a full sheet of paper for each problem. Maintain the proportions of the given figures.

[29]

(a)   (b)   (c)

(d)   (e)   (f)

(g)   (h)   (i)

Ex. 1.2 Sketch the principal views of the blocks shown above. Use a full sheet for each problem.

Lesson 2

Identifying Points, Lines, and Surfaces

Numbering the corners of an object in the principal and pictorial views serves to prevent gross errors in projection and provides an easy means of identifying the edges and surfaces of an object. A mastery of this numbering system is essential to projection techniques which will be developed in future lessons.

In Figure 2–1 the pictorial and principal views of an object have been sketched. The corners of the object are to be numbered in all views to verify the projection. The numbering proceeds as follows:

1. Each corner in the pictorial (including hidden corners) is assigned a number.
2. The views are next numbered in a manner consistent with the pictorial. When two or more points appear superimposed, the point closer to the observer for the particular view is given first. For example, the vertical line at the left front edge of the object is labeled 3, 2 in the top view, signifying that point 3 lies above, that is, closer to the observer for the top view than point 2. Similarly in the front view we see the point view of a line connecting points 4 and 6 called 4, 6 to signify that 4 lies in front of 6, or closer to the observer's position for the front view. The side view has been left for you to number. Do this now, referring only to the pictorial.
3. The principal views having been numbered to agree with the pictorial; it only remains to check that they agree with one another by tracing the projectors between views. For example, 3, 4, 5, 6 must all lie on the same horizontal projector, 5, 6, 7, 8, 9 must all lie in the *FDP*, and so on. Note that the numbering checks only the location of points and not the visibility of lines or surfaces.

Since the numbers are merely a device to aid in the checking or solution of a problem, they are not considered to constitute a part of the solution. Hence, numbers should be written lightly (but legibly) so as not to detract from the appearance of the drawing.

Calling Points by Letter

Points are frequently designated by letters, particularly in problems dealing with lines and planes in space. In such problems the letters are essential to the statement of the problem and so constitute a part of the solution. They are written as capitals and carry the subscripts H, F, or P in the top, front, and side views, respectively.

Consistent Configuration

In our illustrative problem, Figure 2–1, all corners have now been identified by number. We may conveniently use those numbers to identify the edges of the object and, in turn, the surfaces bounded by those edges.

A surface is described by calling the corners sequentially. Thus, 2–3–7–8 or 2–8–7–3 are equally acceptable identifications of the vertical quadrilateral at the left end of the object. The sequence of numbers defining the boundary of a given surface must be consistent in all views. For example, if the boundary 2–3–7–8 were established in the pictorial view, but in one of the principal views these points were joined in the sequence 2–7–3–8, the solution is necessarily incorrect.

A further useful check is provided by the fact that lines parallel in space must necessarily appear parallel in any orthographic view of the lines. (Is the converse of the statement true?) Consider in Figure 2–1 the lines 2–3, 8–7, and 9–5 which are known from the pictorial to be parallel in space. Do they indeed appear parallel in each of the principal views?

Next let us examine the lines 3–7, 2–8, and 4–5 which appear parallel in the top view. Are any of these lines really parallel to one another? All three of these lines can be thought of as lying in a family of parallel planes. Sketch the outline or *trace* of those planes on the surface of the enclosing box in the pictorial view, and consider the appearance of those planes in the principal views.

It is both good practice and good sense to check the configuration of all surfaces and to examine all edges for parallelism upon completion of any drawing.

Sketching Curves

A convenient technique for sketching circular arcs and ellipses is illustrated in Figure 2–2. Here we are required to sketch the principal views of a truncated cylinder. The front view is first sketched in, followed by the outline of the enclosing square in the side view. The sides of the square are then divided by eye in the proportion 2–3–2 as indicated. Connecting these points produces a nearly perfect octagon which circumscribes the required circle. The same procedure is followed to produce the octagon circumscribing the ellipse in the top view. Carefully sketch in the curves, striving for tangency at the midpoint of each side of the octagons.

Note the use of center lines in this figure to indicate the symmetry of the object. Center lines are drawn dark so as to reproduce well, but are made thin to contrast with the outlines (often called *object lines*) of the figure. They are frequently omitted from pictorial drawings.

A method of treating irregular curves is shown in Figure 2–3. The surface of the enclosing box for the given pictorial is divided by eye into a uniform grid which is then reproduced in the required principal view. The intercepts of curve and grid are transferred from the given to required view. The grid may be further subdivided as indicated in the figure if additional points are desired. Transfer the intercepts in this figure and sketch in the curve. How would you extend this procedure to a case in which the given curve lay in a plane which was not parallel to one of the surfaces of the enclosing box?

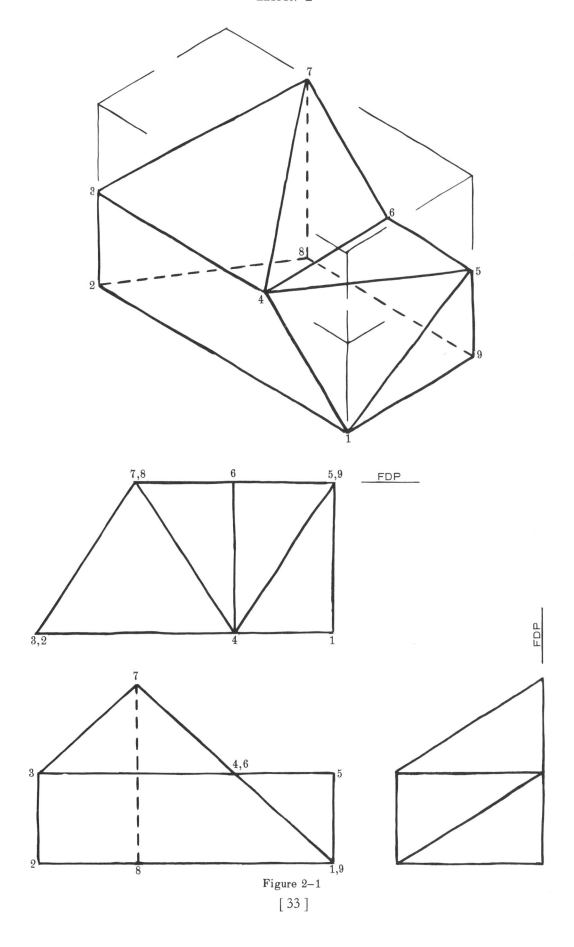

Figure 2–1

[33]

SUPPLEMENTARY NOTES

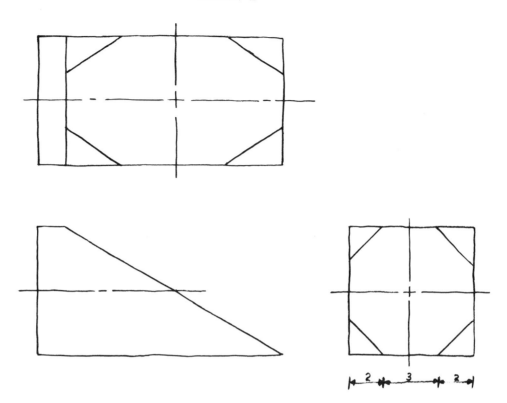

Figure 2–2

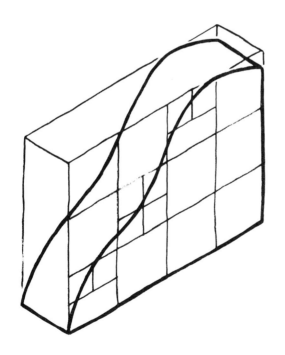

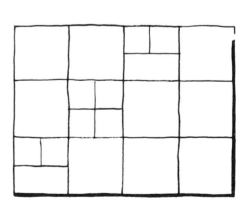

Figure 2–3

SUPPLEMENTARY NOTES

SUPPLEMENTARY NOTES

Exercises

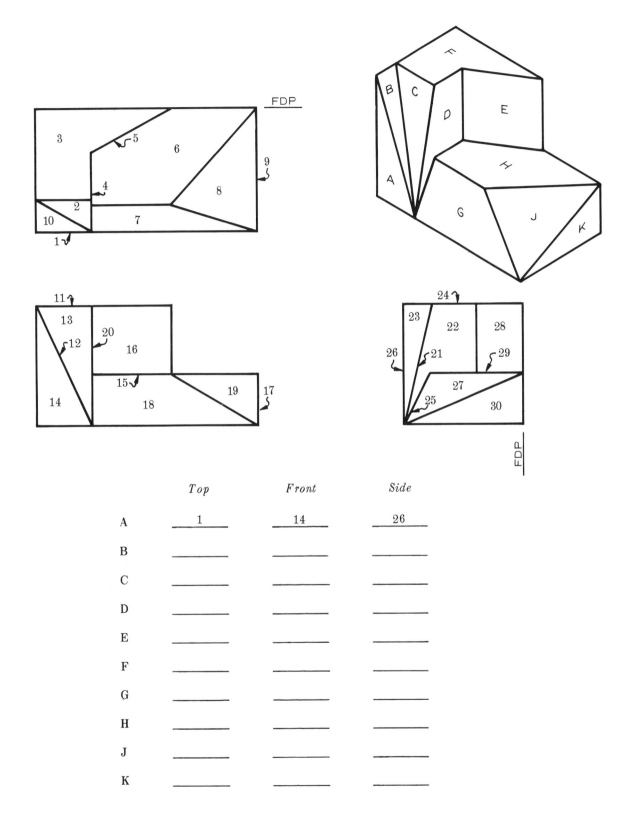

	Top	*Front*	*Side*
A	1	14	26
B			
C			
D			
E			
F			
G			
H			
J			
K			

Ex. 2.1   Enter in the table the numbers corresponding to the lettered surfaces.

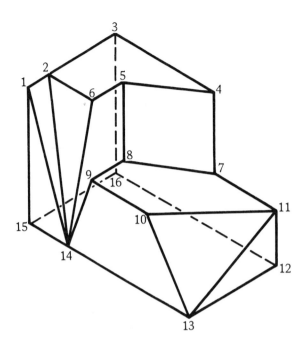

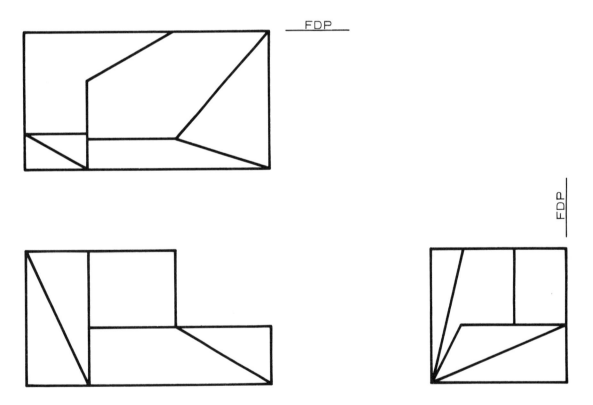

Ex. 2.2 Number the principal views to agree with the numbering given on the pictorial.

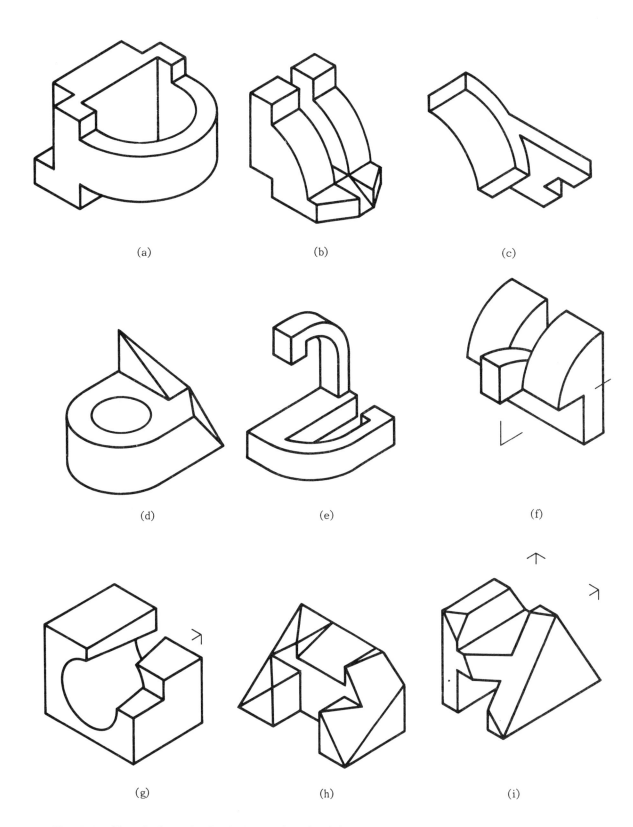

(a) (b) (c)

(d) (e) (f)

(g) (h) (i)

Ex. 2.3 Sketch the principal views of each of the objects shown above. Use a full sheet for each problem. Maintain the given proportions.

Lesson 3

Theory of Isometric Views

Thus far in our consideration of orthographic projection we have chosen to orient all objects with as many surfaces as possible parallel to the principal planes of projection. This was a choice of convenience. There is no such restriction imposed by theory. In later lessons we will learn to draw views of objects in any position, but one particular orientation is of immediate importance.

A cube with its faces parallel to the planes of projection is shown in Figure 3–1. If the position of the cube with respect to the principal planes is shifted so that the diagonal 1–2 appears as a point in the front view, the three principal views, top, front, and side, become those of Figure 3–2. The front view is unique. It is a pictorial and conveys a full shape description of the object. It is complete of itself and not dependent upon the adjacent views for interpretation. Because the edges of the cube make equal angles with the diagonal they also form equal angles with the plane of projection and are therefore equally foreshortened and appear at 120° to one another. Since the edges are all foreshortened by the same amount, the same scale applies to all. The view is called *isometric*, meaning literally, *equal measure*. The edges, and all lines parallel to them, are referred to as *isometric lines*. The surfaces of the cube are said to lie in *isometric planes*. It is important to note that nonisometric lines, for example the diagonals of the faces, do not appear in true proportion. Furthermore, all angles are distorted and can be drawn only by the use of offsets measured along isometric lines.

All of the pictorials given in the problems for Lessons 1 and 2 are isometric drawings. The shape of the object is quite immaterial. Each pictorial is drawn to an arbitrary scale which applies to each isometric line and these lines intersect at 120°. In each case if the object happened to be cubic, we would see the point view of one of its diagonals.

Isometric Sketching

In this lesson we will sketch the isometric pictorials of objects for which the principal views are given. Unfortunately it is not possible to spell out a specific sequence of steps which will lead to easiest or most rapid solution for all cases. However, the various factors which are to be considered can be brought out in a sample solution.

The top, front, and right side views of an object are given in Figure 3–3(a).

To develop the isometric sketch, the object is first imagined replaced by a rectangular block of the same overall height, width, and depth. The pictorial of the simple block is lightly sketched as in Figure 3.3(b) in the desired orientation. In this instance, the block is viewed so as to expose the upper, front, and right surfaces. The final view will be designated a *UFR isometric*.

From the given top view it is quite evident that the entire front-right portion of the block is cut away as in Figure 3–3(c). Next we may observe the easily identifiable top-horizontal and right-profile surfaces added in Figure 3–3(d), and then the upper-right rectangular portion removed to produce Figure 3–3(e).

[40]

Examining the given views, we find that surface 1–2–3–4–5–6–7 appears as an area in the front and side views, but not in the top. It must necessarily, then, show as an edge coincident with the first cut which was made. The outline of this area is therefore sketched on the front face of the original block, using offsets measured along the edges, and the corners are then projected back into the cut surface along isometric lines as shown in Figure 3–3(f).

The remaining surfaces should now be easily recognized. Add them to Figure 3–3(g) completing the final pictorial. Check the result by "reading" the isometric to verify the given views.

Are you satisfied that this pictorial was made in the best orientation for clarity? Make quick sketches of the *UFL* and *UBR* isometrics to satisfy yourself on this point.

Would a more natural appearance have been obtained if one set of isometric lines had been placed horizontal instead of vertical?

Do you think it necessary or desirable to show hidden lines on this pictorial? Can you suggest other objects for which it might be necessary to do so?

Sketching Circles in Isometric

Isometric views of circles are sketched by the same procedure used in the principal views. The isometric of the enclosing octagon is lightly drawn in and the required ellipse is then inscribed as illustrated in Figure 3–4.

In cases where the ellipse is to be drawn in a nonisometric plane, the regular octagon is first sketched on an isometric face and then projected into the required plane as shown in Figure 3–5. Sketch in the ellipse tangent to the sides of the inclined octagon at their midpoints.

In Figure 3–6 sketch the intersection of the given cylinder with the oblique plane containing points *a*, *b*, and *c*.

Cutting Plane Problems

The significance of lines and areas on pictorial and multiview drawings is well demonstrated by problems in which successive cutting planes are passed through a basic rectangular block, one portion of the object being discarded after each cut. The operations are most readily performed on an isometric drawing. When the isometric is completed, the steps can then be retraced in the principal views without undue difficulty.

To illustrate, consider the *UFL* isometric of the prism shown in Figure 3–7(a) with the location of points 1 through 7 given. It is desired to remove the following portions of the block: (a) the part above a plane through points 1–2–3; (b) the part to the left of a plane through points 3–4–6; (c) the part to the right of a plane through points 4–5–7.

The first cut is shown in Figure 3–7(b). Line 1–2 lies on the top surface of the original block, and 2–3 on the left face. The trace of the cutting plane on the right face, 1–*a*, must be parallel* to 2–3 since these lines are the intercepts of the same transverse plane with a pair of parallel planes. The trace on the front face is *a*–3.

The outline of the second cutting plane on the original block is 6–3–4–*b* in Figure 3–7(c). The intercepts 3–4 and 6–*b* are both frontal, and therefore are parallel. 6–3 and

---

* From the familiar theorem of solid geometry, "If a pair of parallel planes are cut by a third plane, the lines of intersection are parallel."

b–4 are horizontal and parallel. Since *b*–4 and 1–2 lie in the same horizontal plane, they must intersect in some point *c*, which is one point on the line of intersection of the two cutting planes. A second point on the line of intersection is 3, which was given as lying in both planes, and *c*–3 may be drawn.

The final cut is added in Figure 3–7(d). Line 4–7 is horizontal and intersects the top surface 1–7–*b*–*c* in line 7–*d*. Line 4–5 is frontal and intersects the front face of the object in line *e*–5. Points *d* and *e* each lie in both plane 4–5–7 and *a*–1–2–3. The line of intersection of these two planes, then, is *d*–*e*. Line 7–5, the trace of the cutting plane on the right profile face, completes the outline of the surface.

Test your understanding of this process by making one additional cut. Pass a plane through points 2–4–6 and discard the portion containing the front-left corner. Shade the cut surface.

In Figure 3–8 each of the above steps has been repeated in the orthographic views of the block. Follow the steps carefully, noting how points *a*, *b*, *c*, and *d* were established in all views. In the final figure add the cut through 2–4–6 as you did in the pictorial view.

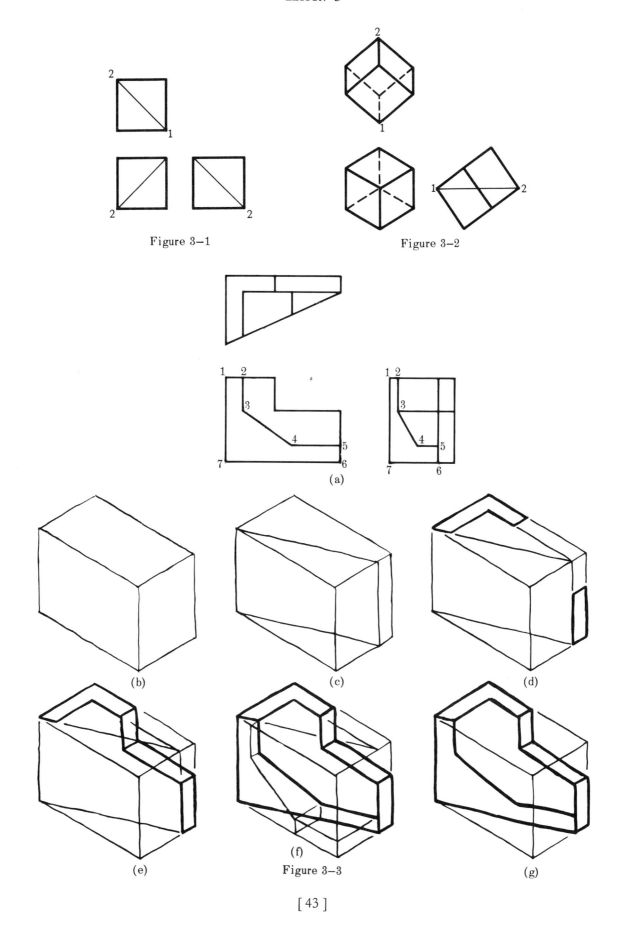

Figure 3-1

Figure 3-2

(a)

(b)

(c)

(d)

(e)

(f)

Figure 3-3

(g)

SUPPLEMENTARY NOTES

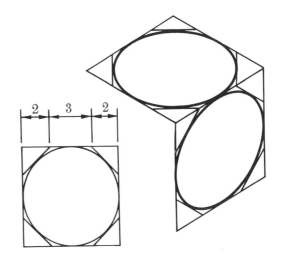

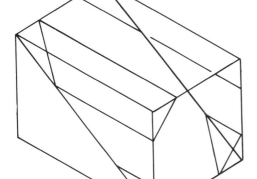

Figure 3–4

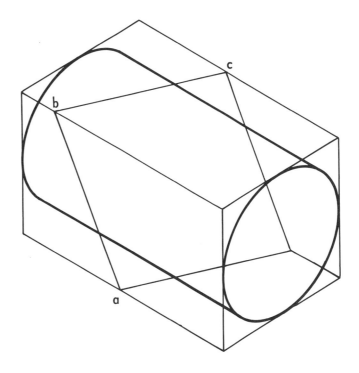

Figure 3–5

Figure 3–6

SUPPLEMENTARY NOTES

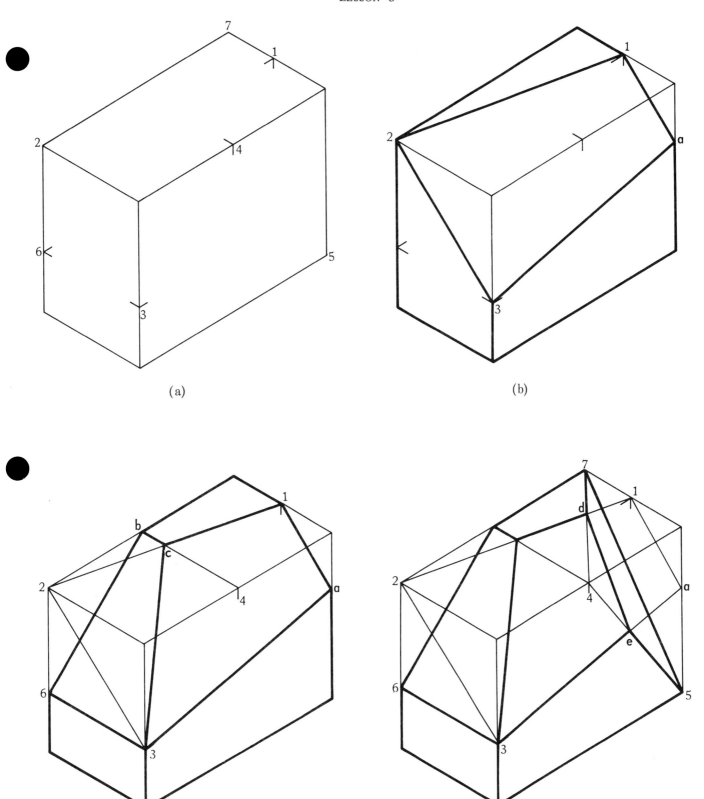

(a)

(b)

(c)

(d)

Figure 3–7

SUPPLEMENTARY NOTES

SUPPLEMENTARY NOTES

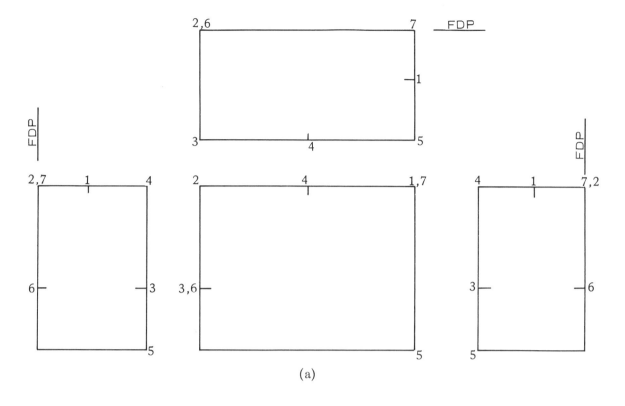

(a)

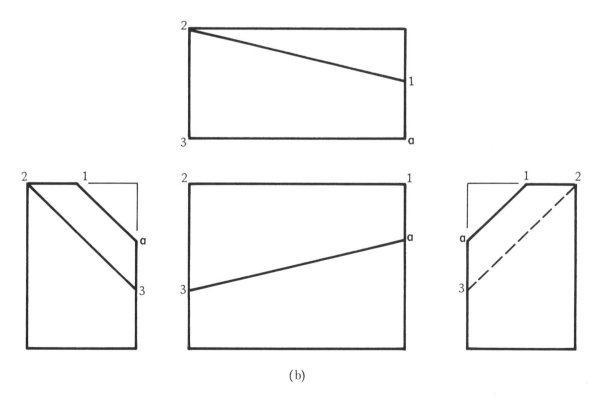

(b)

Figure 3—8

SUPPLEMENTARY NOTES

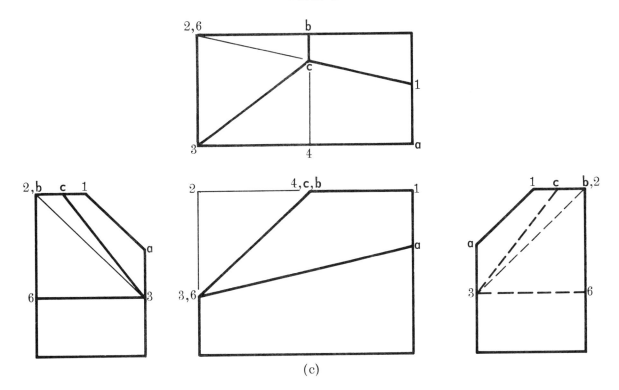

(c)

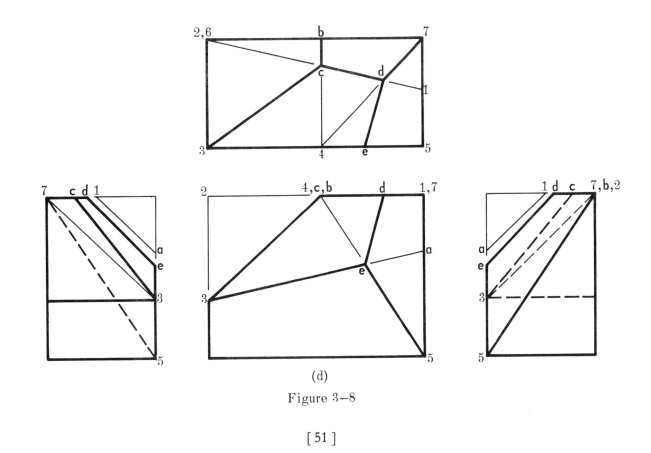

(d)

Figure 3–8

[51]

SUPPLEMENTARY NOTES

Exercises

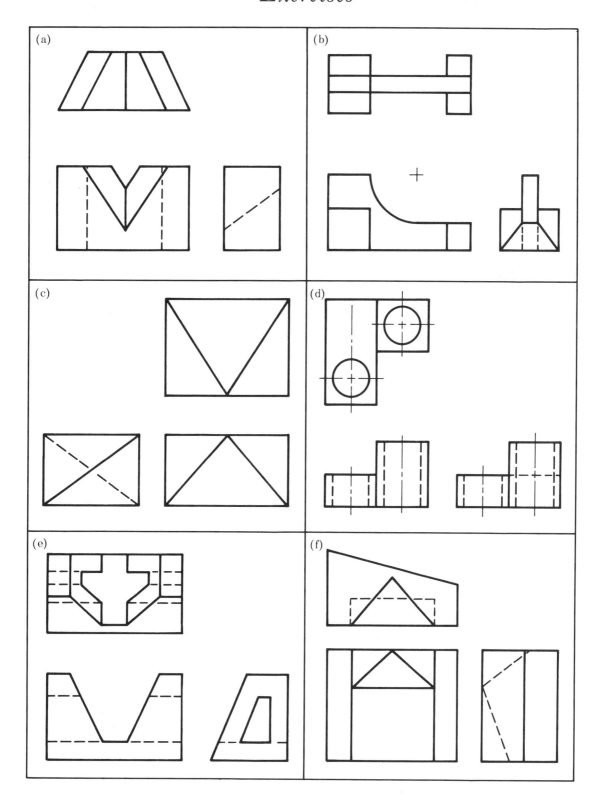

Ex. 3.1 Sketch a full-page isometric pictorial of each object above. Orient for greatest clarity. Number all corners on the pictorial, then directly on this sheet number the given views to conform.

[53]

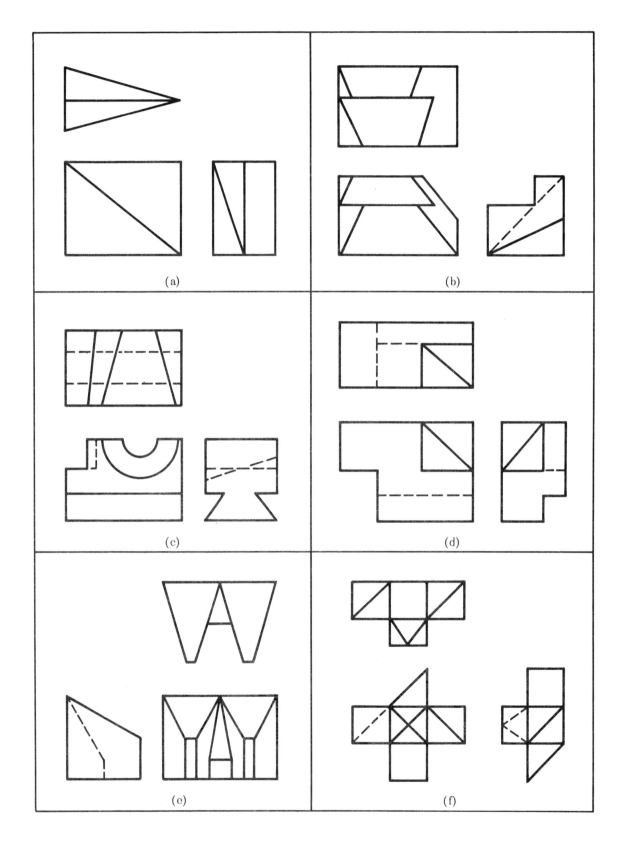

Ex. 3.2 Sketch a full page isometric pictorial of each object above. Orient for greatest clarity.

Ex. 3.3 Sketch an enlargement of the box at left on a full sheet maintaining the given proportions. Remove the portion of the block above a plane through points 1–3–6. Next remove the portion in front of a plane through 3–9–10. Finally, remove the portion below a plane through 1–8–10. Draw the final pictorial in red showing all hidden lines. On a separate sheet sketch the principal views of the original box and make the successive cuts as for the pictorial. Show the final views in red.

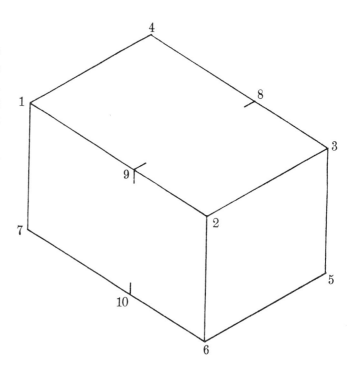

Ex. 3.4 Sketch an enlargement of the box at left on a full sheet maintaining the given proportions. Remove the upper-front portion cut away by a plane through points 1–3–8. Next remove the rear portion which is cut off by a plane through points 7–11–12. Finally, remove the portion to the left of a plane through points 5–9–10. Draw the final pictorial in red showing all hidden lines. On a separate sheet sketch the principal views of the original box and make the successive cuts as for the pictorial. Show the final views in red.

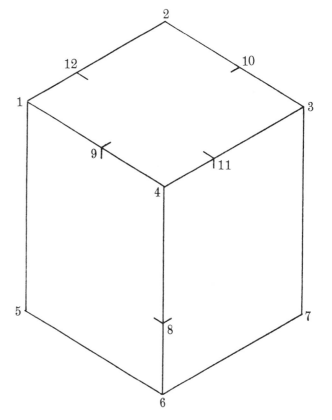

NOTE: You will find it easy to develop your own variations on the type of problems above. They are very effective for study and review.

Lesson 4

Classification of Planes and Lines

Before proceeding further in the study of objects, lines, and surfaces, we must learn the nomenclature of our subject, just as in the study of chemistry one must learn the symbols of the elements before going on to the writing of formulae.

In orthographic projection the views are imagined drawn on the surfaces of an enclosing glass box as illustrated in Lesson 1. The visible surfaces of this box are the *principal planes* of projection, and the views shown on them are the *principal views*. Lines and planes are classified by their relationships to the principal planes. For example (see page 57), normal planes are defined as being perpendicular to two principal planes. Normal planes are subdivided into horizontal, frontal, and profile. The top, front, and right side views of each are shown in the sketch. Notice that a normal plane shows true shape in one of the principal views and as an edge in the others.

Inclined planes are perpendicular to one principal plane, hence show as an edge in one principal view and true shape in none. The names of the inclined planes use the Greek prefix *ortho-*, meaning *perpendicular to*. Thus, an orthofrontal plane is one perpendicular to the frontal plane of projection and shows as an edge in the front view.

Study the following two pages until you are able to reproduce them. Drill yourself with such questions as: What kind of line shows as a point in the side view; shows *TL* (*true length*) in a top view; shows *TL* in two principal views; is parallel to one principal plane; is perpendicular to one principal plane? and so on. Adjacent to each of the classifications on these pages, list by number each line or surface shown in Figure 2–1 which belongs in the particular category. For example, 2–3–7–8 is an *OH* surface, and 7–8 is a *FP* line.

It is most important that your mastery of this nomenclature be complete because the terms will be used freely throughout the course.

CLASSIFICATION OF PLANES

NORMAL: Perpendicular to two principal planes

HORIZONTAL (H)

FRONTAL (F)

PROFILE (P)

[56]

INCLINED: Perpendicular to one principal plane

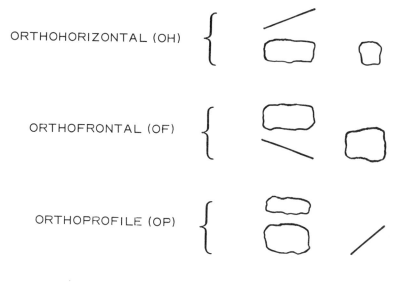

ORTHOHORIZONTAL (OH)

ORTHOFRONTAL (OF)

ORTHOPROFILE (OP)

OBLIQUE: Perpendicular to no principal plane

OBLIQUE (O)

CLASSIFICATION OF LINES

NORMAL: Parallel to two principal planes

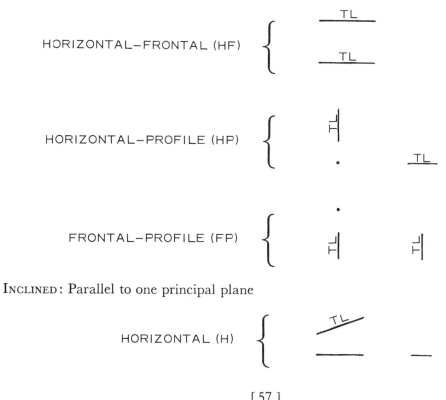

HORIZONTAL–FRONTAL (HF)

HORIZONTAL–PROFILE (HP)

FRONTAL–PROFILE (FP)

INCLINED: Parallel to one principal plane

HORIZONTAL (H)

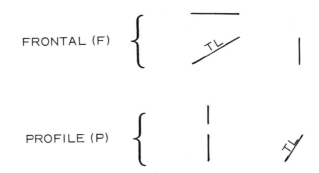

FRONTAL (F)

PROFILE (P)

Oblique: Parallel to no principal plane

OBLIQUE (O)　No view TL.

Direction of a Line

The direction of a line is described by the key letters of the principal directions, usually on the front view, given in the following sequence:

First		Second		Third	
Upward	(U)	Forward	(F)	Right	(R)
Downward	(D)	Backward	(B)	Left	(L)

The direction of a line AB is the direction from A to B, whereas the direction BA is the direction from B to A. If a line is not designated by letters or numbers, it is usual to read its direction from left to right.

By way of illustration the directions of several lines from Figure 2–1 are given below. Note that oblique lines have three direction designators; inclined lines have two; and normal lines, one. Complete the table.

Oblique line	Direction	Inclined line	Direction	Normal line	Direction
4–7	UBL	5–4	$-FL$	2–1	$--R$
3–7	UBR	4–1	$D-R$	9–1	$-F-$
7–3		1–5		4–3	
7–4		7–6		9–5	

Exercises

Ex. 4.1 Complete the statements below supplying the appropriate classification of each line of intersection.

An *H* plane intersects a *F* plane in a ___*HF*___ line.

H	*OF*	_____
H	*OP*	_____
H	*OH*	_____
F	*P*	_____
F	*OF*	_____
F	*OP*	_____
F	*OH*	_____
P	*H*	_____
P	*OF*	_____
P	*OP*	_____
P	*OH*	_____
OF	*OF*	_____
OF	*OP*	_____
OF	*OH*	_____
OP	*OP*	_____
OP	*OH*	_____
OH	*OH*	_____
O	*H*	_____
O	*F*	_____
O	*P*	_____
O	*OF*	___ or ___
O	*OP*	___ or ___
O	*OH*	___ or ___
O	*O*	___ , ___ , ___ or ___

Ex. 4.2 Supply the words necessary to complete the following statements:

The intersection of two normal planes is always a _____ line.

The intersection of an inclined plane with a normal plane is either a _____ line or a _____ line.

The intersection of an oblique plane with a normal plane is always a _____ line.

The intersection of two inclined planes is either a _____ line or a _____ line.

The intersection of two oblique planes is either a _____ line or a _____ line.

[59]

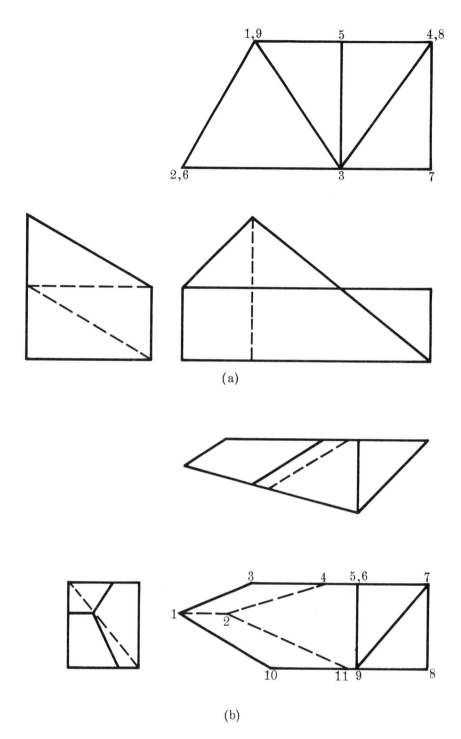

(a)

(b)

Ex. 4.3 Sketch the given views on a full sheet of paper. Supply the right side view. On a second sheet sketch the isometric pictorial. Number all corners on the pictorial and principal views to conform with the given numbers. Make a list of all numbered lines and planes, giving the classification of each line or plane and the direction of each line.

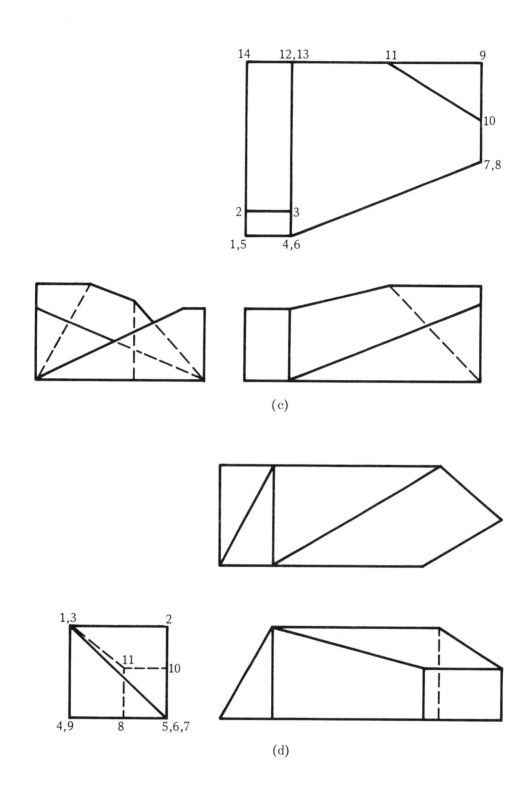

(c)

(d)

Lesson 5

Visualization of Missing View

Missing view problems are of little practical importance. Only on rare occasions does a puppy or small child chew up a third of a drawing to leave one faced with the problem of supplying a missing view. Such problems are unsurpassed, however, as a device for developing our powers of visualization and insight into the interrelation of orthographic views. Their solution often involves a complex combination of imagination, intuition, judgement, along with an element of luck. No two persons are likely to approach a problem in exactly the same way. In fact the same person may attack two successive problems in quite different ways. In many instances more than one solution may be possible for a problem and it is not uncommon for entirely unanticipated solutions to turn up from time to time.

It is possible to set down certain guide-lines to aid in the solution of missing view problems. These are best illustrated by example. A typical problem is shown in Figure 5–1(a). The top and front views are given and the right side view is required. The usual approach is to develop a complete pictorial sketch of the object and then to draw the missing view from visualization of the pictorial.

In the illustration our first step is to sketch the grid of the projectors in the missing view and to rough in a pictorial of the enclosing box oriented to show the faces corresponding to the principal views. In this instance the sketch is a *UFR* isometric. In complicated problems it may prove helpful to sketch the given views and the projector grid of the missing view lightly on the exposed surfaces of the pictorial. (Do this in Figure 5–1(a) and you may find that you can visualize the object immediately.)

Next let us examine the given views for points or lines which are uniquely defined. For example, we find that point *a* in the top view has only one possible corresponding position in the front view. Similarly, points *b* and *c* in the top view necessarily represent the lines *b–b'* and *c–c'*, respectively, in the front view. These points may be located in the pictorial with confidence.

Now we study the given views to discover any surfaces which can be identified in both views without ambiguity. In Figure 5–1 (b) we will probably first recognize triangle *b–d–e* lying on the top surface of the enclosing box, and the triangle *e–f–a* lying on its front face. These are shown sketched in on the pictorial.

Upon further inspection of the given views we may conclude that: *e–b–b'* must be *OH*; *e–b'–c* is *OF*; *e–c–a* is *O*; and, finally, that *c–c'–a* is *OH*. Add each of these surfaces to the pictorial and visualize the object. Check carefully to see that the pictorial agrees with the given principal views.

With the pictorial completed it should now be a routine exercise to complete the sketch of the missing view.

The final step is to number the pictorial completely, and from it, to number the three principal views. A check of the projection of the numbered points between the principal views will now provide a final verification of the solution.

The complete solution to the illustrative problem is shown in Figure 5–1(c). Because all surfaces of the object appeared to be uniquely defined in the given views, it is unlikely that any alternative solutions exist. However, a slight modification of the given views as shown in Figure 5–2 makes possible the existence of at least two solutions. Visualize both and sketch them on the figure. Compare these solutions with that obtained for the original problem.

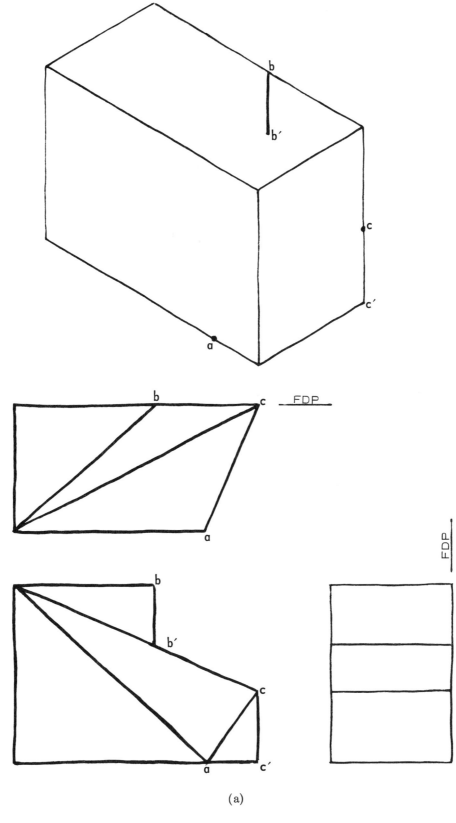

(a)

Figure 5—1

SUPPLEMENTARY NOTES

SUPPLEMENTARY NOTES

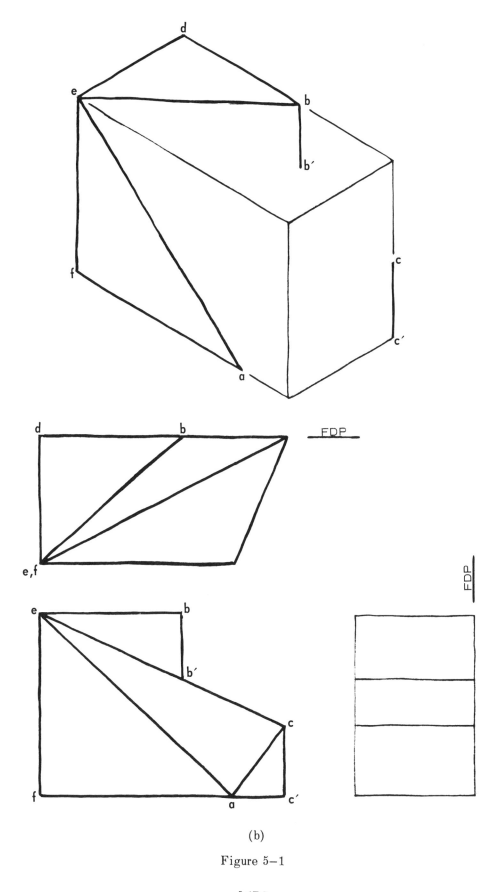

(b)

Figure 5–1

SUPPLEMENTARY NOTES

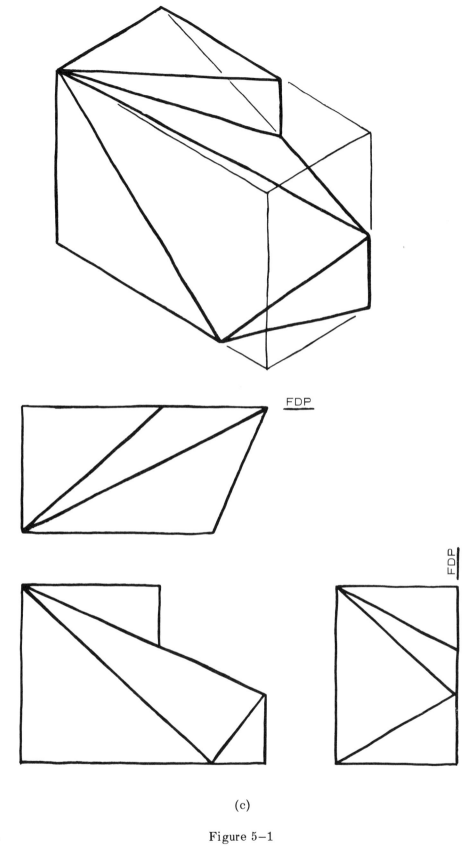

FDP

FDP

(c)

Figure 5-1

SUPPLEMENTARY NOTES

SUPPLEMENTARY NOTES

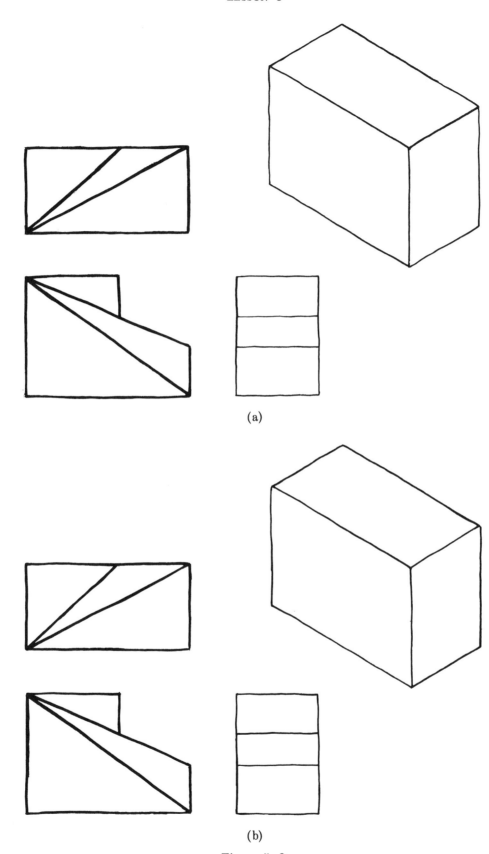

(a)

(b)

Figure 5–2

SUPPLEMENTARY NOTES

Exercises

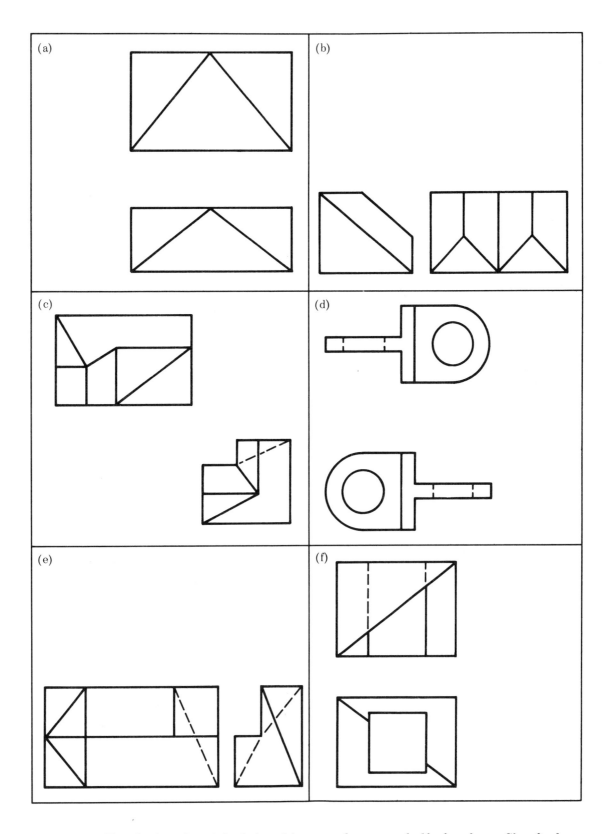

Ex. 5.1 Sketch the pictorial of the object on the upper half of a sheet. Sketch the principal views below. Check solution by numbering several corners.

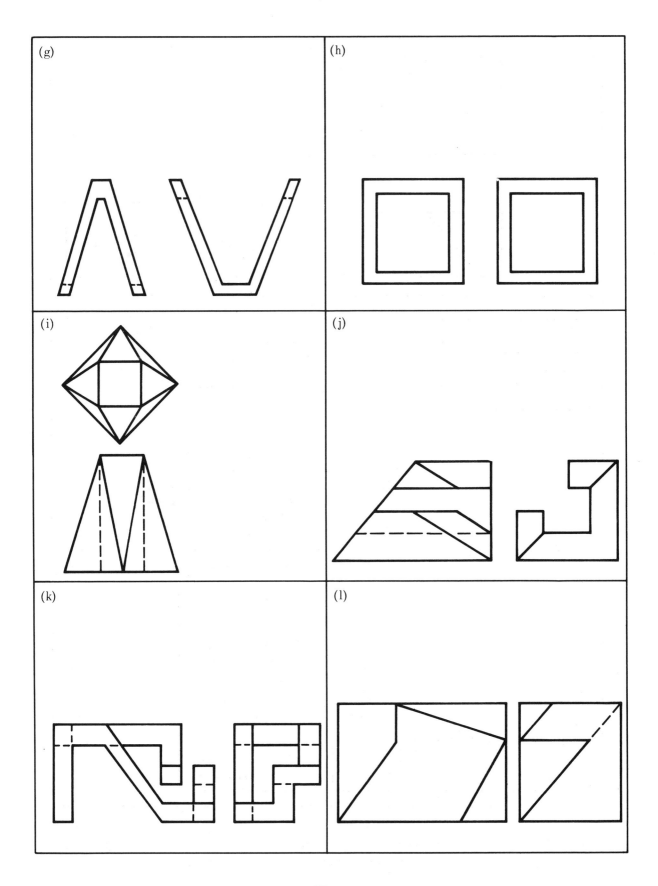

Lesson 6

Nonvisual Procedure for Missing View Problems

Objects having few normal faces are frequently difficult to visualize and do not lend themselves readily to pictorial sketching. In this lesson a nonvisual procedure is presented which leads to a valid solution for this type of problem.

The procedure may be summarized as follows:

1. Establish the grid for the required view.
2. Number the corners of a surface recognized as being visible in the required view. Project the numbers into that view and complete the outline of the surface.
3. Proceed in this manner until the visible surfaces are exhausted.
4. Identify and project each hidden surface and also surfaces which appear as edges in the same fashion until all surfaces have been carried into the missing view.
5. If along the way a contradiction develops in the numbering, return to step 2 and retrace the construction examining each numbered face for possible alternative interpretations until a compatible solution is found.
6. Visualize the object and attempt a pictorial sketch. It may help to distort the proportions.
7. Number the points on the pictorial to agree with the given and required views to check the solution.

The method is demonstrated for the problem shown in Figure 6–1(a). The top and front views of the object are given; the left side view is required. The grid for the required view is first established. Next, the direction of sight for that view is sketched in the given views. The sight lines in the front view immediately indicate that the orthofrontal faces numbered 1–2–3 and 1–4–5 must be visible in the required view. These surfaces are numbered in the given views. The numbers are projected onto the grid and the outlines of the surfaces are drawn.

In Figure 6–1 (b) the top view is next examined. The orthohorizontal face 1–3–7–4 is identified and carried into the missing view. The rear surface, also recognized as being orthohorizontal, allows alternative interpretations. It can be called either 1–2–*a*–*b*–5 or 1–2–6–5. If the first is selected, it eventually leads to a contradiction requiring a second attempt. In the illustration 1–2–6–5 has been chosen and carried into the required view.

All visible surfaces have now been projected, filling the entire outline of the object. All other faces must appear either as edges or as hidden outlines. Surface 3–7–8 is seen to be necessarily frontal and is next projected.

Several possible solutions exist for the right-hand portion. The more obvious is the interpretation that the upper surface consists of one orthofrontal and two oblique faces. Sketch this solution in Figure 6–1(c) and verify the result in a pictorial sketch.

A second solution would have the same portion consist of three orthofrontal and two orthohorizontal faces. Sketch this solution in Figure 6–1(d). Other possible solutions would be combinations of these.

Pictorials of both solutions are given in Figures 6–2(a) and 6–2(b), respectively.

Number these views to agree with the solutions which you obtained by the nonvisual procedure.

Examine the alternative choice offered for the rear orthohorizontal surface 1–2–*a*–*b*–5. Does a compatible solution exist?

In following the nonvisual procedure it has not been necessary to visualize the object as a whole until the problem was fully solved. It was only necessary that one be able to identify the individual surfaces of the object. This is not difficult after a little practice.

In most situations it is convenient to use a combination of methods in working missing view problems. The nonvisual projection of just one or two key surfaces will often provide sufficient insight into the problem such that one can jump to a pictorial sketch or even directly to the required view. In any event it is prudent to complete the numbering as a check.

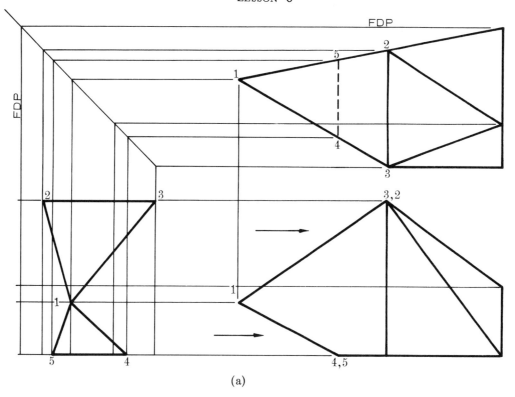

(a)

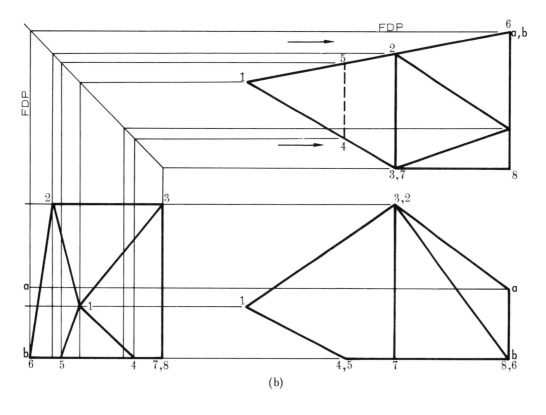

(b)

Figure 6–1

SUPPLEMENTARY NOTES

SUPPLEMENTARY NOTES

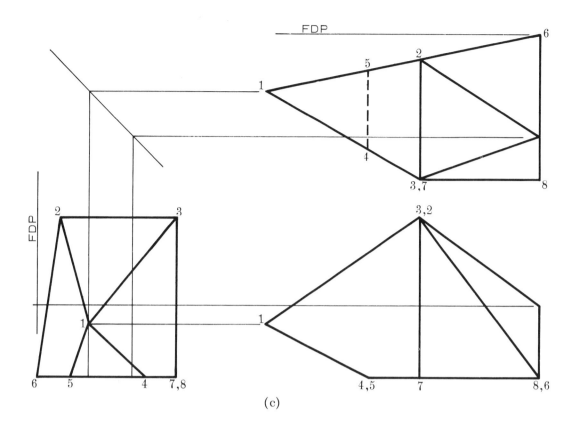

(c)

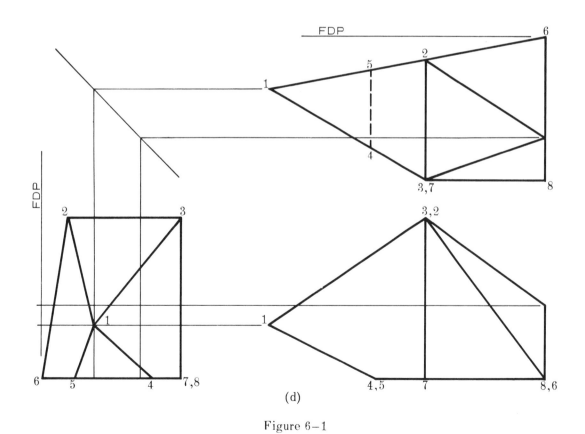

(d)

Figure 6–1

[79]

SUPPLEMENTARY NOTES

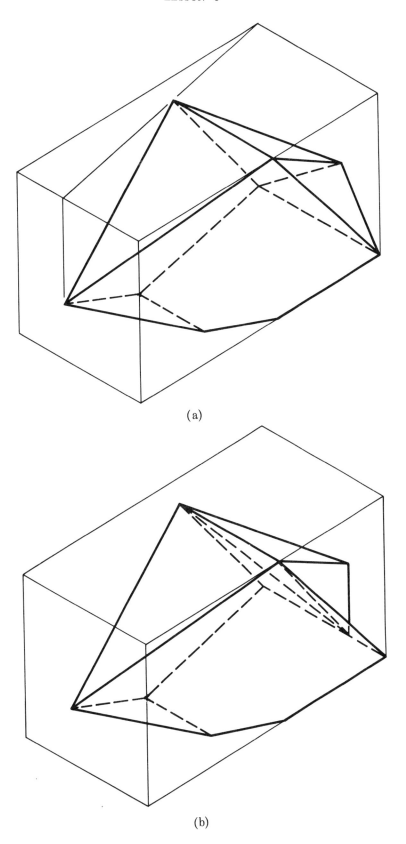

(a)

(b)

Figure 6-2

FIGURE 6–2

SUPPLEMENTARY NOTES

SUPPLEMENTARY NOTES

Exercises

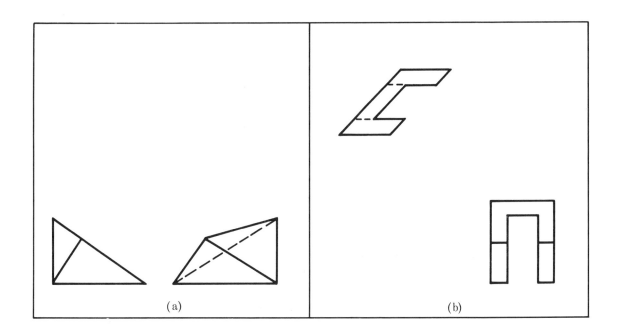

(a)   (b)

Ex. 6.1 Sketch the given views in the upper half of a sheet. Number corners and project by the nonvisual procedure to obtain the missing view. Verify your result by making a numbered pictorial sketch in the lower portion of the sheet.

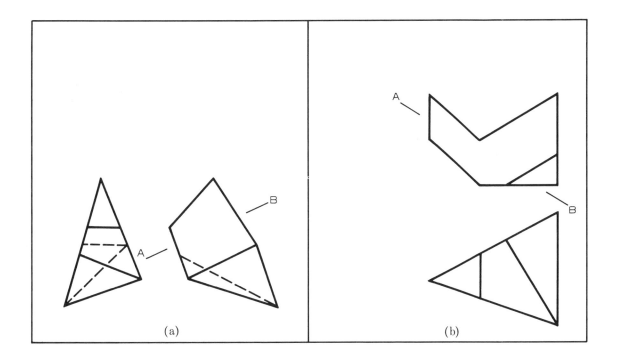

(a)   (b)

Ex. 6.2 Sketch the given views on a full sheet and solve for the missing view by the nonvisual procedure. Verify the solution in a full page numbered pictorial sketch. Redraw the pictorial showing the object as it would appear if cut by an inclined plane through line *AB* and the smaller part removed. Sketch the modified principal views.

[83]

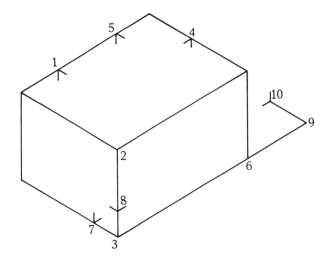

Ex. 6.3 Carefully sketch the pictorial of the box on the upper half of a sheet and the principal views on the lower. Portions of this block are to be cut away in successive steps. It is helpful to use pencils of different color for the various operations. Show each step in both the pictorial and principal views. The problem can be varied by changing the order of the steps. (a) Remove the portion in front of an *O* plane containing points 1–4–9. (b) Remove the portion to the left of an *OF* plane through points 5–8. (c) Remove the portion above an *OP* plane containing points 1–6.

Ex. 6.4 Same basic figure and general instructions as Ex. 6.3. The following successive cuts are to be made: (a) Remove the portion to the left of the *OH* plane through points 1–3. (b) Remove the portion above an *O* plane containing points 2–5–6. (c) Remove the portion in front of an *OH* plane through points 2–4. (d) Remove the portion in front of the *OP* plane through points 4–7. (e) Remove the portion behind an *O* plane containing the points 4–1–6.

Ex. 6.5 Same basic figure and general instructions as Ex. 6.3. The following successive cuts are to be made: (a) Remove the portion above an *O* plane containing points 1–8–10. (b) Remove the portion behind an *OH* plane through the points 1–9. (c) Remove the portion to the left of an *OF* plane through points 1–3.

Lesson 7

Geometric Constructions

Geometric constructions in orthographic views parallel those developed and proven in plane geometry with but one important difference. In Euclidean constructions the only working tools permitted were the compass and straight-edge, whereas in engineering graphics these are supplemented by triangles, T-square, dividers, scales, and protractor. Our objective in this lesson is to learn to use these tools to best advantage.

The triangle and T-square permit the instantaneous construction of parallels and perpendiculars, and the laying out of angles in increments of 15°. The dividers offer a rapid means of dividing lines or arcs into equal parts by trial and error. The manipulative techniques will be demonstrated in the classroom. The analytical aspects of the various constructions will be explored in the following paragraphs.

Tangencies

The fundamental property of lines tangent to a circle is that the tangent line is perpendicular to a radius drawn to the point of tangency. To construct a tangent to a circle from a point outside the circle, we simply draw the line of best fit, and then locate the exact point of tangency by turning a right angle through the center of the circle with our triangles. How many tangents can be drawn to a circle from a point outside the circle? On the circle? Inside the circle?

Circles are said to be tangent to one another when they are both tangent to the same line at the same point. The point of tangency lies on the line of centers of the two circles.

Two circles may have common tangents as indicated below. The tangents crossing the line of centers are called *internal tangents*, and the other pair *external tangents*.

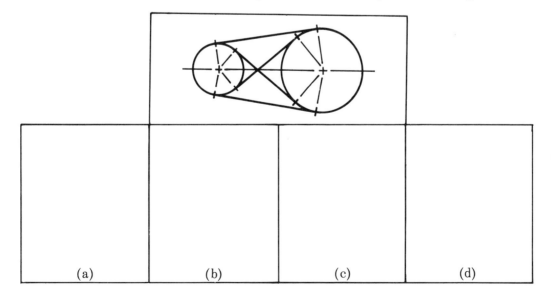

(a)   (b)   (c)   (d)

In the spaces provided, sketch two circles having: (a) one internal tangent and two external tangents; (b) two external and no internal tangents; (c) one internal and no external tangents; (d) no common tangents.

Locus Concepts in Plane Geometry

Most graphical constructions in engineering work stem from the fundamental concept of the line as a locus. For this reason it is sensible for us to review briefly the locus theorems from plane geometry.

1. The locus of a point at a specified distance from a given point is a circle having the given point as a center and the specified distance as a radius.
2. The locus of a point at a specified distance from a given line is a pair of lines, one on either side of the given line, each parallel to the given line, and at the specified distance from it.
3. The locus of a point which is equidistant from two given parallel lines is a line which is parallel to the given lines and midway between them.
4. The locus of a point equidistant from the sides of an angle is the line which bisects the angle.
5. The locus of a point equidistant from two given points is the line which is the perpendicular bisector of the line joining the two given points.
6. The locus of the right angle of a right triangle whose hypotenuse is given is a circle which has the given hypotenuse as one of its diameters.

Locus Analysis

From the above theorems deduce the loci and indicate each locus on the following sketches.

1. Find the locus of the center of a circle having radius r and which passes through point A.

2. Find the locus of the center of a circle of radius r which is tangent to the given line AB.

3. Find the locus of the midpoint of a chord of length l in a given circle O of radius r.

4. Find the locus of the center of a circle of radius r which is tangent to a given circle O of radius R.

5. Find the locus of the vertex of a triangle having given the base AB and the length l of the median on the base.

A———————B

6. Find the locus of the center of a circle which is tangent to a given circle O at a given point A on the circumference of the given circle.

A

7. Find the locus of the center of a circle tangent to the legs of angle ABC.

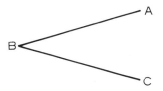

Practical problems usually involve finding points which satisfy two or more locus conditions. In the following brief exercises sketch the construction to find the required points. The simple analysis involved will prepare you for the problems of this lesson.

1. Locate the center of a circle passing through points A, B, and C.

2. Locate the centers of all circles of radius r which are tangent both to line AB and the circular arc O.

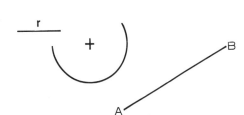

3. Locate a point on line AB which is equidistant from two points C and D which are not on the line

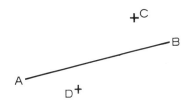

4. Locate a point on line LM which is equidistant from the sides of angle ABC.

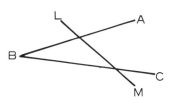

5. Locate the centers of all circles of radius *r* which are tangent to the given circles *O* and *O'*

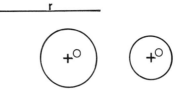

6. Locate the vertex *C* of triangle *ABC*, given side *AB* and the median *m* on *AB*, and the altitude *a* on *BC*.

7. Locate the center of the inscribed circle in an isosceles triangle *ABC* given the base *AB* and *r*, the radius of the circumscribed circle.

Locus in Three Dimensions

In later lessons we shall have occasion to use locus concepts drawn from solid geometry. The pertinent theorems are stated here for future reference.

1. The locus of a point at a specified distance from a given point is the surface of a sphere which has its center at the given point and a radius equal to the specified distance.

2. The locus of a point at a specified distance from a given line is the surface of a circular cylinder (all right sections are circles) whose axis is the given line and whose radius is the specified distance.

3. The locus of a point which is equidistant from a given pair of parallel lines is a plane parallel to the lines and which passes through the midpoint of, and is perpendicular to, a line which connects the given lines and is perpendicular to them. (Illustrate this theorem by a sketch in the margin. Show the end view of the parallel lines.)

4. The locus of a point equidistant from the sides of a dihedral angle is the plane which bisects the angle.

5. The locus of a point equidistant from two given points is a plane through the midpoint of, and perpendicular to, the line joining the given points.

6. The locus of the right angle of a right triangle having a given hypotenuse is the surface of a sphere having the given hypotenuse as one of its diameters.

7. The locus of a line parallel to a given line and at a specified distance from that line is the surface of a circular cylinder having the specified distance as its radius.

8. The locus of a line through a given point on a given line which makes a specified angle with the given line is a circular cone (two nappes) with its vertex at the given point, its axis coincident with the given line, and its vertex angle equal to twice the specified angle.

9. The locus of a line through a given point which makes a specified angle with a given plane is a right circular cone whose vertex is the given point, whose axis is perpendicular to the given plane, and whose base angle is equal to the specified angle.

[88]

Exercises

Where tangencies exist in each of the following problems, indicate the point of tangency with a $\frac{1}{8}''$ tic mark perpendicular to the tangent.

Ex. 7.1 Without using dividers or protractor, construct a regular octagon $1\frac{1}{2}''$ on a side such that one axis of symmetry is inclined to the T-square at 30°.

Ex. 7.2 The sides of a regular hexagon are each $2''$ long and two of them are T-square lines. Erect perpendiculars to the sides at the third points and draw the small hexagon formed by these lines. Calculate the ratio of the area of the small to that of the large hexagon.

Ex. 7.3 Construct a right triangle whose hypotenuse is a $5''$ ortho-T-square line. The altitude to the hypotenuse is to be equal to the median drawn to that side. Inscribe a circle in the triangle.

Ex. 7.4 Construct a triangle with sides $2\frac{1}{2}''$, $3\frac{1}{2}''$, and $4''$ long. Extend the sides to the edges of the sheet. Construct all possible arcs of $\frac{3}{4}''$ radius tangent to each pair of lines.

Ex. 7.5 Two circles have their centers $3''$ apart on a T-square line. The diameter of one is $2''$, and that of the other is $1\frac{1}{4}''$. Construct all possible arcs of $2\frac{1}{2}''$ radius tangent to both circles.

Ex. 7.6 *AB*, a $6''$ T-square line, is the hypotenuse of a right triangle *ABC*. Side *AC* is $\frac{3}{5}$ the length of *AB*. Let *C* be the center of a $2\frac{1}{2}''$ diameter circle and *B* the center of a $1''$ diameter circle. From *A* construct the tangents to circle *C*, then join circles *B* and *C* with all possible common tangent lines.

Ex. 7.7 The equal legs of an isosceles triangle are $3\frac{1}{2}''$ long. The altitudes to the equal legs are $2\frac{1}{2}''$. From the midpoint of one leg construct a line making a 30° angle with the base extended. Drop perpendiculars from the three vertices to intersect this line in points *A*, *B* and *C*. Divide the base of the triangle into segments proportional to *AB* and *BC*.

Ex. 7.8 On the upper half of the sheet draw an irregular pentagon inscribed in a $4''$ diameter circle. On the lower half, without use of scale or protractor, reproduce the pentagon $\frac{3}{4}$ size and rotated 60° clockwise.

Lesson 8

Construction of Missing Views

The exercises in this lesson provide additional practice in the use of drawing instruments. Strive for top quality work. Drawings should be clean and bright. Linework should be dark, crisp, and uniform in both instrument and freehand work. Keep triangles and T-square clean at all times, and, if you are troubled by sweaty hands, always keep a piece of scrap paper under your palm while working. This is a good time to check your pencil sharpening technique with your instructor to be sure that you are getting perfectly conical points.

The analytical procedures required for the problems in this lesson are the same as those already presented in Lessons 5 and 6. It is suggested that you review this material before starting on the current assignment.

Exercises

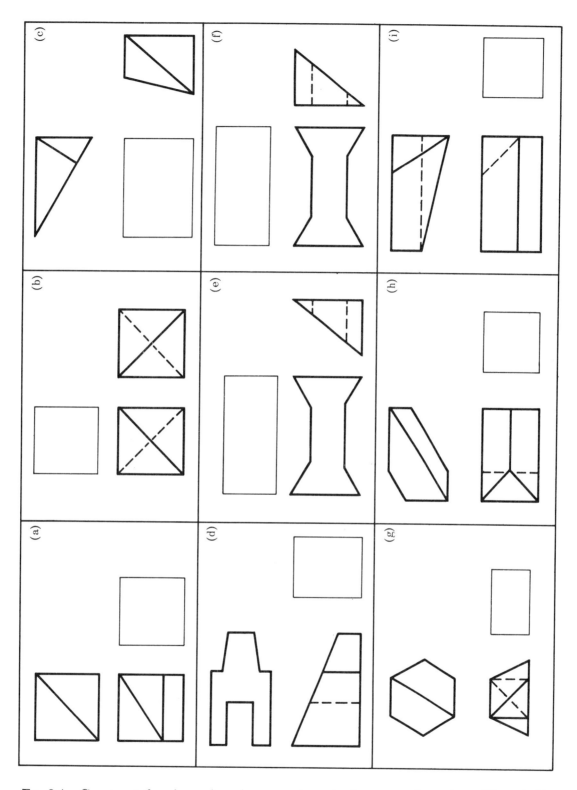

Ex. 8.1 Construct the given views in approximately the proportions given. Use a half page for each layout. Be sure corresponding points are in alignment. Construct the third principal view. Choose convenient orientation. Make a pictorial sketch on the other half of the sheet.

[91]

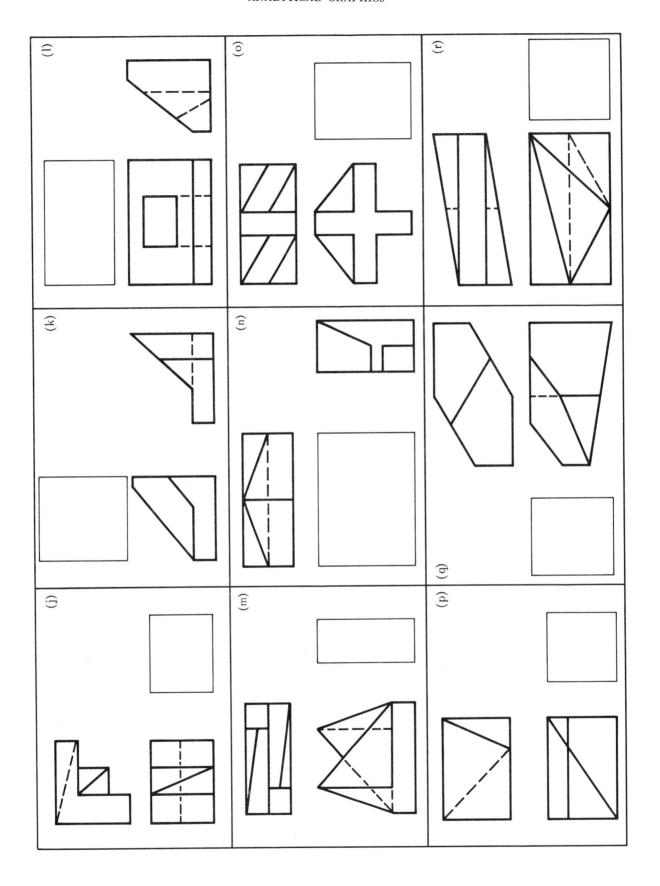

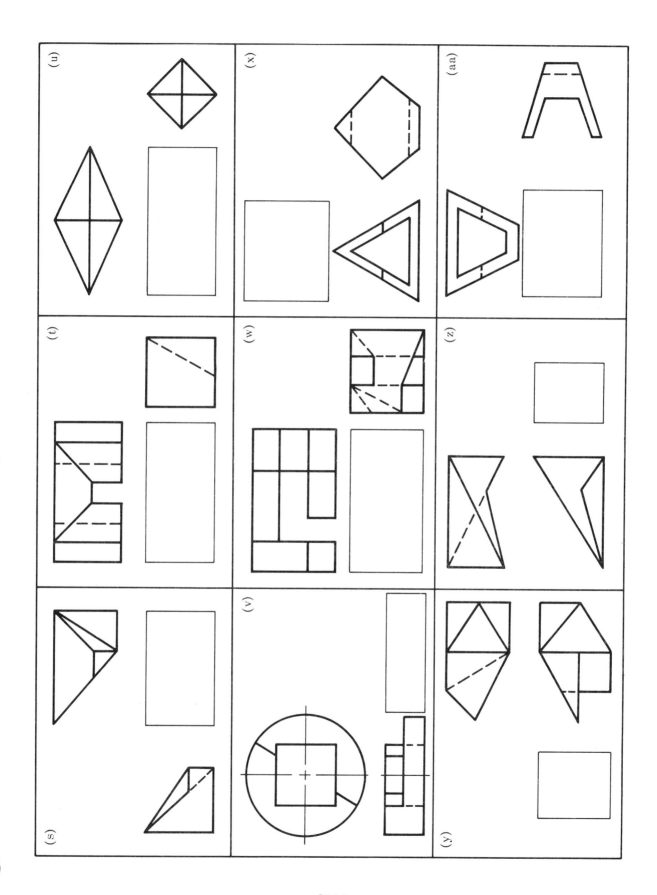

Lesson 9

Ellipse by Projection

The ellipse is the most commonly recurring curve in practical graphics. The method for obtaining an ellipse by direct projection is illustrated in Figure 9–1. We are given the front and right side views of a truncated right cylinder, the top view being required. As is usually the case with symmetrical objects, the frontal datum plane is selected through the center line of the object, and projectors are conveyed from the side view to the front view and thence into the top view. Depth measurements are transferred in the usual way from the side to the top view by dividers. If projectors are selected so as to be symmetrical about the horizontal axis, each setting of the dividers will be used to transfer four points (1–2–1′–2′, for example).

This point-by-point plotting procedure may be used for any curve or outline which is known in two adjacent views.

After sufficient points have been located in the required view, a freehand curve is lightly drawn in. The French curve is then fitted to the freehand line and the final line is drawn. Usually the French curve will have to be repositioned several times to complete the curve. Sufficient overlap should always be allowed between successive positionings to assure a smooth curve.

Note that A, A', B, and B' are the endpoints of the major and minor diameters of the ellipse. When these four points have been established in a required view, a number of other procedures are available for completing the curve.

Trammel Method

In Figure 9–2(a) we see the semimajor diameter OA and the semiminor diameter OB laid out from a point O' on a straight edge of paper. As this paper, or *trammel* is shifted, keeping points A' and B' on the axes as indicated, point O' traces a true ellipse.

This may be readily proven if we recall from analytic geometry the equation of the ellipse:

$$\frac{X^2}{a^2} + \frac{Y^2}{b^2} = 1, \quad \text{or} \quad X = \frac{a}{b}(b^2 - Y^2)^{\frac{1}{2}}$$

in which $a = \overline{OA}$, and $b = \overline{OB}$

Assigning coordinates (X,Y) to point O' and taking C as the projection of O' on the x axis, we have:

$$\overline{O'C} = Y, \quad \text{and} \quad \overline{O'B'} = b$$

whence: $\overline{B'C} = (b^2 - Y^2)$.

In triangle $OB'A'$, $\overline{B'A'} = a - b$.

Then, by similar triangles, $\overline{OB'} = \dfrac{a-b}{b}(b^2 - Y^2)^{\frac{1}{2}}$

But $X = \overline{OC} = \overline{OB'} + \overline{B'C}$

Substituting and simplifying, we obtain:

$$X = \frac{a}{b}(b^2 - Y^2)^{\frac{1}{2}}$$

which verifies the construction.

This method is excellent when the major diameter is considerably greater than the minor. When they are more nearly the same length, that is, as the ellipse approaches a circle, the length $A'B'$ becomes quite short and accuracy is lost. In that event the alternate trammel layout shown in Figure 9–2(b) is to be preferred. You can quickly prove its validity as an original exercise.

Circular Arc Approximation

A reasonable approximation of an ellipse can be drawn with a compass by the procedure given in Figure 9–3. Given the major and minor diameters, we first swing an arc AC with center at O. Line AC is drawn. With center at B we next swing arc CD and then construct the perpendicular bisector of AD, cutting the axes at E and F. E' and F' are located symmetrically by dividers. These four points are the centers of the arcs used to draw the approximate ellipse. The arcs will be tangent at the lines of centers.

The resulting curve is pleasing pictorially and is sufficiently accurate for most purposes. Note, however, that it should not be used when it is necessary to represent tangent lines or curves at any points other than the endpoints of the major and minor diameters.

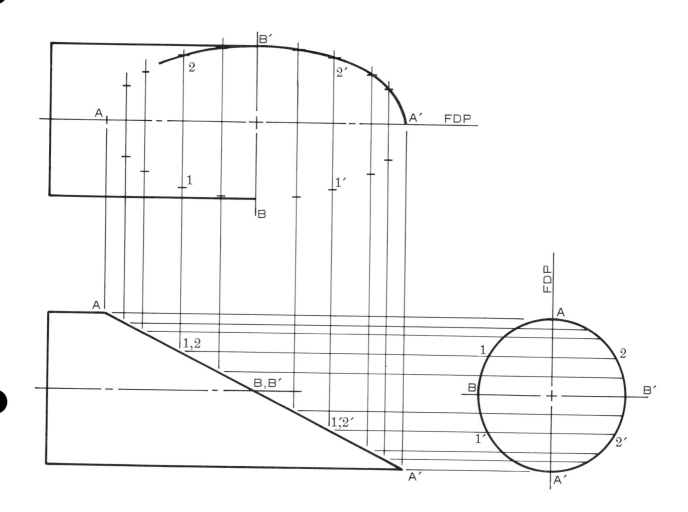

Figure 9–1

SUPPLEMENTARY NOTES

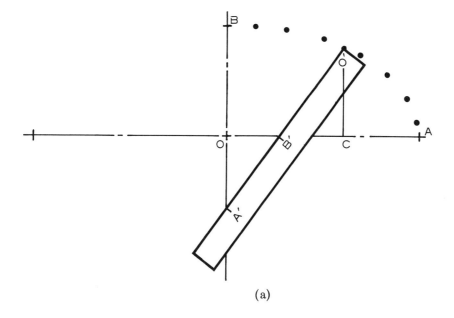

(a)

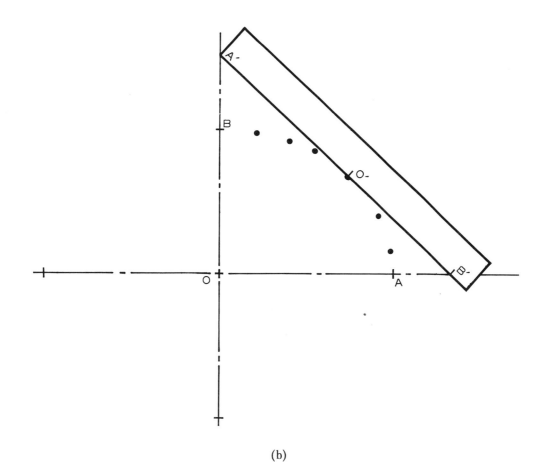

(b)

Figure 9–2

FIGURE 9–2

SUPPLEMENTARY NOTES

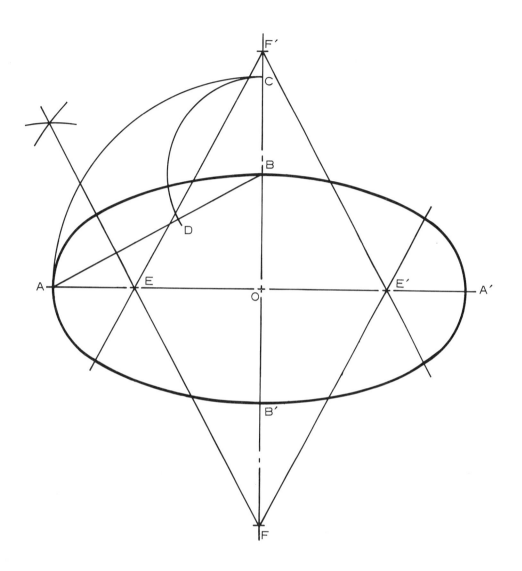

Figure 9–3

SUPPLEMENTARY NOTES

Exercises

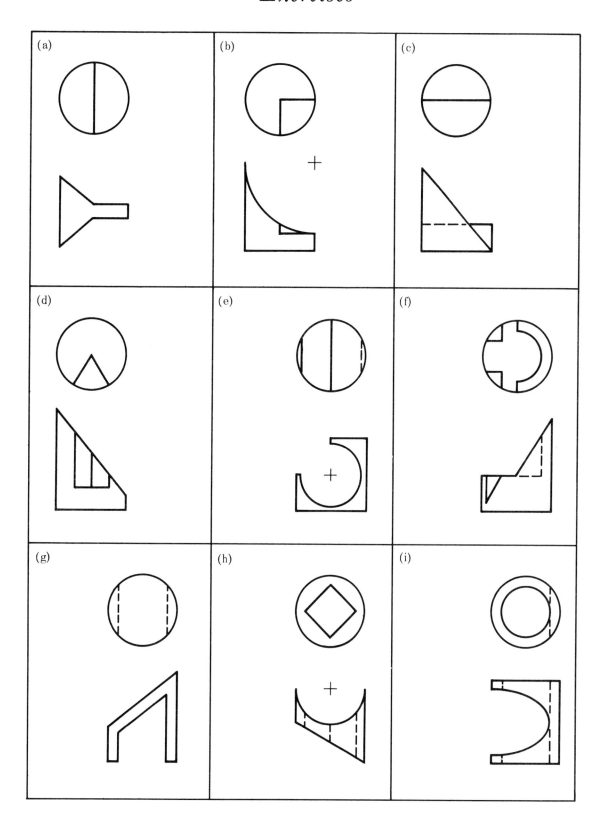

(a) (b) (c) (d) (e) (f) (g) (h) (i)

Ex. 9.1 Construct three principal views of each object above. Maintain the proportions shown. Sketch pictorials as assigned.

Lesson 10

Sectional Views

Many objects are not adequately described in their principal views because much of the significant detail is hidden in the interior. This leads to a maze of hidden lines in the principal views. The difficulty may be overcome by the addition of sectional views, or by the substitution of sectional views for one or more of the principal views.

Full Sections

The pulley shown in Figure 10–1 is an obvious candidate for sectional representation—most of the significant detail is hidden.

To obtain the sectional view, we shall, in this illustration, pass a frontal cutting plane through the centerline of the object. The portion in front of the cutting plane is discarded, resulting in the highly descriptive full section shown in Figure 10–2. All of the surfaces which have been produced by the action of the cutting plane are drawn cross-hatched. Nothing in the portion of the object behind the cutting plane has been changed, omitted, or disturbed in any way.

In Figure 10–3 we have the unsectioned principal views of this object. The full section front view of Figure 10–4 gives a much clearer picture. It is not only easier to read, but is much more practical to dimension as we will see in the next lesson.

Notice that in these figures we have produced a *full* sectional view by removing one-half of the object.

In the case of a fully symmetrical piece, such as that shown in this illustration, it is permissible to omit half of the circular view. This may be seen applied in the given figures for Exercises 10.2(a) and 10.2(b) which appear on page 119. Because the full front views are shown, the rear portion of the top view is omitted. However, when the front views are drawn as sections, the front portions of the top views are omitted, since this tends to reflect the action of the cutting plane.

Half Sections

The same pulley is redrawn in the pictorial of Figure 10–5 with only one-fourth of the object removed. The cutting planes are horizontal and frontal. Both pass through the centerline of the piece. The view produced, called a half-section, reveals both interior and exterior detail very effectively. When the front view is drawn as a half-section as shown in Figure 10–6, it too shows both interior and exterior features, but being comparatively difficult to dimension, its usefulness is somewhat limited.

Offset Sections

In order to show as much detail as possible in a single view, sections are frequently taken on offset cutting planes as shown in the two illustrations of Figure 10–7. Notice that the offset, being arbitrary and artificial, is not shown in the sectional view. If the nature of the piece is such that doubt might exist as to which features are intersected by the cutting plane, the edge view of the cutting plane may be indicated by a heavy broken line such as that appearing in Figure 10–11. In this figure the broken line has not been used to indicate offsets, however, but merely to provide identification of the location and direction of sight for Section *DD* which then may be placed anywhere on the sheet.

Other Types of Sections

The use of *broken out* sections like those seen in Figure 10–8 is fairly common for revealing local interior details in shafts, cylindrical fasteners, keys, and other small features which are not usually drawn in section.

Revolved sections are shown in Figure 10–9. The plane of the section is perpendicular to that of the view upon which it is superimposed. The axis of revolution coincides with the edge view of the cutting plane. The piece may be "broken" in the vicinity of the section to provide a clear space.

Violations of Projection

It is sometimes expedient to violate the strict rules of projection for the sake of clarity. In Figure 10–10 the true projection shown at the right has several obvious shortcomings, whereas the conventionalized section is very descriptive of the actual object. In the conventionalized view the stiffening webs and the bolt holes have been revolved into the cutting plane prior to projection into the sectional view. Crosshatching has been omitted from the webs to suggest their comparative fragility, an effect which contrasts sharply with the impression of massiveness which is given by the true projection.

A number of other conventional violations of projection are indicated in Figure 10–11. The true curve at *A–B–C* is quite complex in form. It is often convenient to represent the curve simply as a circular arc constructed through the three points. The location of *B* is obtained by projection from the side view. The center of the arc is given by the intersection of the perpendicular bisectors of the chords *A–B* and *B–C*.

The figure shows four objects astride the large cylinder. Two of these are wider than the radius of the cylinder. The intersection of the cylinder in the *A–B–C* curve has already been discussed. The block is shown in true projection.

The intersections for the small cylinder and block are idealized in the front view, simply because it would be confusing to attempt to draw the actual intersection.

The removed section *DD* has been shown on this drawing in order to make two points. The first is that a removed section, properly labeled, may be placed anywhere on the sheet. The second point is that it may not always be desirable to show all of the object behind the cutting plane. In this section the vertical cylinder at the left end was omitted. Presumably its inclusion would not have contributed to the purpose for which the section was drawn.

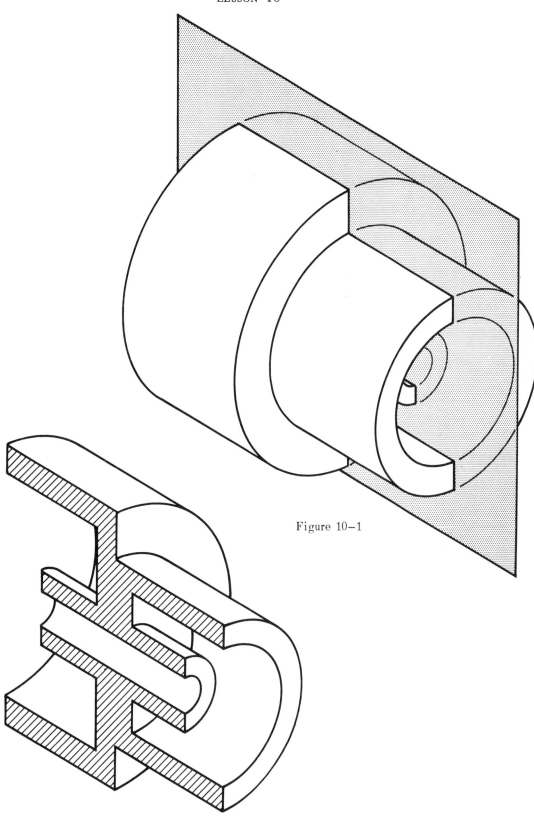

Figure 10–1

Figure 10–2

SUPPLEMENTARY NOTES

SUPPLEMENTARY NOTES

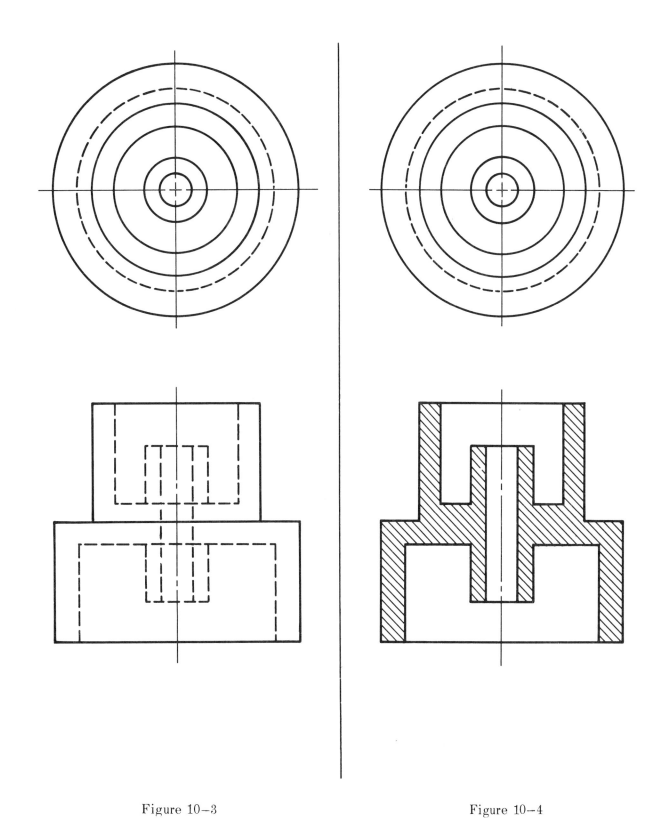

Figure 10–3   Figure 10–4

SUPPLEMENTARY NOTES

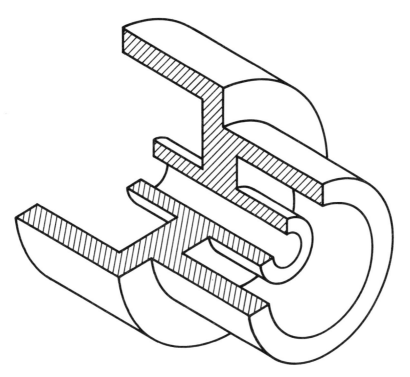

Figure 10–5

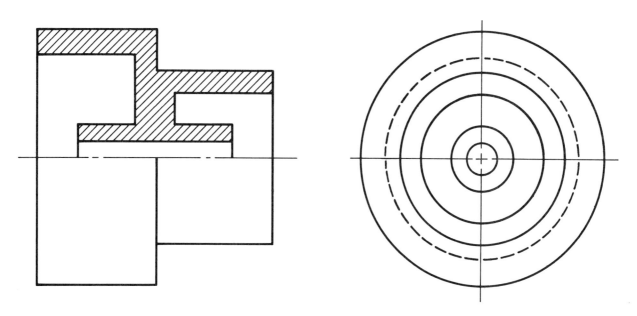

Figure 10–6

SUPPLEMENTARY NOTES

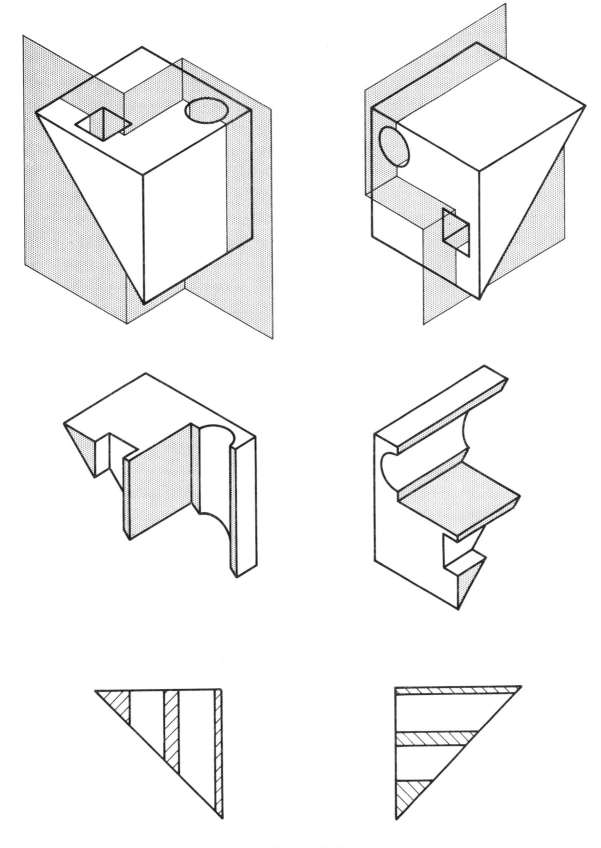

Figure 10–7

SUPPLEMENTARY NOTES

SUPPLEMENTARY NOTES

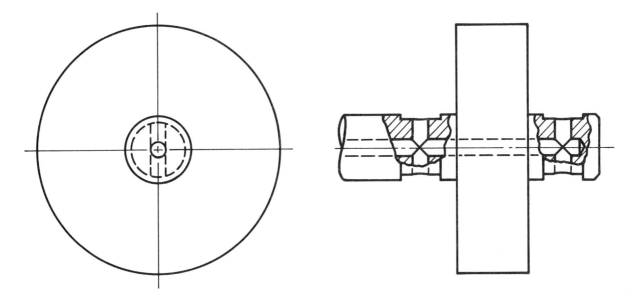

Figure 10--8

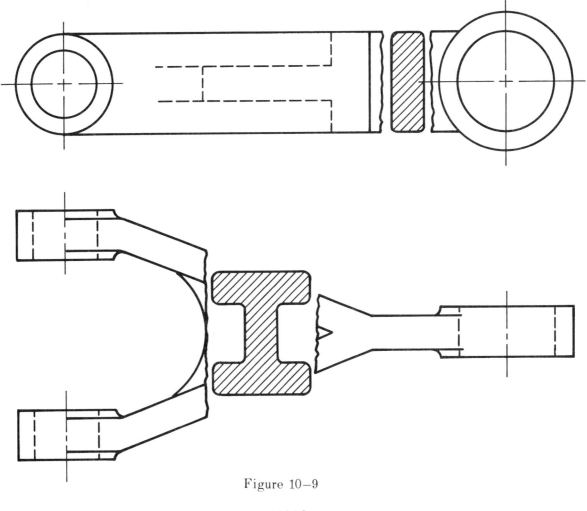

Figure 10—9

SUPPLEMENTARY NOTES

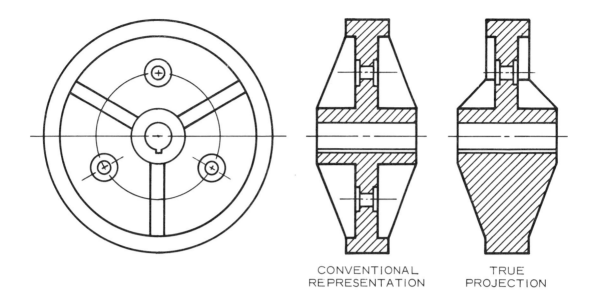

CONVENTIONAL
REPRESENTATION

TRUE
PROJECTION

Figure 10—10

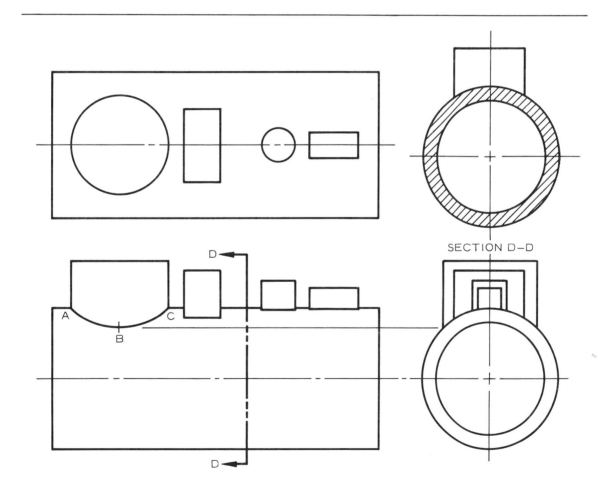

SECTION D—D

Figure 10—11

SUPPLEMENTARY NOTES

Exercises

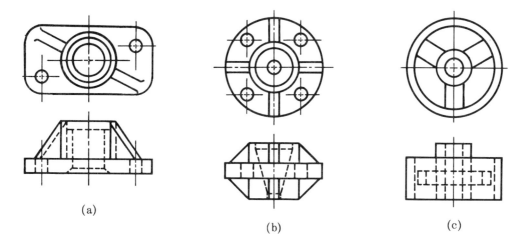

Ex. 10.1 Sketch the circular and full sectional views of the objects above.

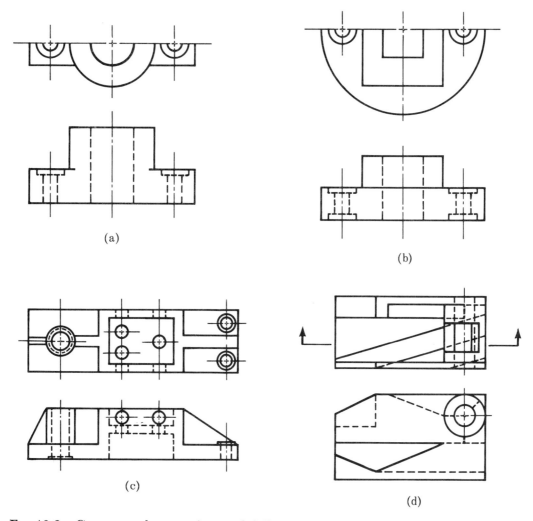

Ex. 10.2 Construct the top view and full section of each of the above objects. Scale: Double Size.

Lesson 11

Use of Scales

Three basic types of scales find wide application in engineering practice. Their names are somewhat misleading because every engineer will, on occasion, make use of all three.

Architects' Scales, used by architects and structural engineers to lay out dimensions measured and recorded in feet and inches, are shown in Figure 11–1. Dimensions are scaled and recorded on a drawing as illustrated in this figure. Examine the given dimensions and then supply those which are missing.

When an architects' scale has been used in constructing a drawing, the title box contains a statement of the scale thus:

$$\text{Scale:} \quad (\text{inches}) = 1'\text{-}0''$$

The scale shown at A would be written:

$$\text{Scale:} \quad 1\tfrac{1}{2}'' = 1'\text{-}0''$$

From this one can deduce that the linear dimensions stated on the drawing are one-eighth their actual size on the object represented.

Because the basic divisions in the subdivided end portions of the architects' scales represent inch parts of a foot, we find that these divisions are whole or fractional multiples of twelfths.

Mechanical Engineers' Scales are used to lay out drawings of equipment and machinery for which all dimensions are recorded in inches and fractions of inches. Use of these scales is illustrated in Figure 11–2. The scale of a machine drawing appears in the title box in the form:

$$\text{Scale:} \quad (\text{inches}) = 1'', \text{ or Full Size, Half Size, etc.}$$

Scale B, for example, might be recorded:

$$\text{Scale:} \quad \tfrac{1}{8}'' = 1'', \text{ or as: Eighth Size}$$

The basic divisions of these scales are usually sixteenth parts of the subdivided portion. This contrasts with the twelve basic divisions of the architects' scales. Hence we note that the two types of scales cannot be used interchangeably.

Observe in Figure 11–2 that scale D is equivalent to scales A and F. D is a type known as "*double* (because two scales superimposed), fully divided or *chain* (because it is subdivided over its entire length and not just at the ends)." The A–F arrangement is referred to as "*opposite* (scales progress from opposite ends) *double divided* (two scales) *open divided* (indicating only end portions are subdivided)." A selection between the types is a matter of personal taste.

Fill in the missing dimensions at B, D, and F.

Civil Engineers' Scales or *chain scales* are used in representing decimal divisions. In Figure 11–3 scale A might be used to represent scales such as $1'' = 10'$, or $100''$, or 1000 fps; and B might be used for such scales as $1'' = 40$ lb., or 4 mi. Note that the

[120]

form is always "one inch equals something." In the dimensions shown the decimal point obviously must be located to suit the particular scale of the drawing. Supply a dimension at *D*.

The required dimensions in Figure 11–1 are 15′–11″, 8′–7½″, and 7′–9″ at *G*, *H*, and *I*, respectively. In Figure 11–2 they are $20\frac{5}{8}$, $5\frac{11}{16}$, and $3\frac{3}{4}$ at *B*, *D*, and *F*, respectively. In Figure 11–3 the missing dimension is a decimal multiple of 112.

Dimensioning

The dimensioning of engineering drawings is not a skill which can be acquired in the two brief lessons allotted to the subject in this treatment. We can, however, gain an appreciation of the underlying philosophy and learn some of the customary practices.

Before one can hope to master dimensioning techniques, he must have a thorough knowledge of the design applications of the part or parts to be manufactured; that is, he must understand the inter-relationships in size, position, and function among the various components of the system under design. In addition he must have an intimate familiarity with the various shop operations and processes which will be utilized in the production of the final product.

Many details of dimensioning practice vary among the several branches of engineering, and indeed within the same branch and among offices doing rather similar work. The important thing is that there must be a complete understanding between the designer and the shop. A large corporation may develop its own standards and procedures and incorporate numerous short-cuts and simplifications without getting into difficulties, but in general practice the designer must be certain that his drawings are so complete and explicit that they cannot be misunderstood by a trained person.

We are going to develop a fairly extensive list of rules relating to dimensioning in this lesson, but just as important as knowing these rules is knowing when to break them. Only a very few rules can be said to have the force of law. We will consider these principles in the next paragraphs.

Cardinal Principles of Dimensioning

The primary purpose of the drawing is to provide the craftsman in the shop with all of the information necessary to the production of the part. Therefore:

1. The drawing must be complete, correct, and unambiguous in all detail. It must be clean and neat and absolutely legible. Mistakes and misunderstandings are always costly, and sometimes disastrous.
2. Every dimension required for manufacture must be explicitly stated. The selection of dimensions supplied will often control the sequence of steps followed in manufacture and the accuracy with which particular features are related to one another. This selection must therefore be carefully considered.
3. The shopman should never find it necessary to scale a drawing (in fact, it is one of *his* cardinal principles that he shall never do so), nor should he be required to perform involved arithmetic, or make an assumption of any sort.
4. Drawings should be accurately drawn to scale in order to provide a visual check on the overall accuracy of the dimensions. When a change is made which throws a dimension on a drawing out of scale, that dimension must be so labeled so that no possible confusion can result.

5. In drawings of mating parts, corresponding dimensions should be used to minimize possible confusion.

Specifics of Dimensioning

The more important features of dimensioning practice will be observed in an examination of the drawings of several simple objects. Since each of these objects appears to be a machine part, dimensions are stated in inches exclusively, making it possible to omit inch marks entirely. When fractions are used, as in these drawings, a tolerance of plus or minus $\frac{1}{64}''$ is implied unless otherwise noted. Where greater precision is required, a decimal form of dimensioning is adopted.

Let us now examine Figure 11–4 and list our observations:

1. Dimensions read to the bottom of the sheet or to the right edge of the sheet. Notes, such as the "$\frac{1}{2}D$", always read to the bottom.

2. Centerlines, dimension lines, and extension lines are of approximately the same weight. They are dark and crisp but considerably thinner than object lines. Arrowheads, letters, numerals and fractions are drawn in approximately the proportions shown. $\frac{1}{8}''$ lettering is used on most drawings. In quality work guide lines are drawn above and below each line of lettering. Special guides and templates are available for this purpose. Note that fraction bars are aligned with the associated dimension line.

3. The thickness of the plate has been shown by a note. It might also have been conveyed on a top or side view, or in the name assigned to the piece, or on the billing or parts list. This is a matter of local practice.

4. Cylindrical holes are usually dimensioned in the circular view where size and position are most graphically described. The size is stated as a diameter, usually by a note as shown. The leader to the note is a radial line. The arrow is external to the circle.

5. Notice that dimensions have been omitted at a and b. This is in keeping with the general proposition that dimensions should not be duplicated. When a string of detail dimensions is given between the same end points as an overall dimension, one of the detail dimensions should be omitted. This space with the omitted dimension is the one in which layout inaccuracies in the shop will accumulate. The dimensions shown are presumably the ones requiring the greater degree of precision and control.

Turning now to an examination of Figure 11–5, we are immediately impressed at how few dimensions are required to completely describe this comparatively involved piece.

1. As in the previous figure we see the size of a cylindrical hole specified by note as a diameter in the circular view. By contrast, the arc at the right end is called by its radius. The leader is drawn from the center of the arc, and the arrowhead touches the inside of the arc. The radius at the upper left end has not been dimensioned because the common centerline forces it to be the same as that to the right.

2. It would be redundant in this case to show overall dimensions for this piece, since all necessary dimensions are already given. If we wished to add redundant dimensions for reference or checking purposes we should follow the dimensions with the letters *REF.* to make our intent perfectly clear.

The dimensioning of the object shown in Figure 11–6 illustrates the proposition that a particular feature of an object should be dimensioned in the particular view which provides the most definitive shape description of that feature. On this object, the forked shape, for example, is dimensioned in the top view, while the prominent "L" shape is fully dimensioned in the front view.

1. As a general rule it is considered desirable to place dimensions between views. On the other hand neatness requires that we attempt to keep extension lines reasonably short, and that we attempt to avoid developing mazes of intersecting extension and dimension lines. The arrangement shown appears to be the most expedient in the present circumstances. The drawing is extremely clear, so it is quite unimportant how many of the so-called rules we have violated in producing it.

In the sectional view of the pulley shown in Figure 11–7 it appears that we have violated one of the dimensioning principles stated earlier; namely that cylindrical holes are dimensioned in their circular views. But the rule has been violated to good purpose. The note which would be required to completely describe the hole through the center of the piece if it were dimensioned in the top view would be very involved and probably quite confusing. A clear and compact arrangement has been obtained confining the dimensions to the rectangular view of the part.

1. Notice in this figure how dimensions have been staggered to avoid interference with one another.
2. The locations of the small bolt holes can be specified in several ways. We might choose to draw the complete top view and show as dimensions the arcs of angle between the holes. If it were necessary to relate the positions of these holes to some fixed features such as a keyway or stiffening ribs, those locations would undoubtedly be fixed by dimensioned arcs. In the present case, the given note is a neat way of handling the situation. The note might be expanded to read "$\frac{1}{2}D$. 3 HOLES, EQUALLY SPACED ON $6\frac{1}{2}D$ B.C." The diameter of the bolt circle (B.C.) could then be omitted from the rectangular view.

The object shown in Figure 11–8 approaches in complexity those which we will consider in the exercises for this and the following lesson.

1. In dimensioning this object, we are faced with numerous decisions as to which of several alternative dimensions shall be selected for incorporation into the drawing. We may proceed on some such reasoning as this:

a. We must give the diameters of circles and the radii of arcs, preferably in their circular views.
b. We must rigidly fix the locations of the centers of those arcs and circles, both with respect to one another and with respect to the surfaces of the object.
c. We must decide which surfaces are functionally most important and tie our control dimensions from the various centerlines to those surfaces. In this illustration the control dimensions have been drawn to the inner surfaces of the part.

2. The overall height, width, and depth dimensions shown on the figure should, strictly speaking, be noted REF. since they are redundant. In point of fact, however, this is frequently omitted when, as in this instance, there is virtually no chance that the shopman might misunderstand the intent and use those dimensions for control. If in doubt, use REF.

Certain additional complications arise in dimensioning the plate shown in Figure 11–9.

1. In all previous examples we have carefully avoided placing dimensions within the outline of the object. This is good general practice, but, as in the present instance, exceptions do arise. Long and cumbersome extension lines would be required causing a good deal of unnecessary confusion. There is ample room within the figure for the necessary dimensions, and they do not seriously detract from the clarity of the view as a shape description.

2. The plate has been dimensioned with the assumption made that the position of the holes with respect to one another is most important, and that these should be controlled with respect to the upper and left edges of the plate. These considerations make it necessary that there be two extension lines crossing the dimension line for the 11 inch measurement. We have managed to avoid such interference in previous illustrations, but here we see that, if done with discretion, the practice is not harmful and need not be shunned.

Much more detail on dimensioning practices for various types of engineering drawings is available in innumerable reference works and these should be consulted by a student who aspires to assume a design function in industry.

ARCHITECT'S SCALES

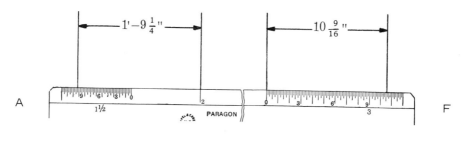

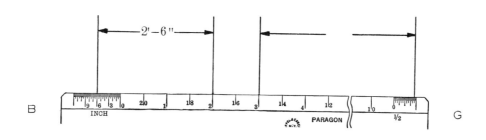

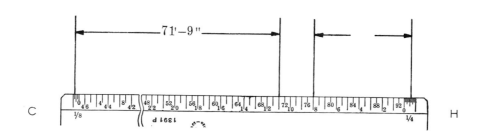

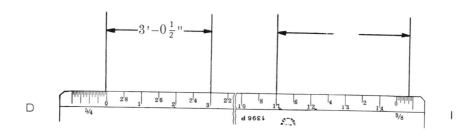

Figure 11–1 (Courtesy Keuffel & Esser Co.)

FIGURE 11–1

SUPPLEMENTARY NOTES

MECHANICAL ENGINEER'S SCALES

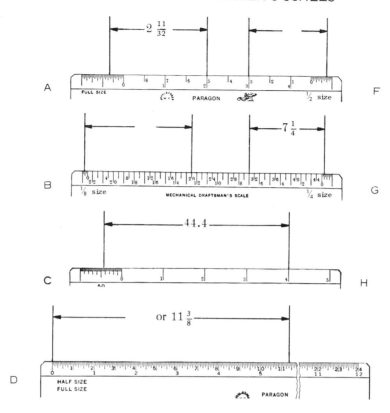

Figure 11–2 (Courtesy Keuffel & Esser Co.)

CIVIL ENGINEER'S SCALES

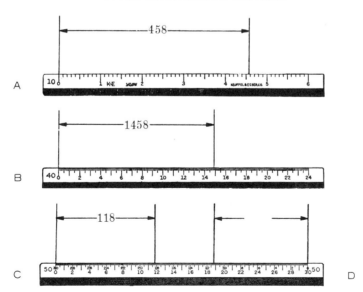

Figure 11–3 (Courtesy Keuffel & Esser Co.)

SUPPLEMENTARY NOTES

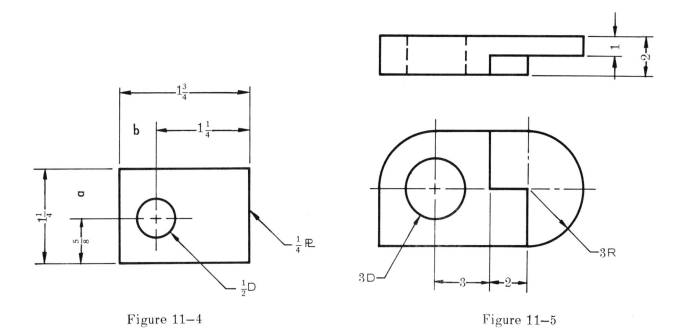

Figure 11–4   Figure 11–5

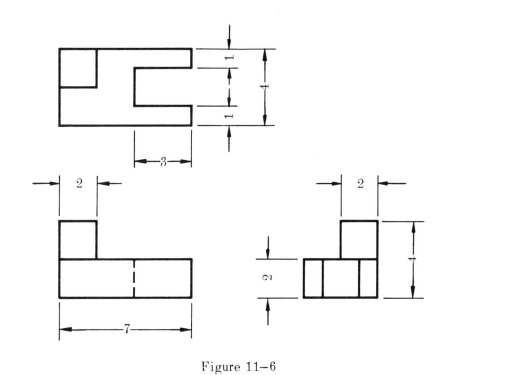

Figure 11–6

[129]

SUPPLEMENTARY NOTES

SUPPLEMENTARY NOTES

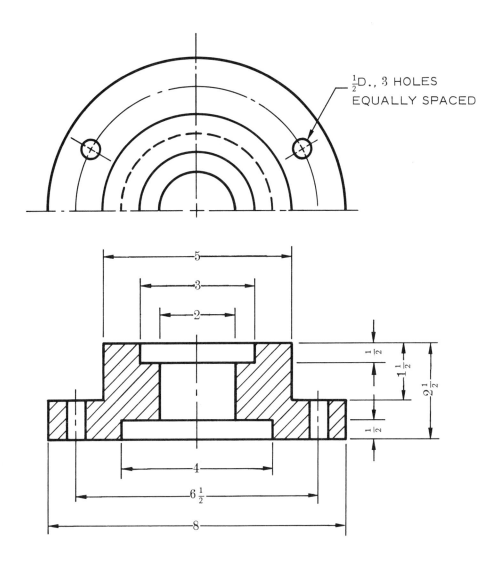

$\frac{1}{2}$D., 3 HOLES
EQUALLY SPACED

Figure 11–7

SUPPLEMENTARY NOTES

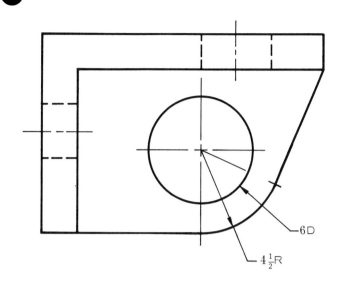

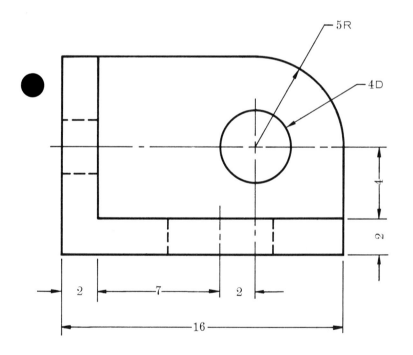

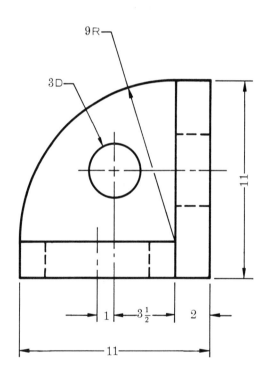

Figure 11–8

[133]

SUPPLEMENTARY NOTES

SUPPLEMENTARY NOTES

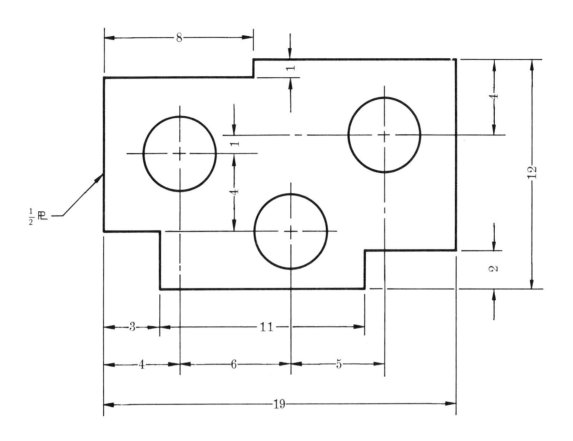

Figure 11–9

SUPPLEMENTARY NOTES

Exercises

Ex. 11.1 Draw T-square construction lines spaced every $\frac{1}{2}''$ down the sheet beginning $1\frac{1}{2}''$ from the upper edge. Two inches from the right edge label these lines A through R. Draw an object line $1''$ from and parallel to the left edge, extending slightly beyond the top and bottom horizontal lines.

In the following table are listed various dimensions, the scales to which they are to be laid out (or the ratio of length on drawing to length on object), and the type of scale to be used.

For each case in turn, scale the length along the construction line from the reference line at the left, and mark the end point with a tic mark. Draw the dimension line superimposed on the construction line, paying particular attention to line weight and arrowheads. Record the dimension in proper form using $\frac{1}{8}''$ lettering.

LINE	TYPE SCALE	LENGTH ON OBJECT	SCALE	SIZE RATIO
A	ARCH	$3'-10\frac{1}{2}''$	$1'' = 1'-0''$	
B	ME	$5\frac{17}{32}$	$\frac{3}{4}'' = 1''$	
C	CE	$124.5'$	$1'' = 50'$	
D	ARCH	$32'-7''$		$\frac{1}{96}$
E	ME	$17\frac{13}{16}$		$\frac{1}{4}$
F	CE	$36.3'$		$\frac{1}{120}$
G	ARCH	$2'-11\frac{1}{4}''$	$\frac{1}{2}'' = 1'-0''$	
H	ME	$1\frac{5}{64}$	$2'' = 1''$	
I	CE	$72.4'$	$1'' = 30'$	
J	ARCH	$22'-1''$	$\frac{1}{8}'' = 1'-0''$	
K	ME	$5\frac{9}{32}$	$\frac{3}{8}'' = 1''$	
L	CE	$1015'$	$1'' = 600'$	
M	ARCH	$18'-0\frac{1}{2}''$		$\frac{1}{48}$
N	ME	$2\frac{11}{64}$		$\frac{1}{1}$
O	CE	$.0725''$	$1'' = .04''$	
P	ARCH	$1'-2\frac{7}{8}''$		$\frac{1}{4}$
Q	ME	$8\frac{9}{16}$		$\frac{1}{4}$
R	CE	$11.85''$		$\frac{1}{5}$

Complete the columns of Scale and Size Ratio in the above table as part of the solution.

[137]

Ex. 11.2 Sketch the necessary views of the objects above. Indicate required dimensions and notes by supplying dimension lines, leaders, and extension lines.

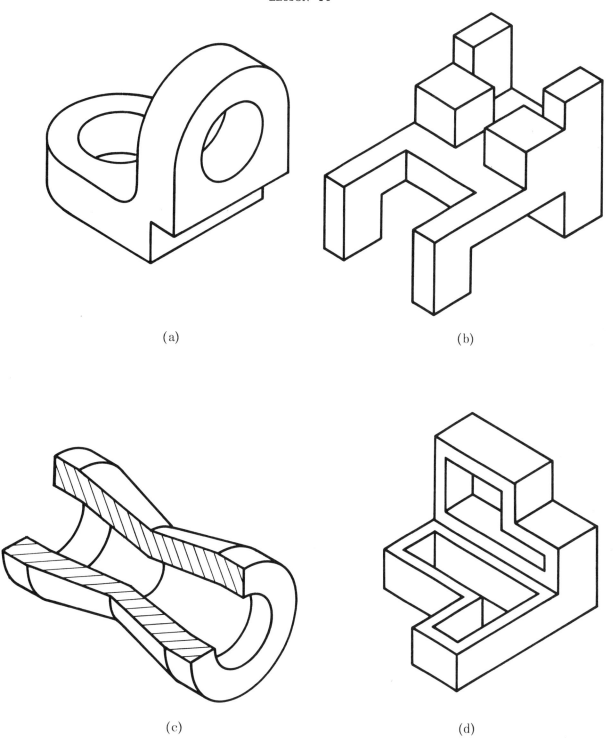

(a)

(b)

(c)

(d)

Ex. 11.3 The isometric drawings above are constructed to the scale $\frac{1}{2}'' = 1''$. Layout the necessary principal views to the scale $\frac{3}{4}'' = 1''$ and dimension fully. Use an entire page for each problem.

Ex. 11.4 Layout and dimension the principal views of objects assigned from Ex. 1.1 and 2.2 as in Ex. 11.3.

Lesson 12

Additional Dimensioning Exercises

Dimensioning theory developed in the preceding lesson is again applied in the exercises that follow.

It should perhaps be re-emphasized that each engineering speciality has evolved its own standards of practice which will come to your attention as you enter your professional field.

Exercises

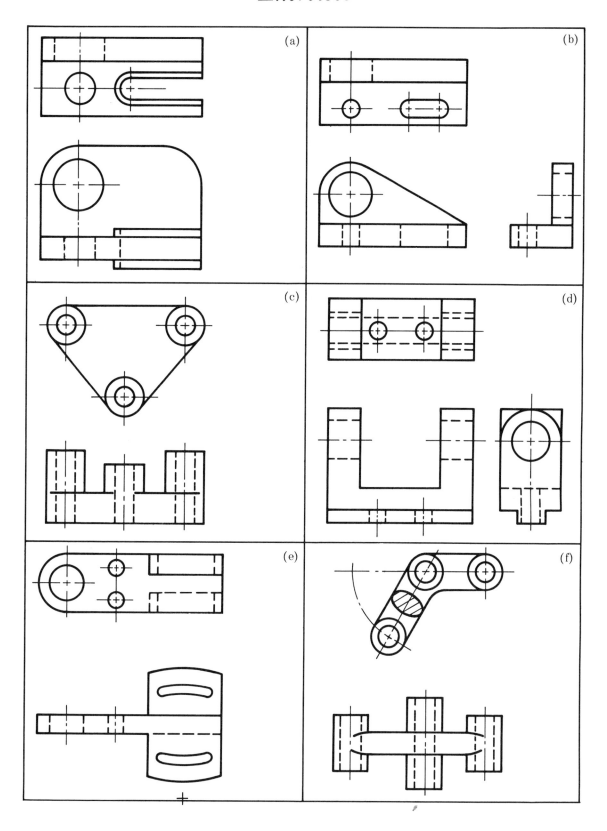

Ex. 12.1 Construct double size the principal views of the objects above. Scale as accurately as possible from the given views. Dimension fully to a scale to be assigned.

Lesson 13

Construction of Isometric Drawings

The use of drawing instruments makes it practical for us to attempt pictorial drawings of objects considerably more complicated than those considered in the lessons associated with freehand representation. Of course all of the theory and projection techniques previously discussed apply equally to freehand and instrument drawings.

As an illustration of the type of problem we shall attack in this lesson, consider Figure 13–1(a). The basic object is a prism with a cross section in the shape of a *G*. We are required to construct a pictorial of the object, two portions having been removed; that to the left of an *OF* plane through point *A* and the lower-front-left corner of the enclosing box, and, secondly, that which is above an oblique plane containing points *A*, *B*, and *C*. For clarity we shall consider the various stages of the construction individually, although these would doubtless be combined in a normal solution to avoid duplication of effort.

The pictorial in Figure 13–1(a) has been laid out by scaling the given views. The dashed outline of the *G* on the right face would, of course, normally be omitted if this were the final drawing of the object.

The required orthofrontal cut is shown in Figure 13–1(b). The entire construction has been performed on the pictorial. Initially the trace of the cutting plane was laid out on the surface of the enclosing box, and the *G* outline plotted on the left isometric face. Lightly shade in the *G* with colored pencil to clarify the drawing. Depth coordinates have been transferred into the inclined plane by a series of frontal cutting planes. Their traces appear on the top, left side, and *OF* surfaces. With black pencil lightly shade in the typical cutting plane *a–b–c*. The height and width coordinates are carried into the *OF* plane from the left face by isometric projectors in the frontal cutting planes, as, for example, line 1–2 in plane *a–b–c*. All significant points in the inclined plane having thus been determined, the figure is easily completed. Note that all parallel lines appear parallel in the pictorial as well as the principal views.

Horizontal cutting planes could have been used in the above construction with equal success, or individual points in the inclined plane could have been located by offsets measured in the principal views. It is not unusual to use a combination of all these techniques in a given problem.

The intersection of the given oblique plane with the *G* prism is found in Figure 13–1(c). The enclosing box has been extended to accommodate the complete intersection *ABCD* of the box with the oblique plane. In this solution horizontal cutting planes such as *a–b–c–d* have been used to locate the required points in the oblique plane, although frontal planes such as 1–2–3–4 could have been used with equal effectiveness. Note that the intersections of all horizontal cutting planes with the oblique plane are parallel to *AB* and *CD*, while those of frontal cutting planes are parallel to *AC* and *BD*.

The intersection of the right face of the original prism with the oblique plane is the line *BE*. The *G* outline in that plane is again shown by dashed lines. Note that a part of this outline and a portion of the *G* shape in the oblique plane will be discarded in the final solution.

The final pictorial of the block is shown in Figure 13–1(d). Note the right portion especially. It is possible you may still have difficulty visualizing some details. Should this be the case, add all possible hidden lines to the figure.

As a final step the front view of the object has been completed in Figure 13–1(d). This may have been accomplished either by taking offsets from the pictorial, or by the addition of a top view to provide the necessary width coordinates.

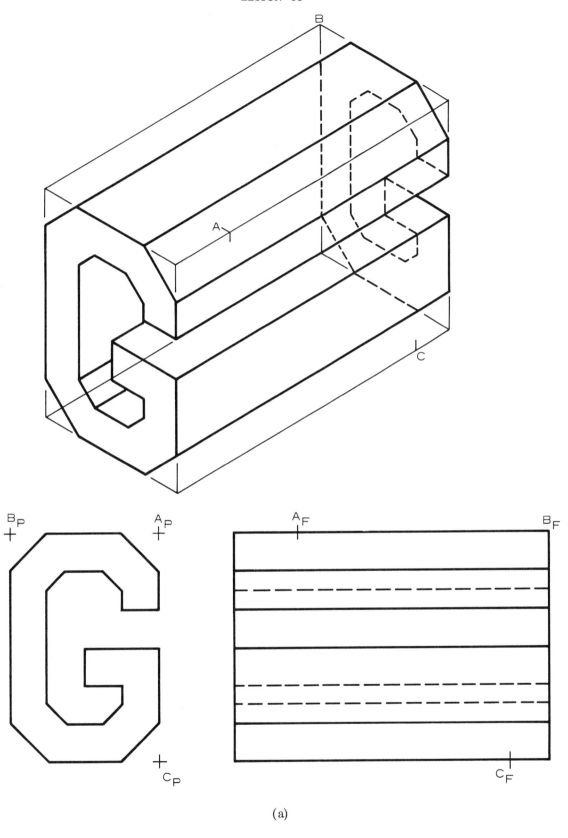

(a)

Figure 13-1

SUPPLEMENTARY NOTES

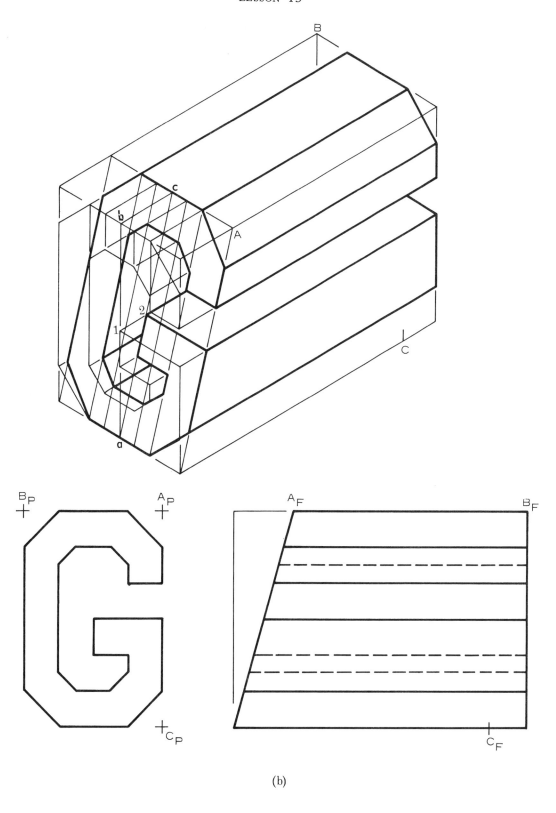

(b)

Figure 13–1

FIGURE 13–1 B

SUPPLEMENTARY NOTES

SUPPLEMENTARY NOTES

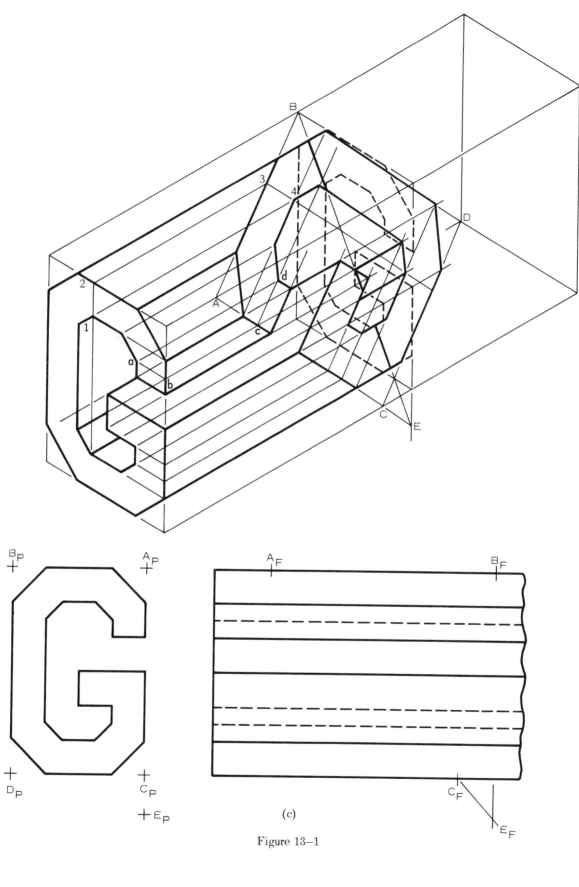

(c)

Figure 13–1

SUPPLEMENTARY NOTES

(d)

Figure 13–1

SUPPLEMENTARY NOTES

Exercises

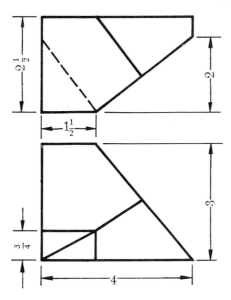

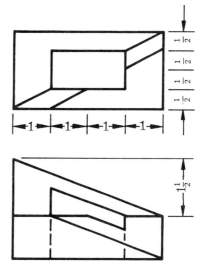

Ex. 13.1 Each surface of the block above is either normal or inclined. Construct the *UFR* isometric by taking successive cuts from the basic rectangular solid. All necessary dimensions are given. Do not scale the given orthographic views.

Ex. 13.2 Construct the *UFR* isometric. Inclined horizontal lines are parallel as are the inclined frontal lines. All necessary dimensions are given. Do not scale the given views.

Ex. 13.3 Construct double sized isometric pictorials of assigned objects from Ex. 3.1, 5.1, and 8.1.

Ex. 13.4 Construct the *UFR* isometric drawing of a block 4″ wide, 3″ deep, and $2\frac{1}{2}$″ high. Consider the 4″ × $2\frac{1}{2}$″ faces to be frontal. Remove portions of the basic block as described below to complete the drawing. The problem may be varied by changing the sequence of operations. Overlay sheets or colored pencils are suggested. (a) Remove the upper right portion of the block which is cut off by an *OF* plane containing the lower right edge and intersecting the top surface 1″ from the right face. (b) Remove the upper front portion cut off by an *OP* plane containing the longitudinal centerline of the top surface and passing through the lower front left corner of the object. (c) Remove the upper portion of the block cut by a plane which passes through the upper left rear corner and intersects the front left and rear right *FP* edges of the original block at mid-height. (d) Cut a $1\frac{1}{2}$″ × 3″ rectangular hole through the mutilated block from front to rear. Center the hole in the front face of the original block. Place the long sides horizontal.

Lesson 14

Constructing Curves in Isometric

Any curve may be established in an isometric drawing by the use of point-by-point plotting the height, width, and depth coordinates measured along isometric lines. While this process is somewhat tedious, the resulting line, if accurately plotted, is an exact representation of the required curve.

The most common problem which we are called upon to handle is that of the circle drawn in an isometric plane. Fortunately a number of relatively simple procedures are available for this construction. Two of the most convenient are discussed in the following paragraphs.

Circumscribed Octagon Method

An exact ellipse giving a true representation of a circle in an isometric plane may be obtained by using a modification of the enclosing octagon technique which was developed for sketching ellipses in Lesson 3.

Referring to Figure 14–1 (a) we will recall that the ratio of the lengths 1–2:2–3:3–4 was taken as 2:3:2 for sketching purposes. The actual ratio, to an accuracy required for construction, is 2.121:3:2.121, and is obviously not a convenient form for construction purposes.

Two practical alternative approaches present themselves. The first of these is to calculate the length of a–b from the geometry of the octagon, obtaining a–b = 0.41421 times the radius of the circle. This length may then be laid off on the sides of the iso-metric rhombus from the known centerpoints of the sides, and these points connected to complete the octagon.

A preferred approach is to partially layout the octagon in a principal view to establish length a–b which is then transferred to the rhombus in the isometric. A convenient form of this procedure is illustrated in Figure 14–1(b), in which the partial principal view and the isometric are superimposed one on the other. A circle of the given diameter is lightly drawn at O, the center of the required isometric ellipse, and the intercepts of this circle with the isometric diameters are used to establish the enclosing rhombus. Lines a–b and c–b, a portion of the enclosing octagon, are drawn, and a–b is then transferred to the rhombus as in Figure 14–1(c). Note that the sloping sides of the octagon are inclined at 30° and 60° to the horizontal, are perpendicular to the diagonals of the rhombus, and are bisected by the diagonals. These points of intersection with the diagonals, numbered 1–2–3–4 in the figure, are the end points of the major and minor diameters of the required ellipse.

With eight points on the curve known, and the tangent lines at those points established, an accurate ellipse may be sketched lightly. The French curve is then fitted to the sketched line and the final curve drawn. If the ellipse is large requiring additional points on the curve these may be quickly obtained by the trammel method since the major and minor diameters have been established.

The same procedure is shown in Figure 14–2 for the case of a circle in a horizontal

LESSON 14

plane. Observe that in this case it is necessary to draw the portion of the original octagon in a rotated position. In all other respects the construction is the same as the foregoing.

Approximate Isometric Ellipse

A four-center approximation of the isometric ellipse is generally used in cases not requiring accurate plotting. The procedure is shown in Figure 14–3. The enclosing rhombus is first constructed. The perpendicular bisectors of each side are next constructed. Because of the special geometry of the isometric figure, these perpendiculars will pass through the opposite vertex facilitating construction. The intersections of these lines locate the four centers of the circular arcs which approximate the required ellipse. The points of tangency of the several arcs occur at the midpoints of the sides of the rhombus.

The same figure also serves to illustrate the point that the construction of cylindrical objects in isometric can be developed from the various centerlines and that the enclosing box may often be omitted. Complete the sketch of the cylinder projecting from the front face of the block in the figure to see this. Many of the assigned problems with this lesson will further clarify this point.

A comparison of the exact isometric ellipse (solid curve) with the approximate version (dashed curve) is given in Figure 14–4. It is evident that the approximate curve departs significantly from the true ellipse and should be used with restraint.

Curves in Non-isometric Planes

When faced with the problem of constructing a curve which lies in a nonisometric plane in an isometric view of an object, it is usually helpful to first construct the projection of the required curve in one of the isometric faces of the enclosing box and to then utilize a series of cutting planes to establish the corresponding points in the required plane.

The procedure is illustrated in Figure 14–5 in which we are required to construct the isometric view of a cylinder truncated by an orthofrontal plane through points 1–2, and by an oblique plane through 2–3–4. In the solution shown, the true ellipse representing a right section of the cylinder was constructed in the left isometric face. A series of frontal cutting planes was then used to transfer points on the curve into the required planes. If you will lightly shade in the frontmost of these cutting planes the drawing will become considerably clearer.

As an alternate procedure we might have chosen to construct the enclosing octagon in the left isometric face. The corners of the octagon would then be projected into the truncating planes and the required ellipse drawn tangent to the resulting octagons. In this case, however, we should note that the major and minor diameters of the ellipses are unknown and it is not possible to add additional points by trammel.

[155]

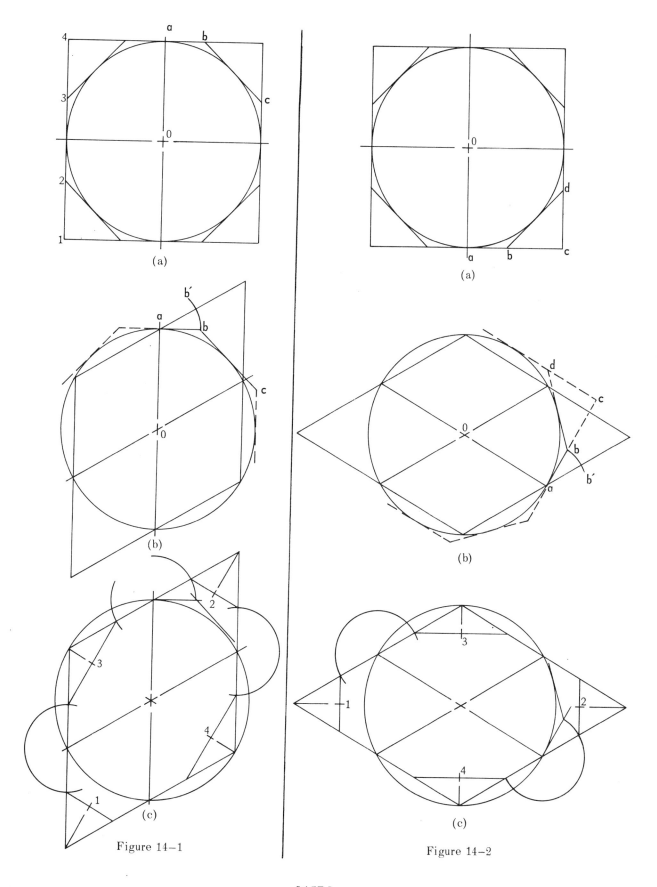

(a)

(b)

(c)

Figure 14-1

(a)

(b)

(c)

Figure 14-2

SUPPLEMENTARY NOTES

SUPPLEMENTARY NOTES

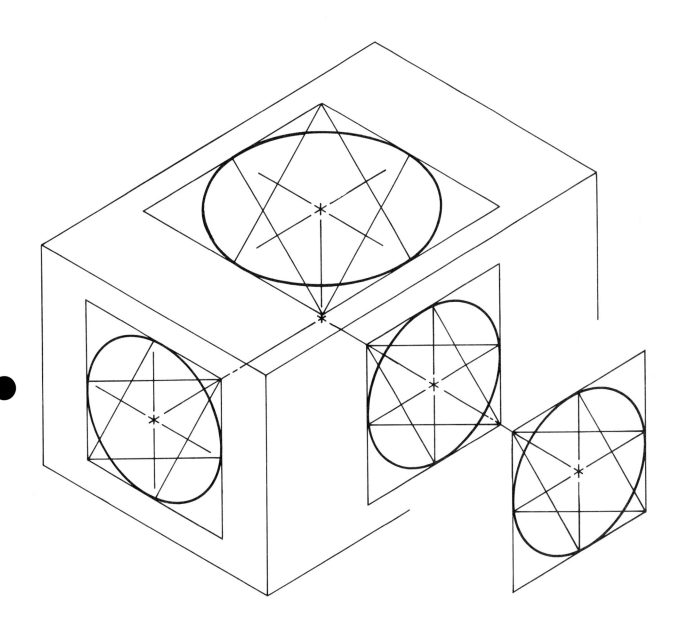

Figure 14–3

SUPPLEMENTARY NOTES

SUPPLEMENTARY NOTES

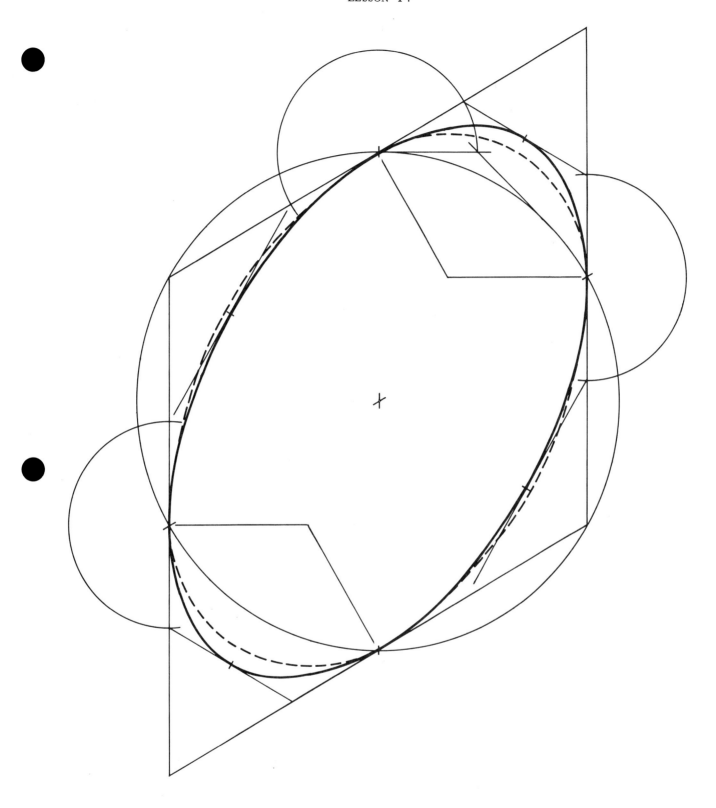

Figure 14–4

SUPPLEMENTARY NOTES

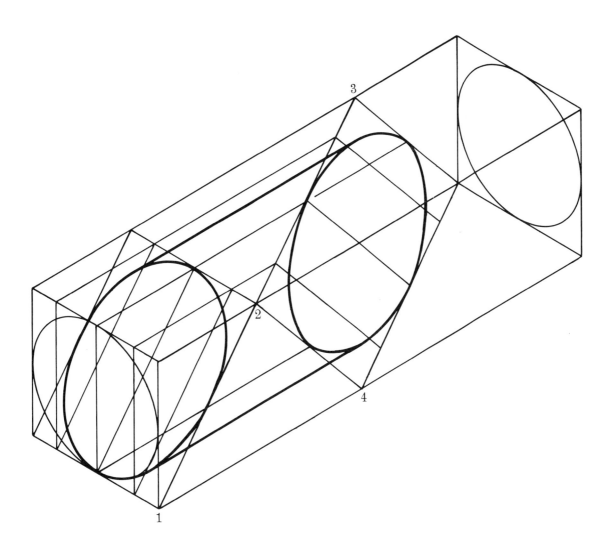

Figure 14–5

FIGURE 14–5

SUPPLEMENTARY NOTES

Exercises

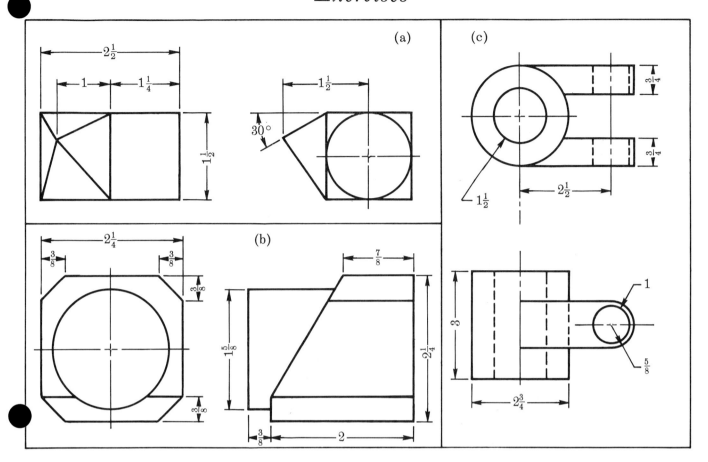

(a)
(c)
(b)

Ex. 14.1 Construct the full size isometric drawing of each of the objects above. Orient in the best position for clarity.

Ex. 14.2 Construct the *UFR* isometric drawing of a 4″ diameter globe. Show the equator and the meridians in the isometric planes.

Ex. 14.3 The centerlines of two 8″ diameter circular sheet metal pipes intersect in a right angle. Show the intersection in an isometric drawing to a convenient scale.

Ex. 14.4 A block 4″ long, 2″ high and 2½″ deep is oriented with the 4″ × 2″ face frontal. A 1½″ diameter hole is drilled through the block on the longitudinal centerline. The upper front portion of the block is then removed by a cutting plane passing through the diagonal of the upper face which runs forward and to the left and also through a point on the lower front edge 1″ to the left of the right face. Construct the *UFR* isometric drawing.

Ex. 14.5 Construct double sized isometric drawings of the objects of Ex. 9.1 as assigned. Choose various orientations for the given views, i.e., take circular view as either top, front, or side.

[165]

Lesson 15

Position in Space

A position in space defines a point. It may be considered as the intersection of three normal planes in orthographic projection. The intersecting planes establish mutually perpendicular axes x, y, and z.

Point B in Figure 15–1 is defined by the intersection of the horizontal xz, frontal xy, and profile yz datum planes. The position of any other point A may then be expressed in terms of measurements perpendicular to the datum planes (parallel to the coordinate axes).

Point A in the figure may be described as being $1''$ above, $1\frac{1}{2}''$ in front of, and $2''$ to the right of point B. This is to say that A lies in the frontal plane which is $1\frac{1}{2}''$ in front of the FDP and which is the locus of all points $1\frac{1}{2}''$ in front of point B. Similarly, A lies in the H plane $1''$ above the HDP, the H plane being the locus of all points $1''$ above B. The profile plane containing A is the locus of all points $2''$ to the right of B.

Sketch in all views the locus of all points which lie $1\frac{1}{2}''$ above B and $1''$ behind A.

Note in the figure the coincidence of the datum planes and the coordinate axes.

Point on a Line

A point on a line must appear on the line in all views.

In Figure 15–2 it is required that point C be located on the line AB $\frac{1}{2}''$ to the right of point A. The profile locus plane (PLP) containing all points $\frac{1}{2}''$ to the right of A is first established. The point at which AB pierces that plane is the required point C.

Line in a Plane

A line lies in a plane if it contains two or more points which lie in the plane.

In the Figure 15–3 the line AB, given in the top view, is to be drawn in the front view so as to lie in the plane of LMN. Since AB is required to lie in the plane, it must intersect LN at 1 and when extended, must meet MN at 2. Then AB lies along line 1–2 in the front view.

Point in a Plane

A point lies in a plane if it is located on any line which lies in the plane.

Point P, given in the front view of Figure 15–4, is to be located in the side view so as to lie in the plane of ABC. A random line 1–2 lying in the plane is drawn through P in the front view and projected into the side. P must lie on 1–2 in the side view. As a matter of convenience, the random line 1–2 is usually drawn through some known point in the plane, such as A, B, or C.

Sketch the construction using $A_F P_F$ as the random line.

[166]

LESSON 15

Determining the Visibility of Lines

1. Any view of an object is bounded by visible lines.

2. The corner, edge, or surface closest to the observer for a particular view must be visible in that view.

3. Any corner, edge, or surface falling within the outline of a surface previously established as visible must be hidden.

4. Of two edges which appear to cross in a view, the one closest to the observer at the apparent intersection is visible in that view.

Rule 4 is a very powerful tool. Its application is seen in Figure 15–5. The outline of a tetrahedron is given in the top and front views. A vertical line through the apparent intersection in the top view intersects BD in point 1 and AC in 2. Since 1 is higher than 2, which is to say, closer to the observer in the top view, BD crosses above AC and is visible in the top view.

In Figure 15–6 the procedure is repeated to fix the visibility in the front view. The HP line representing the apparent intersection in the front view meets BD at 3 and AC at 4. Since 3 lies in front of 4, line BD is visible in the front view.

This method is perfectly general, although in special cases more than two views may be required to establish the intersections of the edges with the normal line representing the apparent intersection.

Use of the Layout Grid

From this lesson forward many of our problems will deal with the relationships which exist between points, lines, and planes, the traditional content of courses in *descriptive geometry*. Most of the problems in descriptive geometry contain very limited given information—a line, a couple of points, perhaps a triangle. It is therefore practical for us to adopt a kind of shorthand to facilitate the presentation of a generous selection of problems in a limited space. This will be accomplished by means of a special coordinate system* to be used in conjunction with the layout grid which you will find on page 179. (Duplicate copies of this grid are provided at the end of the last Lesson.)

Remove the grid and mount it permanently on your drafting board in careful alignment with the T-square. Drawings are to be made on bond paper working sheets mounted on top of the grid. You will find that the grid is clearly visible through the working sheet.

The method of locating points on the grid is illustrated in Figure 15–7. The coordinates are always used to describe the location of points in the front and top views and no other. For example, the front and top views of point A are uniquely located by the notation "$A(1,2,6)$." This point is shown in Figure 15–7. Note that the first number specifies the ortho-T-square line which contains both the front and top views of the point; that the second specifies a T-square line containing A_F; and that the third locates another T-square line, this one containing A_H.

Verify that the coordinates of point B are given by $B(1\frac{3}{4},1\frac{1}{2},5\frac{1}{4})$.

At times we shall wish to convey only a partial description of the location of a point, as for example, $C(3\frac{1}{2},2\frac{1}{2},X)$. This serves to locate C_F uniquely, and defines a locus for C_H

* This grid and coordinate system was devised by Professor C. E. Rowe and first used in his text *Engineering Descriptive Geometry* published in 1939 by D. Van Nostrand Company. Many other systems have been presented since, but none has proven to be as versatile or convenient.

[167]

which is shown labeled L/C_H on the figure. Similarly, note the locus for D_F which is properly specified in the notation $D(X,1\frac{1}{2},X)$, and the locus for E_H given by $E(X,X,7\frac{1}{2})$.

A notation such as "triangle $A(3,1,5)$ B $C(1,1,7)$ indicates that A and C are given points, but that B is an unknown in the statement of the problem.

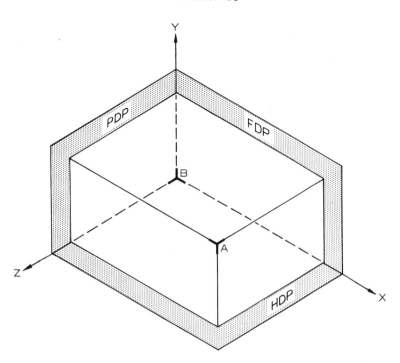

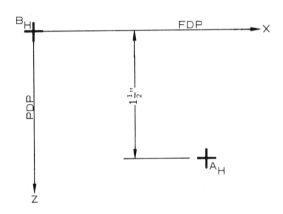

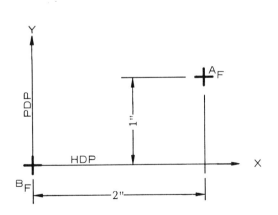

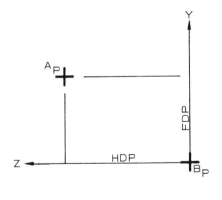

Figure 15–1

FIGURE 15-1

SUPPLEMENTARY NOTES

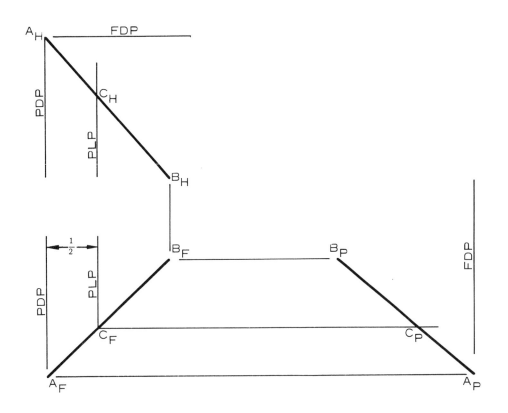

Figure 15–2

SUPPLEMENTARY NOTES

SUPPLEMENTARY NOTES

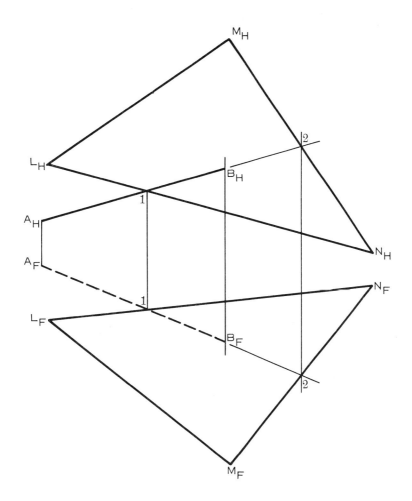

Figure 15–3

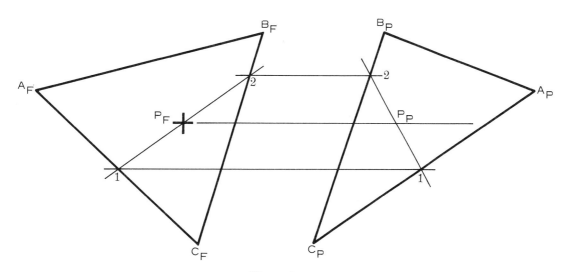

Figure 15–4

SUPPLEMENTARY NOTES

SUPPLEMENTARY NOTES

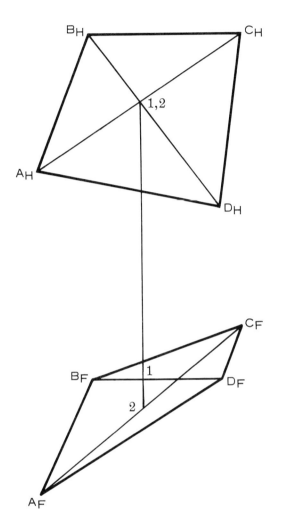

Figure 15–5

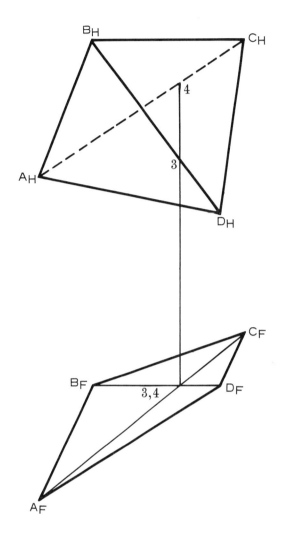

Figure 15–6

SUPPLEMENTARY NOTES

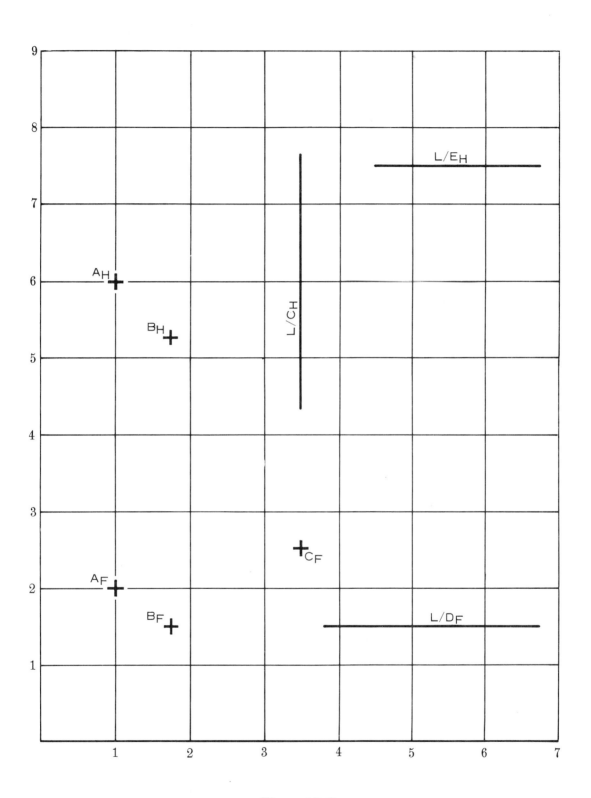

Figure 15–7

SUPPLEMENTARY NOTES

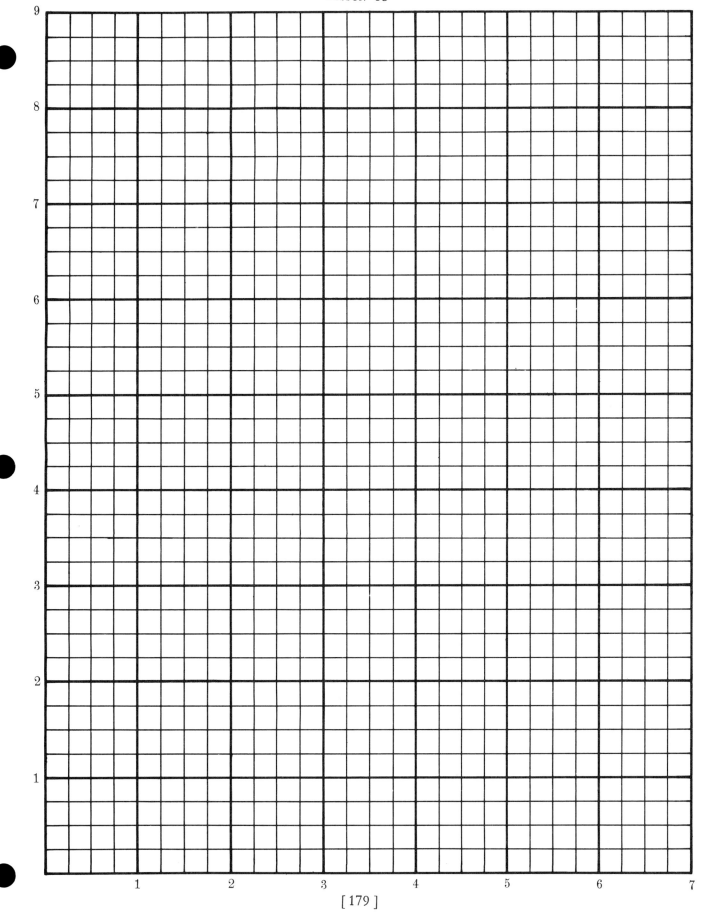

Exercises

Ex. 15.1 Given the following facts, construct the three principal views of the lines $A(1,X,6)B$ and $X(1,3,X)$ $Y(3,2,X)$. (a) Point A is $\frac{1}{2}''$ behind the frontal line XY. (b) Point B lies in the same profile plane as point Y. (c) Point B is $\frac{1}{2}''$ below point X and lies behind X and Y. (d) Line AB is horizontal and $2\frac{1}{2}''$ long.

Ex. 15.2 Given the following facts, construct the three principal views of the lines $AB(1,2,X)$ and $X(3,X,6)Y$. (a) Point Y is in the same profile plane as point B. (b) Line AB is horizontal and has the direction $-FL$. (c) Line XY is frontal and has the direction U–L. (d) Both lines are $2\frac{1}{2}''$ long. (e) Point B is $\frac{3}{4}''$ in front of X and $1''$ to the left of A. (f) Point X is $\frac{3}{4}''$ below point A.

Ex. 15.3 Given lines $A(1,3,5\frac{1}{2})$ $B(1,3,8)$ and $C(0,1,7)$ $D(3,3\frac{1}{2},5\frac{1}{2})$. Construct the following lines to connect AB and CD: (a) a blue horizontal line $2\frac{1}{4}''$ long; (b) a green profile line $1\frac{3}{4}''$ long; (c) a red frontal line $1\frac{3}{4}''$ long.

Ex. 15.4 $A(1,3,7)$ $B(X,2,X)$ and $C(3,X,X)$ are points on the circumference of a circle with center O. Both AB and AC are frontal and each is $3''$ long. B and C are to the right of and below A. Measure the diameter of the circle.

Ex. 15.5 Locate points P and Q in the plane of triangle $A(2\frac{1}{2},4,5\frac{1}{2})$ $B(0,3,7)$ $C(3\frac{1}{2},0\frac{1}{2},7\frac{1}{2})$ in the three principal views. P lies $2''$ to the right of B and $\frac{3}{4}''$ behind A. Q is $1''$ to the left of A and $\frac{1}{2}''$ above C.

Ex. 15.6 Construct the top, front, right and left side views of the tetrahedron $A(4,2,7)$ $B(2\frac{1}{2},1,5\frac{1}{2})$ $C(3,3\frac{1}{2},5)$ $D(4\frac{1}{2},3,6)$.

Ex. 15.7 Construct the principal views of tetrahedron $A(0,4,7)$ $B(1,2,8)$ $C(3,3,7)$ $D(2,4,6)$.

Ex. 15.8 Given the centerlines of the three $\frac{1}{4}''$ diameter rods $A(3,3,6)$ $B(0,1\frac{1}{2},7)$, $C(2,1\frac{1}{2},5)$ $D(0\frac{1}{2},3\frac{1}{2},7\frac{1}{2})$, and $E(3,3\frac{1}{2},5\frac{1}{2})$ $F(1,1,5\frac{1}{2})$. Complete the principal views. Omit hidden lines. Sketch the ends of the rods freehand.

Ex. 15.9 Construct the principal views of the opaque triangles $A(6,5,8)$ $B(3\frac{1}{2},2,6\frac{1}{2})$ $C(5,2,9)$ and BCD $(5,6,6\frac{1}{2})$ showing correct visibility.

Ex. 15.10 Construct the principal views of the tetrahedron $A(3,1,7)$ $B(6,4,7)$ $C(4,1,8)$ $D(4,4,6)$.

Ex. 15.11 Construct the top and front views of the tetrahedron $A(1,3,5)$ $B(3,1,8)$ $C(6,4,5)$ $D(4,3,6)$.

Lesson 16

First Auxiliary Views

The mechanics of the construction of auxiliary views is treated in considerable detail in this text. The technique is of the greatest importance, being fundamental to the solution of the majority of problems in descriptive geometry. The student is urged to attain a complete mastery of the principles and steps involved.

As previously shown, the principal views of an object are those projected onto the normal planes of projection; that is, onto the horizontal, frontal, and profile planes. For these views the directions of sight are normal lines; frontal-profile, horizontal-profile, and horizontal-frontal, respectively.

Frequently circumstances require that views be taken with directions of sight which are either inclined or oblique. Such views are called *auxiliary views* because they supplement the principal views. In any view the direction-of-sight line for that view appears as a point. When the observer looks at an object along an inclined sight-line, he sees a first auxiliary view of the object. A given oblique direction of sight leads to an *oblique* or *second auxiliary*. Auxiliary views of higher than second order also will be found to correspond to oblique directions of sight.

First auxiliary views may be projected from any principal view. In Figure 16–1, for example, a group of views projected from the front view of an object are shown pictorially. The top, bottom, and side views are seen to be the same as if pictured on the surface of the familiar rectangular enclosing glass box. Note that the directions of sight for these views are normal lines and that the planes of projection are normal planes. The direction-of-sight lines for the four auxiliary views are frontal lines, however, and they are perpendicular to the orthofrontal planes of projection. For all eight views the sight lines show true length, and the planes of projection appear as edges in the front view of the object. Note also that, while the height and width dimensions are distorted in the auxiliary views, the depth is common to all and is in true proportion. Depth measurements can therefore be made from any convenient frontal plane taken as a datum.

The planes of projection for the eight views have been revolved through 90° into the plane of the drawing in Figure 16–2, just as the glass box was unfolded in the case of the principal views. The height and width characteristics for each view are seen to be determined by the projectors from the front view, but the depth dimension must be supplied from another source. Because the other views are all obtained by projection from the front, they are called *related views* and the front view is, in this case, the *common view*. The depth measurement is "missing" from the related views, that is, not supplied by projectors, but since it is identical in all of them, it is measured from a convenient frontal datum plane (*FDP*). The *FDP* was arbitrarily taken through the frontmost edge of the object. Therefore, in this case, depth measurements were made toward the back of the object or away from the front view in all related views. Had the datum been taken through the back surface of the object, measurements in all related views would have to be made toward the front view. A violation of this procedure would result in an inverted view, a mirror image of the required view.

To aid in visualizing the position of the auxiliary in space, the view is oriented and named. A vertically-down or *plumb* line is represented in all views as an arrow. It will of course show foreshortened in the auxiliary views. The name of the view is placed below the object, perpendicular to the plumb line. This is the bottom horizontal position on the particular view, and any other lettering placed on that view is oriented as though this were the bottom of the sheet. The subscript A is used for lettered points appearing in a first auxiliary view.

The views are readily named if one imagines the object to be temporarily replaced by a normally oriented cube. The name is then taken from the surfaces of that cube which are visible in the auxiliary. The key letters for the surfaces are written in sequence:

First	Second	Third
Upper (U)	Front (F)	Right (R)
Lower (L)	Back (B)	Left (L)

Since all planes parallel to the datum plane show as edges in the auxiliary view, only two surfaces of the normally oriented cube will be visible in the case of a first auxiliary view. Thus in auxiliaries projected from the front view, all frontal surfaces show as edges, so neither Front nor Back can appear in the name of the view. The missing designator is indicated by a dash. The mechanics of naming and orienting views are the same, regardless of from what view the projection is made.

A family of related views projected from the top view is shown in Figure 16–3. In this case the direction-of-sight lines are horizontal, the planes of projection are ortho-horizontal, and the datum plane are horizontal (*HDP*). The datum plane provides the base for the measurement of height, the dimension not conveyed by the projectors from the top view. The general term *elevation* is frequently applied to any view projected from the top or *plan* view.

The side view is taken as the common view in Figure 16–4. Since the side view contains the dimensions height and depth, the projectors automatically supply these dimensions to the auxiliary. The width measurements are made from a profile datum plane (*PDP*). The directions of sight are profile lines and are perpendicular to the orthoprofile planes of projection.

Construction Procedure

The step-by-step procedure for the construction of a first auxiliary view will now be illustrated. In Figure 16–5(a) the object is first visualized in a pictorial sketch and the corners of the object are numbered in all views. A plumb line is identified on the object, or, if no frontal-profile line is present, one is added. The direction of sight for the required view is established (given in this instance) and shown in the principal views. It immediately reveals that the upper and right surfaces of a normally oriented cube would be visible. The name of the auxiliary is therefore *U–R AUX*.

The corners of the object are shown projected by number into the auxiliary in Figure 16–5(b). The projectors from the common view convey height and width. Depth is measured from a convenient *FDP*, in this case taken through the rear of the object so as to contain a maximum of the numbered points. Measurements in the related views are then made toward the front view, and locus lines parallel to the datum plane are drawn in the auxiliary to complete the grid. The plumbline 3–4 is then drawn, and the name of the view is placed in the bottom-horizontal position. The *FDP* is lettered to read from the right with respect to the position of the name of the view. Note that the direction of sight plots as a point in the auxiliary.

The numbered corners are shown joined in accordance with the rules of visibility in Figure 16–5(c) to complete the required view. The outlines of surfaces known to be visible are always plotted first. The direction-of-sight arrow in the front view immediately identifies surfaces 2–3–6–5 and 1–2–3 as visible. The sight arrow in the top view shows that the orthohorizontal surface 1–2–3–4 must also be visible in the auxiliary. Since the auxiliary is projected from the front view, it is known that all frontal surfaces should appear as edges in the auxiliary. This is the case with 1–5–6–7. At this juncture the entire outline of the figure has been filled with visible surfaces, so all remaining outlines must be hidden. The remaining surfaces are plotted. The profile face 3–4–7–6 provides the hidden line 4–7 and the remaining plane, the horizontal triangle 1–4–7, checks the entire construction.

Throughout this entire procedure it has been unnecessary to visualize the view under construction. In many cases this can easily be done, but the foregoing procedure is rapid, and if carefully done, prohibits mistakes. Certainly one should take a long, careful look at the finished product and check the work by mental visualization.

The steps in the construction can be summarized very briefly.

1. Visualize the object in a pictorial sketch.
2. Number corners in all views.
3. Identify or provide plumb line.
4. Establish direction of sight in principal views and determine name of required auxiliary.
5. Establish datum in related views.
6. Draw projectors and complete grid.
7. Draw plumb line and record name of view in bottom-horizontal position.
8. Plot visible surfaces by number.
9. Plot all remaining surfaces.
10. Verify work by visualization.

A specimen solution is given in Figure 16–6 in which auxiliary views of a tetrahedron are developed in all quadrants to illustrate the proper naming and orienting of all possible first auxiliary views.

The essential relationships between sight lines, datum planes, planes of projection, and names of views are given in Table 16–1. Complete the remaining portions of the table.

TABLE 16–1 First Auxiliary Views

Direction of sight*	Project from	Plane of projection	Missing dimension	Datum plane	Name of view
Horizontal	Top view	Orthohorizontal	Height	HDP	–FR Aux
					–FL Aux
					–BR Aux
					–BL Aux
Frontal					U–R Aux
					U–L Aux
					L–R Aux
					L–L Aux
Profile					UF– Aux
					UB– Aux
					LF– Aux
					LB– Aux

* Note: Recall that the direction of sight for a particular view shows as a point in that view.

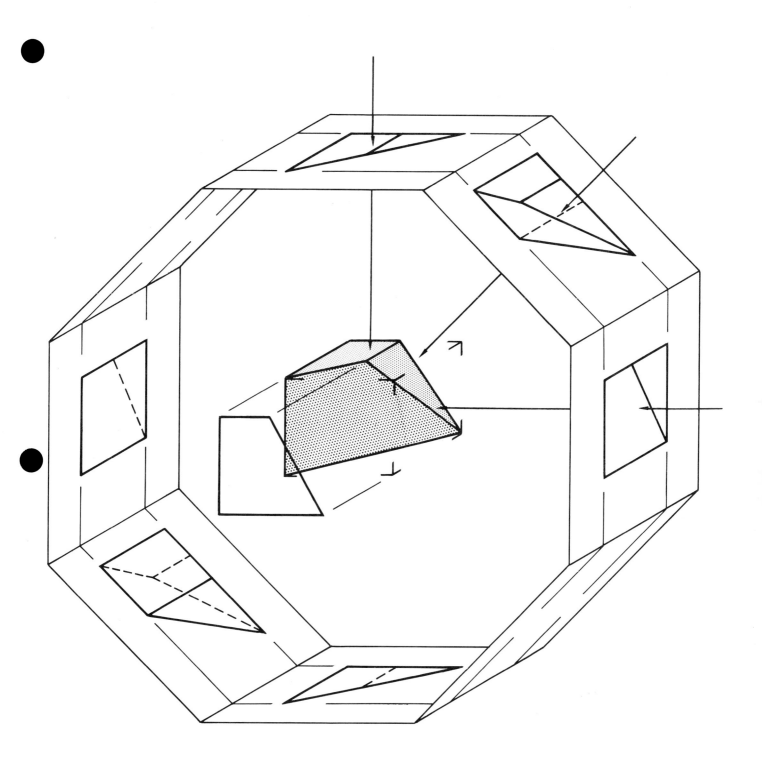

Figure 16–1

SUPPLEMENTARY NOTES

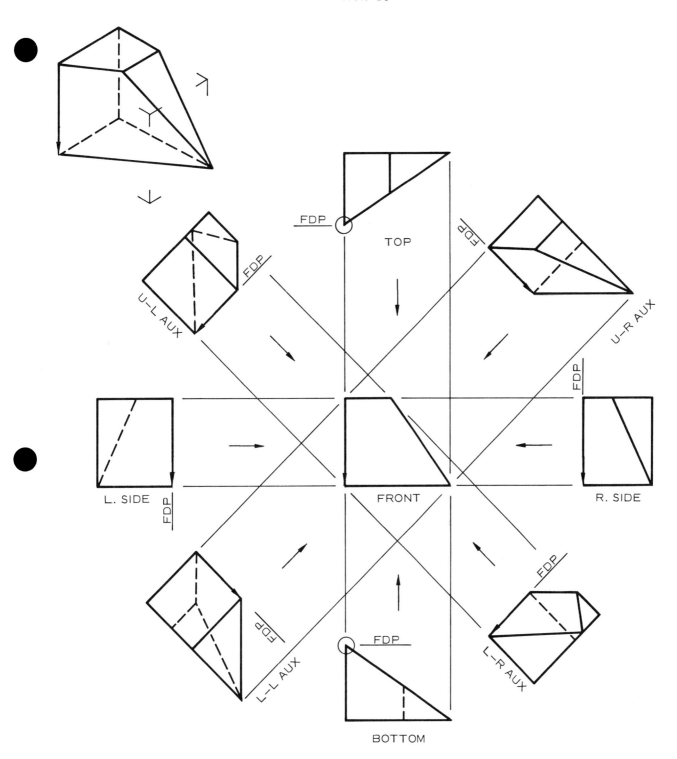

Figure 16-2

[189]

FIGURE 16-2

SUPPLEMENTARY NOTES

SUPPLEMENTARY NOTES

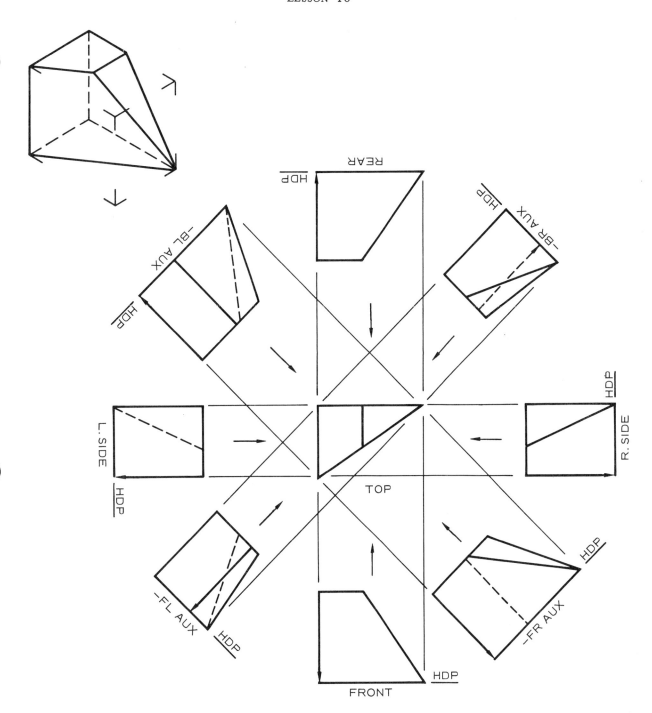

Figure 16–3

[191]

SUPPLEMENTARY NOTES

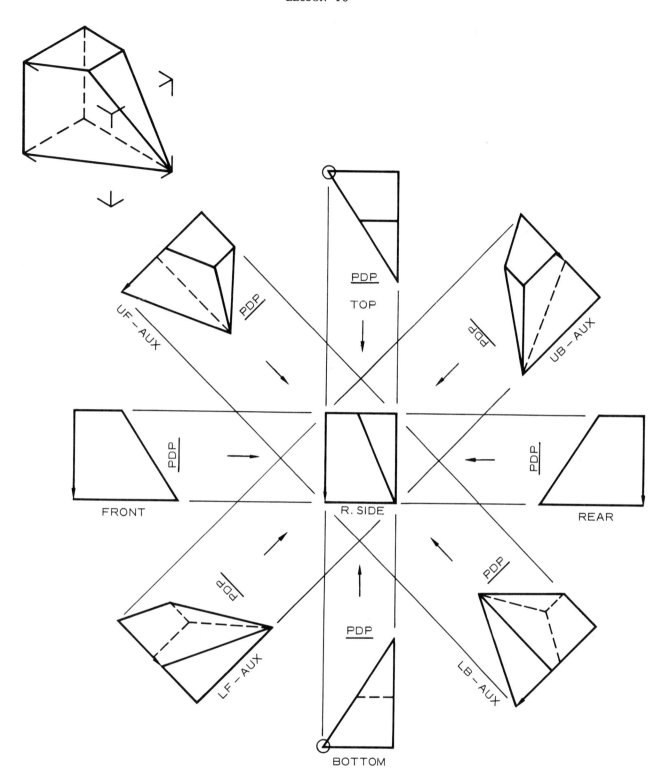

Figure 16–4

SUPPLEMENTARY NOTES

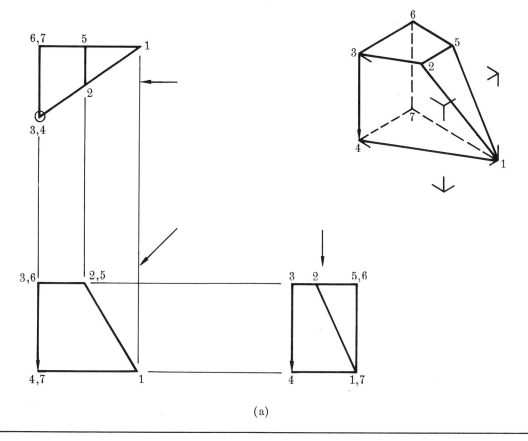

(a)

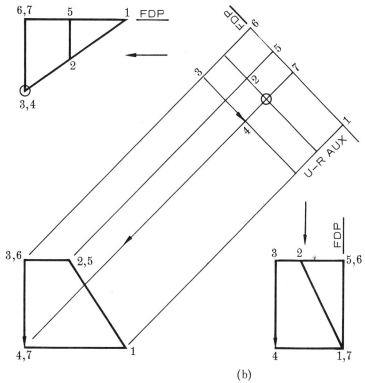

(b)

Figure 16-5

SUPPLEMENTARY NOTES

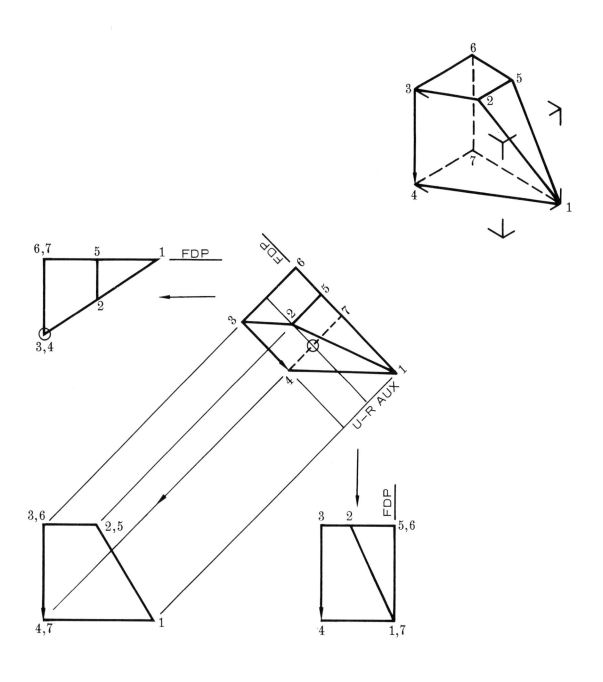

(c)

Figure 16–5

SUPPLEMENTARY NOTES

SUPPLEMENTARY NOTES

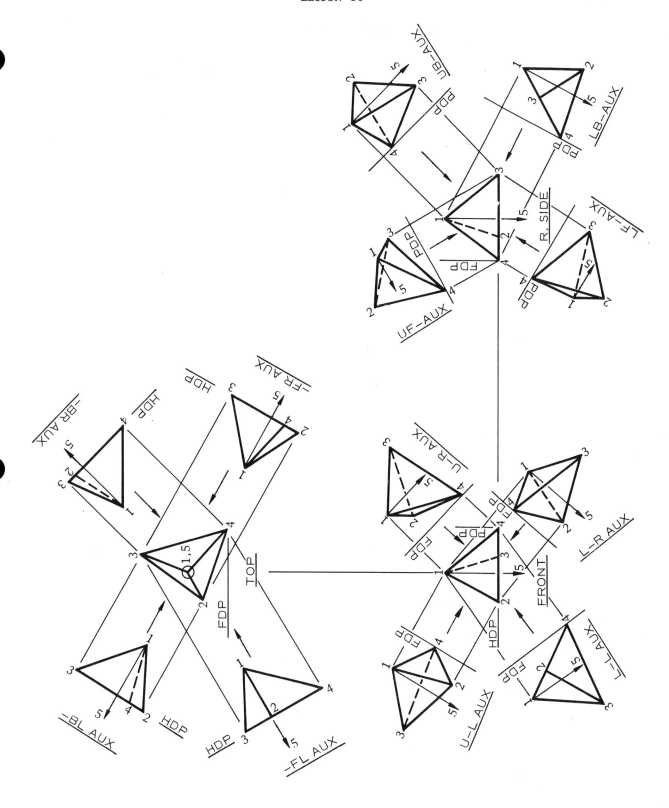

Figure 16–6

SUPPLEMENTARY NOTES

SUPPLEMENTARY NOTES

Exercises

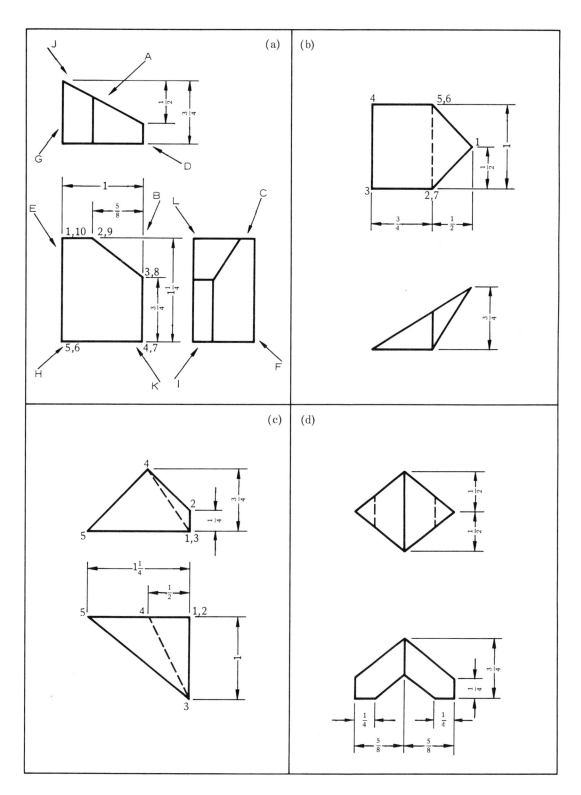

Ex. 16.1 For each of the objects shown above, construct auxiliary views as indicated in (a). Name and orient auxiliaries. Construct the required views in alphabetical sequence. Make layout in the manner of Figure 16–6.

Lesson 17

True Shape of an Inclined Plane

An inclined surface is seen in true shape (TS) in the auxiliary view whose direction of sight is perpendicular to the surface. It follows that the plane of projection is parallel to the surface.

In Figure 17–1 the true shape of the orthofrontal plane 2–3–4 is required. The direction of sight is necessarily frontal and perpendicular to the edge view of the plane. The required auxiliary is constructed mechanically.

Study the figure and then consider what the appearance of the solution would have been, had 2–3–4 been given as a triangle in space rather than as a surface on an object.

How would you go about obtaining the true shape of the surface 2–4–5?

True Length of an Oblique Line

An oblique line may be thought of as lying in an inclined plane. In a view showing the true shape of that inclined plane, the oblique line must show in true length (TL).

The line AB is given in Figure 17–2. An orthofrontal plane containing AB is imagined and the auxiliary view is plotted, which would be the true shape of that plane. The true length of AB is measured in the auxiliary.

Could the true length of AB have been obtained by projection from the top view? From the side view?

Point View of an Inclined Line

A view of a line taken with the direction of sight parallel to the line shows the line as a point. Recalling that the sight arrow for an auxiliary must be true length, it is evident that the projection must be made from the view showing the line in true length.

In Figure 17–3 line AB is horizontal, hence true length in the top view. The direction of sight is parallel to AB and gives the point view in an auxiliary elevation.

Can you prove that all views projected from the point view of a line must show the line in true length?

Edge View of an Oblique Plane

A plane will appear as an edge in any view which shows some line in the plane as a point. As we have just seen, a point view of a line can be obtained only by projection from a true length view. It is therefore a necessary preliminary that a true length line in the plane be identified. The construction is illustrated in Figure 17–4.

Line AB of the given triangle is frontal, hence TL in the front view. The auxiliary view giving the point view of AB shows plane ABC as an edge.

How might the problem be attacked if the edges of the triangle were all oblique lines?

Auxiliary Views by Inspection

The true shape of an inclined surface is frequently required for dimensioning purposes. Such views can often be obtained by mental visualization alone without the necessity of numbering corners and projecting mechanically.

Consider the *E*-shaped prism of Figure 17–5. The front and right side views are given, and the view of the entire object which shows the orthoprofile face in true shape is required.

Surveying the problem, the student should immediately recognize by the principle of consistent configuration that the *E* shape must appear at either end of the prism as shown. The completion of the solution by the addition of the horizontal surfaces with proper visibility is left to the student.

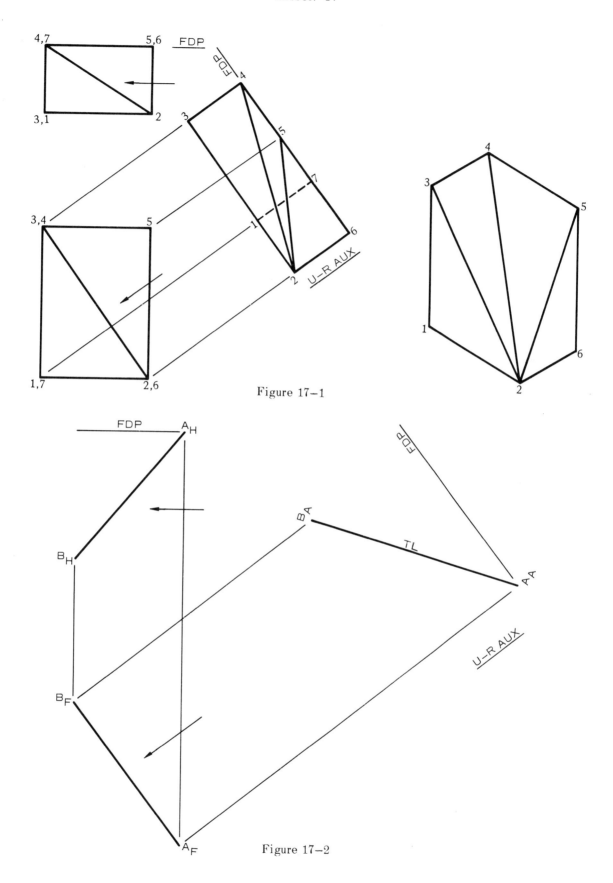

Figure 17–1

Figure 17–2

SUPPLEMENTARY NOTES

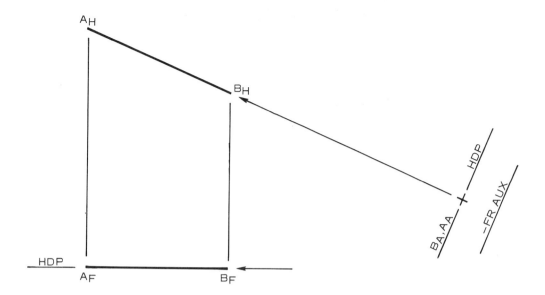

Figure 17–3

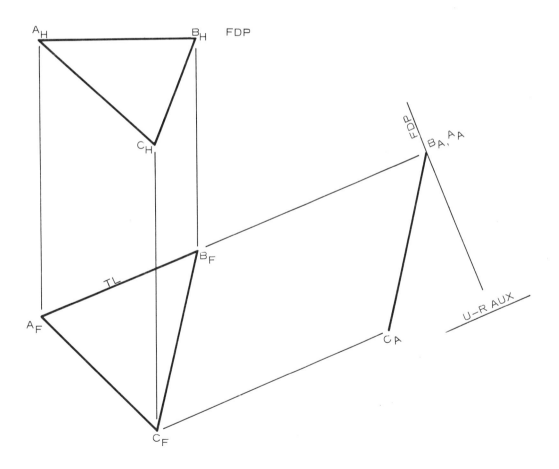

Figure 17–4

SUPPLEMENTARY NOTES

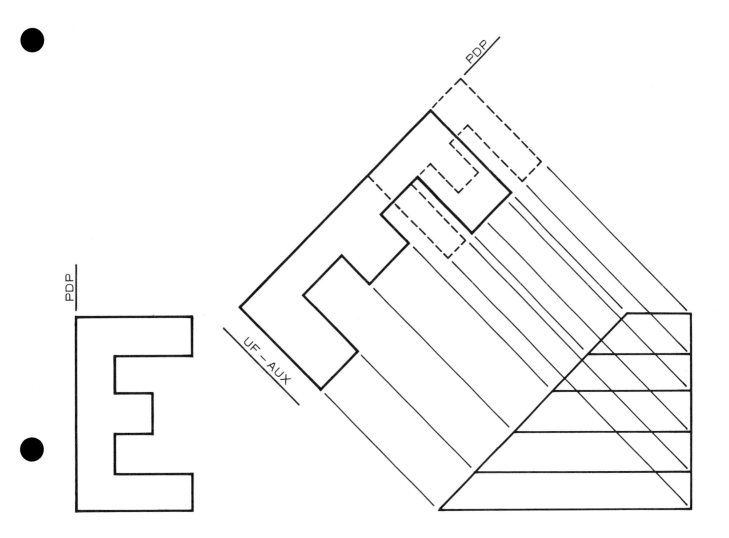

Figure 17—5

SUPPLEMENTARY NOTES

Exercises

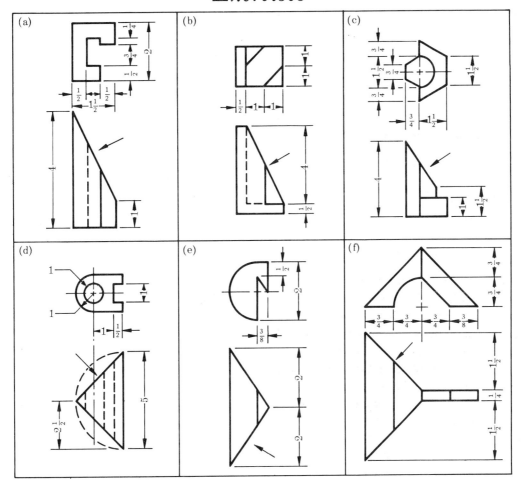

Ex. 17.1 Construct the given views and the indicated auxiliary view of the entire object to show the inclined surface in true shape for each problem shown above.

Ex. 17.2 Construct a view of tetrahedron $A(1,3,8)$ $B(3,4,8)$ $C(2,3,6)$ $D(2,1,6)$ in which line BA appears as a point.

Ex. 17.3 Find and record where measured the true length of line $A(1,1,6)$ $B(3,3,8)$. Project from the top view and then check in a projection from the side view.

Ex. 17.4 Obtain the view of tetrahedron $A(1,1,6)$ $B(3,3,8)$ $C(3,4,6)$ $D(3,1,6)$ in which surface ABC appears as an edge. Also obtain the view showing ABD as an edge.

Ex. 17.5 The tetrahedron of Ex. 17.4 is cut by an OF plane through line $L(3,0,7)$ $M(1,3,8)$ and the portion to the right of the plane is discarded. Construct the view of the entire remaining portion which shows the cut surface in true shape.

Ex. 17.6 The irregular pentagon $A(0,1,7)$ $B(1,0,8)$ $C(3,1\frac{1}{2},7)$ $D(3,X,6)$ $E(2,X,5)$ is the base of an oblique pyramid with vertex at $V(0\frac{1}{2},3,9)$. (a) Complete the top and front views. (b) The pyramid is cut by an OF plane through line $L(0\frac{1}{2},4,8)$ $M(3\frac{1}{2},0,6)$ and the right-hand portion is discarded. Construct the view of the entire remaining portion which shows the cut surface in true shape.

[211]

Lesson 18

Plane Perpendicular to a Line

A plane which is perpendicular to a given line must show as an edge and at right angles to the line in any view showing the line in its true length. For example, the base of a right pyramid would show as an edge in all TL views of the axis. In a view showing the axis as a point, the base would, of course, show in TS.

Locus Planes in Auxiliary Views

Locus planes parallel to the datum plane may be drawn in a first auxiliary view to convey a principal dimension (height, depth, or width).

AB is the given axis of a right prism in Figure 18–1. The bases of the prism are equilateral triangles which may be inscribed in $2''$ diameter circles. One corner of the base at B is behind and $\frac{3}{4}''$ below B. Problem: Construct the prism.

AB is first identified as being TL in the top view. The planes of the bases are drawn as edges perpendicular to AB in that view. An auxiliary taken with direction of sight parallel to AB and projected from the TL view necessarily shows the bases in TS. The vertices of the required triangles are known to lie on the $2''$ diameter locus circle (LC). In the front and auxiliary views the locus plane (LP) is drawn $\frac{3}{4}''$ below B. In the auxiliary the required vertex must be either X or X'. Carrying both these points back to the top view it becomes at once evident that only X' satisfies the locus condition, "behind B."

Complete the solution drawing the three views of the prism with colored pencil. Always recheck a problem to see that all locus conditions given have been used and that all have been satisfied.

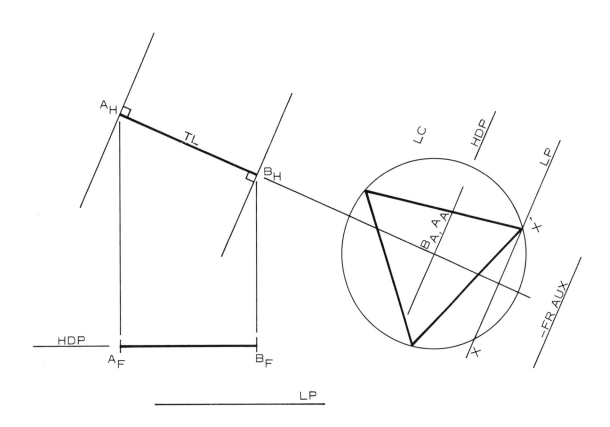

Figure 18–1

SUPPLEMENTARY NOTES

Exercises

Ex. 18.1 $A(0,2,7)$ is the vertex and $B(2\frac{1}{2},2,5\frac{1}{2})$ is the center of the base of a right pyramid whose base is a square having $3''$ diagonals. One corner (X) of the base is behind B and $\frac{3}{4}''$ below B. Complete the top, front, and necessary auxiliary view.

Ex. 18.2 $A(1,3,7)$ $B(2\frac{1}{2},4,7)$ is the axis of a right prism whose bases are equilateral triangles having altitudes of $2\frac{1}{4}''$. One corner (X) of the base at B is to the left of and $1''$ behind B. Complete the top, front, and necessary auxiliary views.

Ex. 18.3 QRS is an equilateral triangle which has an altitude of $2''$ and lies in an orthoprofile plane containing line $A(4\frac{1}{2},0,5)$ $B(5\frac{1}{2},1\frac{1}{2},7)$. Q is $\frac{1}{2}''$ to the right of B and $\frac{1}{2}''$ above A. Points R and S both lie behind and to the left of Q. In the side view QR appears to be $\frac{3}{4}''$ in length. Construct the principal views of QRS and such additional views as may be necessary.

Ex. 18.4 $V(2,3,7)O$ is the axis of a right pyramid. VO is $2''$ long. The vertex V is above and $1''$ in front of O. The base of the pyramid is a rectangle $1\frac{1}{2}'' \times 1''$ and lies in an orthoprofile plane. The short sides of the base are horizontal-frontal lines. Obtain the principal views of the pyramid and any additional views needed.

Ex. 18.5 $A(1,2,7)$ $B(3,3,7)$ is the upper lateral edge of a right prism. The bases are isosceles triangles proportioned such that $1''$ diameter circles may be inscribed. The unequal leg of each base is horizontal. One corner (X) of the base at A is $1\frac{1}{4}''$ below A. Complete the top, front, and necessary additional views.

Ex. 18.6 $V(0,3,6)$ is the vertex and $O(2,3,8\frac{1}{2})$ is the midpoint of the base of a horizontal isosceles triangle. The base is $1\frac{1}{2}''$ long. This triangle is the upper lateral face of a right pyramid. The base of the pyramid is a rectangle $1\frac{1}{2}'' \times 2\frac{1}{2}''$. Complete the top, front, and necessary additional views.

Lesson 19

Second Auxiliary Views

Many problems in descriptive geometry require that views be drawn for which the direction of sight is an oblique line. The procedures for constructing such views are simply an extension of those already studied for first auxiliary views. They are best explained by example.

In Figure 19–1 the top and front views of a pyramid are given along with AB, the direction-of-sight arrow for the required auxiliary view. Since the sight arrow must appear as a point in the required view, the first step must be to obtain a view in which the arrow is shown in TL. In the figure the TL of AB has been obtained in the auxiliary elevation. The direction of sight for this view is indicated by dashed arrows. It must not be confused with the sight direction for the second auxiliary. As we have previously seen, the auxiliary elevation and the front view are related views. Both are projected from the top view, which is the common view in this case, and both contain the same datum plane perpendicular to the projectors joining them to the common view.

The second auxiliary is obtained by projection from the auxiliary elevation to give the point view of AB. Just as the first auxiliary and the front view were related, with the top view being the common view, so the second auxiliary and the top view are related views, both being projected from the auxiliary elevation as the common view. The related views must have the same datum plane shown perpendicular to the projectors joining them to the common view. The datum plane for a second auxiliary is an inclined plane: orthohorizontal when the projection is begun from the top view ($OHDP$), ortho-frontal when begun from the front view ($OFDP$), and orthoprofile when begun from the side view ($OPDP$).

In plotting, care must be exercised to avoid the inversion of a view. The measurement to a point from the datum plane must be made toward the common view in both of the related views, or away from the common view in both. Should confusion arise as to the position of the datum planes, it will be found helpful to think of the first auxiliary as being the front view. Then the second auxiliary would be an L–L Aux and the $OHDP$ would be a FDP. The construction of the oblique would then be identical to that of a first auxiliary.

The subscript o is used for lettered points in second auxiliary views.

A plumb line is carried through the entire construction to orient the oblique view. It is generally advisable to draw it with a colored pencil to avoid confusion with sight arrows. The name of the view is placed horizontally below the view (perpendicular to the plumb line) and, as in the case of first auxiliary views, is taken from the visible faces of a normally oriented cube in the position of the given object. In the top and front views of the example, the sight arrow AB clearly shows that the lower, front, and left faces of such a cube would be visible; hence the name, LFL Aux.

Instead of beginning this solution with a first auxiliary projected from the top view, it would have been equally valid to obtain the true length of the sight arrow in an auxiliary projected from the front view. The point is illustrated in Figure 19–2. Here the given sight line is projected from the top view off to the left and from the front view off to the right. The resulting oblique views, the point views of the sight arrows, are identical except for their orientation on the paper and their datum planes. Why does the datum plane coincide with the plumb line in one of the oblique views, but not in the other?

The mechanics of naming the views is illuminated by the lettered surfaces of the given cube. Using colored pencils add direction-of-sight arrows for each of the first auxiliary views. Number the corners of the cube and verify both projections.

Make sense of the following statement: The plane of projection of the first auxiliary view is in each case the same as the datum plane of the second auxiliary projected therefrom.

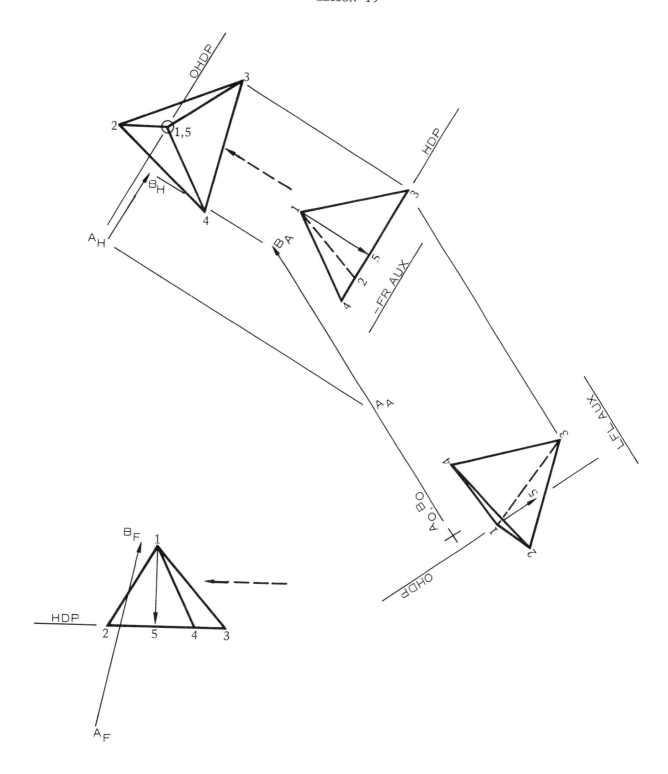

Figure 19—1

SUPPLEMENTARY NOTES

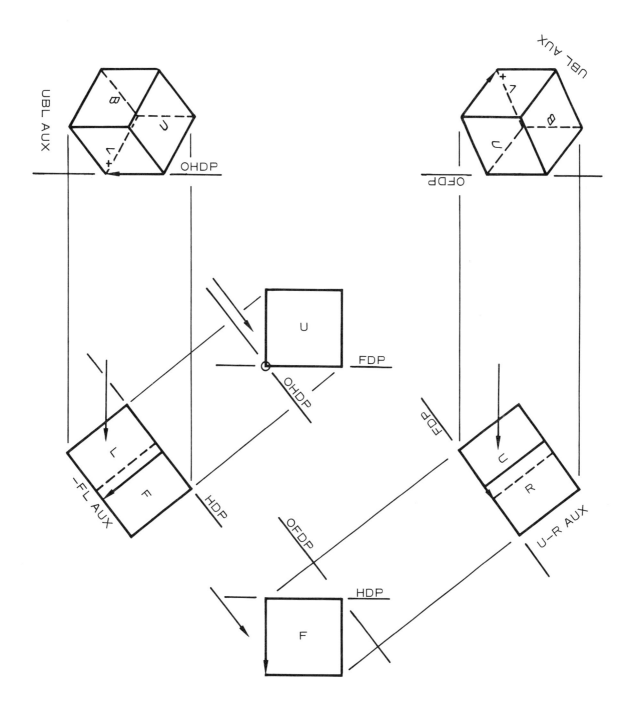

Figure 19–2

SUPPLEMENTARY NOTES

SUPPLEMENTARY NOTES

Exercises

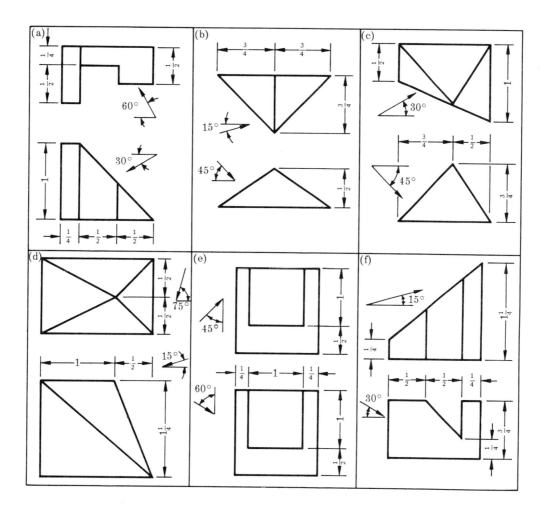

Ex. 19.1 Construct the indicated second auxiliary views of the objects given above. Name and orient all auxiliary views.

Ex. 19.2 Construct the most descriptive isometric projection of each of the objects pictured above. Name and orient all auxiliary views.

Ex. 19.3 $A(4\frac{1}{2},1,8)$ $B(6\frac{1}{2},2,6)$ $C(6,3,8\frac{1}{2})$ $D(4,2\frac{1}{2},6)$ is a quadrilateral which has been folded along line AC. Obtain the view of the figure taken with the direction of sight parallel to AC.

Ex. 19.4 The given views as described by the coordinates are adjacent auxiliary views of line $A(3\frac{1}{2},3\frac{1}{4},7\frac{1}{2})$ $B(3,3\frac{1}{2},7)$ and plumb line $BC(3\frac{1}{2},4,6\frac{3}{4})$. The lower of the two views on the sheet is a *LB-Aux*. Obtain the principal views of AB by projection from the given views. Show all possible solutions and name and orient all views including the given.

Ex. 19.5 The given views are adjacent auxiliary views of a tetrahedron $A(5\frac{1}{2},3,8)$ $B(6,1\frac{1}{2},7\frac{1}{2})$ $C(5,1\frac{1}{2},6)$ $D(4\frac{1}{2},2,7\frac{1}{2})$. The plumb line is $DE(4,1,6\frac{1}{2})$. The lower of the two views on the sheet is a *L–R Aux*. By projection from the given views, obtain the top and front views of the tetrahedron. Name and orient all views including the given.

[223]

Lesson 20

True Length Line in a Plane

A family of parallel true length lines in a plane can be found in any view of the plane. In Figure 20–1 the top, front, and auxiliary elevation views of triangle ABC are given. Any TL line in the plane in the front view is a frontal line and shows as a T-square line in the top view. The T-square line A–1 drawn in the top view is shown projected into the front view where it is TL. Any line parallel to A–1 is also frontal and TL in the front view.

A TL line has been established similarly in the auxiliary elevation. A line which is to show TL in the auxiliary must, in the top view, appear perpendicular to the direction of sight for the auxiliary. One such line, B–2, is drawn in the top view and projected into the auxiliary. Note that since AC in the two views was found to be nearly parallel to the projectors joining the views, point 2 was projected into the front view and then transferred into the auxiliary by means of a horizontal locus plane to give maximum accuracy in plotting.

With colored pencil, project from the auxiliary to obtain a TL line in the top view.

True Shape of an Oblique Plane

The true shape of any plane is obtained in a view taken normal to the edge view of the plane. The edge view of an oblique plane is obtained in a first auxiliary projected with a direction of sight parallel to a TL line in a principal view. The true shape is then found in the second auxiliary projected with direction of sight perpendicular to the edge view of the plane in the first auxiliary. The sight line for the oblique shows as a point in that view and TL in the first auxiliary. It is projected back into the principal views so that the name of the second auxiliary may be determined. Sight lines should be drawn with colored pencil.

Figure 20–2 shows the complete construction for the TS of triangle ABC. Carefully studied, it is self-explanatory.

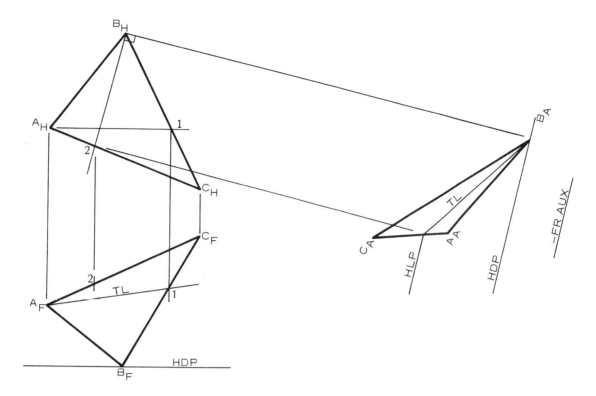

Figure 20-1

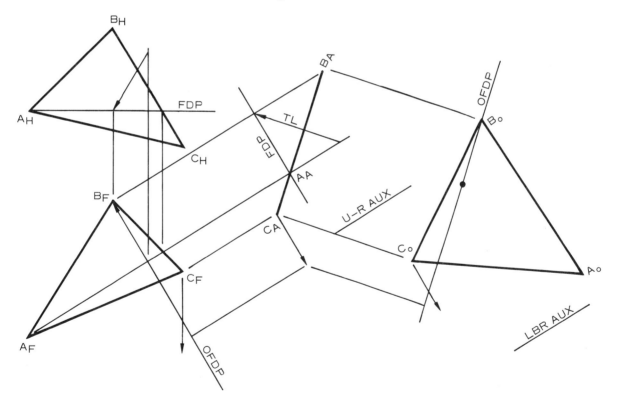

Figure 20-2

SUPPLEMENTARY NOTES

Exercises

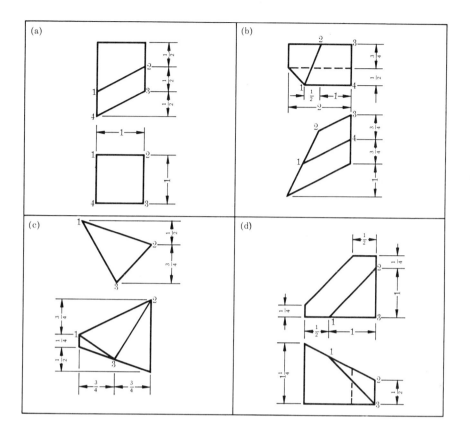

Ex. 20.1 Obtain the true shape view of the triangle $A(6,2,8)$ $B(5,1,6)$ $C(4,3\frac{1}{2},7)$. In the true shape view draw and label a horizontal line, a frontal line, and a profile line in the plane of the triangle. Project from the top view.

Ex. 20.2 Solve Ex. 20.1 by projection from the front view. Observe in the principal views the relation between the sight line for the true shape view and the true length lines in the plane.

Ex. 20.3 Construct the view of the tetrahedron $A(1,5\frac{1}{4},6\frac{1}{4})$ $B(2,3\frac{1}{2},8)$ $C(0,4,7)$ $D(0\frac{1}{2},5\frac{1}{2},8)$ which shows the surface ABC in true shape.

Ex. 20.4 Obtain the view of each of the objects pictured which shows the numbered oblique surface visible and true shape.

Ex. 20.5 Points $A(0\frac{1}{2},2,4\frac{1}{2})$ $B(1,3,5)$ $C(2,0\frac{1}{2},6)$ lie on the surface of a 3″ diameter sphere. In the top and front views show the two possible locations of the center of the sphere, O and O'.

Ex. 20.6 Triangle $A(0\frac{1}{2},3,8)BC$ is isosceles. The base BC coincides with line $L(1\frac{1}{2},1,9)$ $M(1\frac{1}{2},4,7)$. One leg of the triangle, AB, is frontal. Complete the top, front, and necessary auxiliary views.

Ex. 20.7 $A(0,2,7)$ $B(2,2\frac{1}{2},8)$ $C(1,1,X)$ is an equilateral triangle. Locate the possible positions of point C in the top view.

Lesson 21

Successive Auxiliary Views

There is no limit to the number of auxiliary views which can be plotted in sequence. Each view drawn is related to the original orientation of the object by means of the plumb line and the name of the view. In order to name each oblique, it is necessary to carry the direction-of-sight arrow back into the principal views. A separate color should be used for the sight lines for each view.

The mechanics of projection for a fifth auxiliary are identical to those employed in the construction of a first or second auxiliary. The preceding view is the common view. The one before that in the sequence is the related view. The related view and the one under construction show the same datum plane as an edge perpendicular to the projectors from the common view. Measurements are made from the datum toward the common view in both related views, or away from the common view in both.

In the event of a temporary confusion, the two previously completed views can be thought of as being principal views while that under construction is considered to be a first auxiliary. The significance of the datum plane will then become clear.

It will be recalled that the datum plane for a first auxiliary view is a principal plane, and that for a second auxiliary it is an inclined plane. The datum for all higher order auxiliaries is an oblique plane (ODP). When a number of different oblique datum planes appear on the same sheet, they should be given distinguishing subscripts or superscripts such as ODP^2, ODP^3, etc., or they can be labeled with pencils of different color. The subscript o is used for lettered points in a second auxiliary; o' for a third, o'' for a fourth, and so on.

The naming and orienting of a fourth auxiliary view is demonstrated in Figure 21–1. For each of the other auxiliary views add sight lines, datum planes, and the name of the view, properly recorded. Use a different color for the work relating to each of the views. Careful sketching should provide sufficient accuracy.

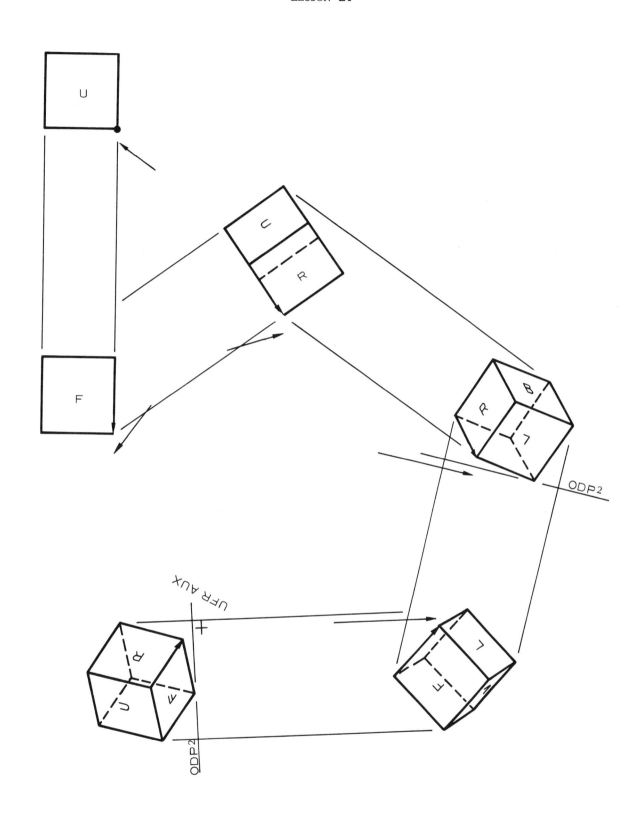

Figure 21–1

SUPPLEMENTARY NOTES

Exercises

Ex. 21.1 Obtain a view of tetrahedron $A(0\frac{1}{2},2\frac{3}{4},6)$ $B(1\frac{1}{4},3\frac{1}{2},5\frac{1}{4})$ $C(0,4,5\frac{1}{2})$ $D(0,3,5)$ in which lines AC and BD both appear true length.

Ex. 21.2 Obtain a view of the tetrahedron of Ex. 21.1 in which lines BC and AD appear parallel.

Ex. 21.3 First obtain a view of the tetrahedron $A(5,3,5)$ $B(6,4,4\frac{1}{2})$ $C(6\frac{1}{4},3\frac{1}{2},5\frac{1}{4})$ $D(6,3,6)$ in which lines CD and AB appear parallel. Then find a view in which the same lines appear perpendicular.

Ex. 21.4 Construct a view of pyramid $V(2,4,5)$ $A(0,3,6)$ $B(0\frac{1}{2},4\frac{1}{2},6\frac{1}{4})$ $C(1,4,6\frac{1}{2})$ $D(1\frac{1}{2},2\frac{1}{2},6\frac{3}{4})$ in which plane VAD appears as an edge and line BC shows in true length. Project from the front view.

Ex. 21.5 $V(1,X,5)$ is the vertex and $O(2,2,6)$ is the center of the base of a right pyramid. The base is a regular pentagon lying in an OH plane. The lowest side of the base is $\frac{3}{4}$" long and horizontal. Using a minimum of projections, obtain a view showing the upper lateral edge in true length and the lower lateral surface as an edge.

Ex. 21.6 $V(1\frac{1}{2},5,6\frac{1}{2})$ $A(0,5,7)$ $B(0\frac{3}{4},5\frac{1}{2},8)$ $C(0\frac{3}{4},4\frac{1}{2},8)$ $D(0,4,7)$ is an oblique pyramid. Obtain the view of the entire object in which line AB appears as a point. Project from that view to obtain one showing the base of the pyramid in true shape. Finally, from this latter view, project to obtain a $-B-$ view of the object.

Ex. 21.7 Triangle $C(0\frac{1}{2},3\frac{1}{2},5\frac{3}{4})$ $D(1,1\frac{1}{2},5\frac{1}{2})$ $E(2,3,5)$ is the common base of two pyramids having vertices at $A(0,2,5)$ and $B(2\frac{1}{2},3\frac{1}{4},6\frac{1}{4})$. Project to obtain a view in which plane BCE appears as an edge perpendicular to line BD. Make the first projection from the front view.

Ex. 21.8 List the steps necessary to the solution of the following problems. Reference may be made to illustrative sketches if desired.

> SAMPLE: Given an OF triangle and a H line. Obtain a view showing the line true length and the plane as an edge.
>
> 1. Project from the front view perpendicular to the edge view of the plane to obtain TS of plane in 1st auxiliary.
> 2. Project perpendicular to the given line from 1st auxiliary to obtain its TL in 2nd auxiliary. Plane appears as edge parallel to $OFDP$ in this view. This is then the required view.

(a) Given the top and front views of a H line segment and a F line segment. Obtain view showing both in true length. (b) Given the top and front views of a square in an oblique position. The square is the base of a right pyramid of a given altitude. Locate the possible positions of the vertex. (c) Given the principal views of an orthofrontal triangle and an orthoprofile square. Obtain a view in which both appear as edges. (d) Given the principal views of a point A and of a triangle QRS, the length of a line AB, and a horizontal plane H. B lies in the plane of triangle QRS and in the given H plane. Locate all possible positions of B satisfying these conditions.

Lesson 22

Circle in an Oblique Plane

Elliptical views of a circle may be drawn by the direct projection of points on the circumference from the circular view as shown in Figure 22–1. It is required that a 2″ diameter circle with center at A and lying in the plane of triangle ABC be drawn in the top and front views. The point-by-point plotting shown is cumbersome and time consuming.

A much more convenient attack is shown in Figure 22–2. The edge view of the plane is obtained by projection from both the top and front views. The major diameter of the required ellipse coincides with the true length line in the plane in both views. The 2″ diameter is laid off in the edge views and projected back in each principal view establishing the minor diameter. The trammel may now be used to complete the ellipses.

An Application of Locus Planes

The line of intersection of two planes shows as a point in the view in which the planes appear as edges. This important observation is applied in the solution of the following problem pictured in Figure 22–3.

V is the vertex and O is the center of the square base of a right pyramid. The diagonals of the base are 2″ long. Corner A of the base is to the left of and $\frac{1}{2}$″ above O. Construct the top, front, and necessary auxiliary views of the pyramid.

The attack on the problem is similar to that given on page 212 which should be restudied before proceeding. The locus plane for point A (LP/A) shows as an edge in an auxiliary elevation which also shows the plane of the base as an edge. The two intersect in A, the point view of horizontal line 1–2. Points 1 and 2 are chosen to lie on the 2″ diameter locus circle in the oblique view and are projected back into the top view in order to determine which satisfies the condition "to the left of O." It is left for you to complete the solution. Sketch with a colored pencil.

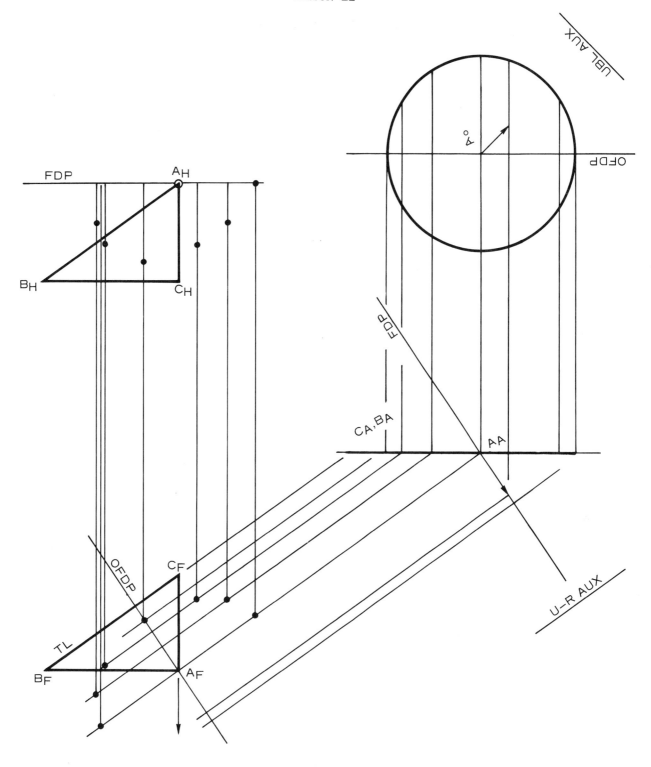

Figure 22–1

SUPPLEMENTARY NOTES

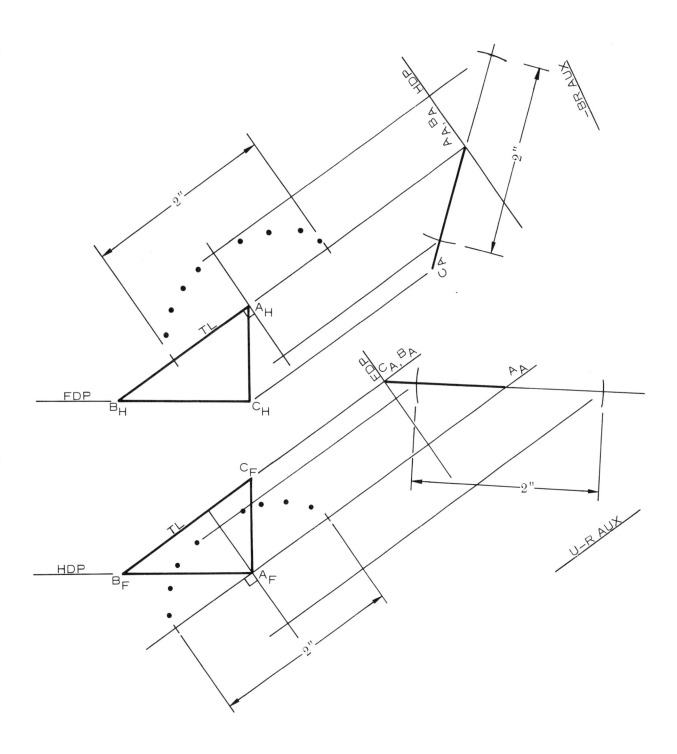

Figure 22–2

FIGURE 22–2

SUPPLEMENTARY NOTES

SUPPLEMENTARY NOTES

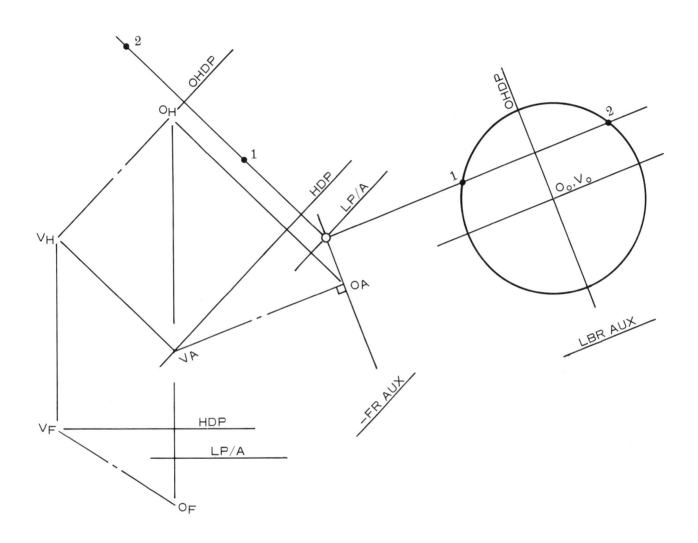

Figure 22–3

FIGURE 22–3

SUPPLEMENTARY NOTES·

SUPPLEMENTARY NOTES·

Exercises

Ex. 22.1 $V(0,3,7)$ is the vertex and $O(1,1,6)$ is the center of the base of a right pyramid. The base is an equilateral triangle which may be inscribed in a $2\frac{1}{2}''$ diameter circle. Corner A of the base is above O and $\frac{3}{4}''$ in front of O. Draw the principal views and necessary auxiliaries.

Ex. 22.2 $A(1,4\frac{1}{2},7\frac{1}{2})$ $B(2\frac{1}{4},6,8\frac{3}{4})$ is the axis of an oblique cylinder whose bases are $2''$ diameter frontal circles. Draw the right section of the cylinder.

Ex. 22.3 $V(0,2\frac{1}{2},5\frac{1}{2})$ is the vertex and $O(1\frac{1}{2},1,4\frac{1}{2})$ is the center of the square base of a right pyramid. The base is $2''$ on a side. Corner A of the base is in front of and $\frac{1}{2}''$ above O. Complete the principal views and the necessary auxiliary views.

Ex. 22.4 $V(2\frac{1}{2},1,6)$ $O(1,2\frac{1}{2},7)$ is the axis of a right pyramid, with V its vertex and O the center of its square base. Corner A of the base is in front of and $\frac{3}{8}''$ to the right of O. The diagonals of the base are $2''$ in length. Complete the principal views and the necessary auxiliaries.

Ex. 22.5 $A_P(4,2)$ $B_P(3\frac{3}{4},3\frac{1}{2})$ is a side view in the alternate position of line AB. $A_F(1,6)$ $B_F(3,7\frac{1}{2})$ is the front view. The orientation of these given views is unknown. Construct the top view of the line. Prove your procedure geometrically valid.

Lesson 23

Locus Plane Exercises

In the previous lesson the following problem was solved: "V is the vertex and O is the center of the square base of a right pyramid. The diagonals of the base are 2″ long. Corner A of the base is to the left of and $\frac{1}{2}$″ above O. Construct the top, front, and necessary auxiliary views of the pyramid." The first projection was made from the top view so that the horizontal LP/A would show as an edge in the auxiliary elevation that showed the base of the pyramid as an edge, thus locating point A in that view. The same problem can be as readily solved by projection from the front or side view, in which case point A is first located in the second auxiliary view.

Figure 23–1 shows the TL of VO and the edge view of the base in a first auxiliary projected from the front view. The LP/A as limited by HP lines through arbitrarily chosen points 1 and 2 shows as the foreshortened shaded area in the first auxiliary. The intersection of this area and the plane of the base is the line 1–2 in the auxiliary. The line 1–2, projected into the second auxiliary, intersects the locus circle in the two possible locations of point A. These locations are carried back to the front view to determine which one satisfies the condition "to the left of O."

Complete the solution in colored pencil.

A procedure similar to that just presented is used when it is desired to establish a horizontal, frontal, or profile line in the oblique plane. It can be seen in Figure 23–1 that in the oblique view the projectors are frontal lines because the intersection of the plane of the base with any frontal plane shows as a point in the first auxiliary. In the oblique the projectors are these lines of intersection. The line 1–2 is a horizontal line in the plane of the base. A profile line could be established similarly. In solving problems of this type, it is usually convenient to use H, F, or P locus planes through point O to minimize construction.

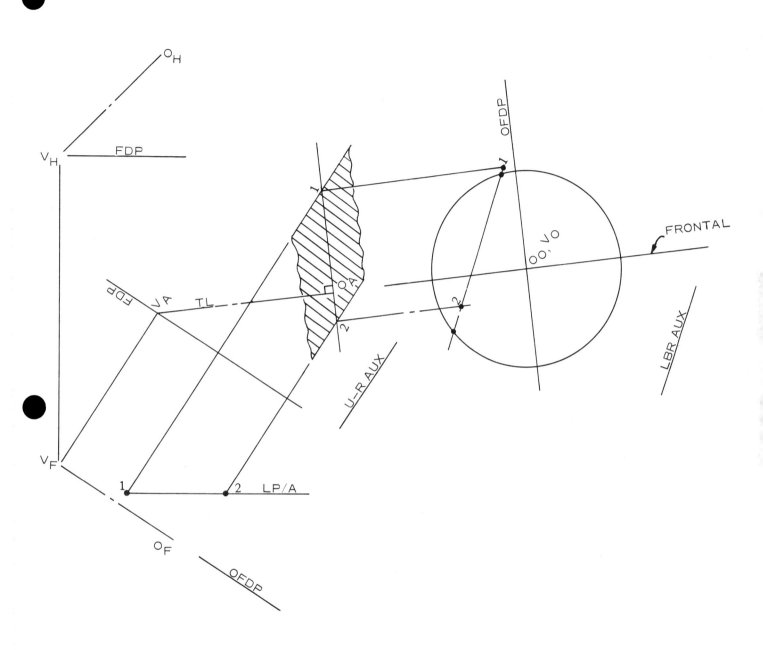

Figure 23–1

SUPPLEMENTARY NOTES

SUPPLEMENTARY NOTES

Exercises

Ex. 23.1 $A(0,3\frac{1}{2},5\frac{3}{4})$ $B(1\frac{1}{4},1\frac{1}{4},7)$ is the axis of a right prism. The bases are equilateral triangles which can be inscribed by circles of $\frac{1}{2}''$ radius. The uppermost side of each base is profile. Draw the top, front, and necessary auxiliary views.

Ex. 23.2 $A(1,2\frac{1}{2},8\frac{1}{2})$ $B(2\frac{1}{2},1\frac{1}{2},7)$ is the axis of a right prism whose bases are $1'' \times 2''$ rectangles. The short sides of the bases are frontal. Solve by projection from the side view. Draw the front, side, and necessary auxiliary views.

Ex. 23.3 In the plane of the three points $A(1\frac{1}{2},4\frac{1}{4},5\frac{1}{4})$ $B(2\frac{1}{4},2\frac{3}{4},8)$ $C(0\frac{1}{2},3,6\frac{1}{4})$, construct an octagon having $\frac{3}{4}''$ sides, with two sides profile and center at C. Show the octagon in the top, front, and necessary auxiliary views.

Ex. 23.4 Pass a plane through point $C(1\frac{3}{4},2,6\frac{1}{2})$ and perpendicular to line $A(0\frac{1}{2},2\frac{1}{2},7)$ $B(2,1,7\frac{3}{4})$ and intersecting AB at D. Construct a horizontal line DH, a frontal line DF, and a profile line DP, each $1\frac{1}{4}''$ long lying in the required plane. Show the lines in the principal views and necessary auxiliaries.

Ex. 23.5 Given the true shape view of triangle $A(3,6)$ $B(4,5)$ $C(2\frac{1}{2},4\frac{1}{2})$. AB is a frontal line, BC is horizontal, and AC is profile. Obtain the principal views of triangle ABC by projection from the given view.

Lesson 24

Additional Locus Plane Exercises

The problems assigned for this lesson are similar to those of Lesson 23 and do not involve any new theory. You will find, however, that the problems are somewhat more sophisticated than those which you have met previously.

Exercises

Ex. 24.1 $V(0,2\frac{1}{2},5)$ is the vertex and $O(2,1,6\frac{1}{2})$ is the center of the base of a right pyramid. The base is an equilateral triangle, one of whose sides lies in the plane of triangle $A(2\frac{1}{4},2,6)$ $B(1,0\frac{1}{2},5)$ $C(1,0\frac{1}{2},8)$. Project from the top view. Complete the top and front views as well as the necessary auxiliary views.

Ex. 24.2 $A(0\frac{1}{2},2,5\frac{1}{2})$ $B(2,3\frac{1}{4},7\frac{1}{4})$ is the uppermost lateral edge of a right prism. The bases of the prism are triangles, each having one side horizontal, one frontal, and one profile. The sides of the bases are tangent to $1''$ diameter circles. Complete the top, front, and necessary auxiliary views.

Ex. 24.3 $V(0,2\frac{1}{2},5)$ is the vertex and $O(1\frac{1}{4},1\frac{1}{2},7)$ is the center of the square base of a right pyramid. The diagonals of the base are $2''$ long. Two sides of the base are parallel to plane $VOA(1\frac{1}{4},2\frac{1}{2},5\frac{1}{4})$. Draw the top, front, and necessary auxiliaries.

Ex. 24.4 $V(2,4\frac{1}{4},7\frac{3}{4})$ $O(1,3\frac{1}{4},5\frac{3}{4})$ is the axis of a right pyramid whose base is a square which may be inscribed in a $2''$ diameter circle. Two sides of the square are parallel to the plane of triangle $A(0,2,6\frac{1}{2})$ $B(2,1\frac{1}{2},6)$ $C(1,3,7\frac{1}{4})$. Complete the given and necessary auxiliary views.

Ex. 24.5 $V(6,3\frac{1}{2},9)$ is the vertex and $O(4,2,7)$ is the center of the rectangular base of a right pyramid. The diagonals of the base are lines that make an angle of $30°$ with the frontal plane through O. They are $3''$ long. Complete the given and necessary auxiliary views.

Lesson 25

Rotation About Normal Axes

The auxiliary view method has been used to obtain a view of an object for any direction of sight. The object has been considered stationary for this method while the observer has moved about, his direction of sight being normal for the principal views, inclined for first auxiliary views, and oblique for higher order auxiliaries. An equally valid and directly comparable procedure can be developed if one considers the position of the observer to be fixed while the object is rotated about a succession of normal lines as axes until the desired orientation is obtained.

The manipulation of views by this rotation method is illustrated in Figure 25–1. The normally oriented principal views of the object are given in space 1. A *HP* axis is indicated in the front view. In space 2 the front view has been rotated 30° clockwise about that axis. The view was traced from space 1 onto a scrap of tracing paper, positioned in space 2, and the corners punched through. The view was then completed in its rotated position. The rotation of the object about the *HP* axis has resulted in a change of all height and width dimensions. The depth dimensions have remained unchanged and have been carried directly across from space 1 to the new top and side views of space 2. In a similar fashion, the side view of space 2 has been rotated about a *HF* axis in moving to space 3. This rotation has changed the height and depth coordinates from what they were in space 2, but has not affected the width which has been carried into the top and front views of space 3. A rotation about a *FP* axis is illustrated in spaces 3 and 4. Notice that the choice of axis determines which dimension remains unchanged and is carried forward. This, in turn, dictates the space to be occupied by the new group of views.

Study the views obtained in the sample problem. Which correspond to principal views? Which to first, second, or third auxiliaries?

It should now be evident that any problem which can be solved by auxiliary views can also be solved by successive rotations, although the procedure is somewhat more cumbersome. As a preliminary to construction always consider the selection of axes and the sequence of rotations to permit the unchanged dimension to be projected into the next space conveniently.

In Figure 25–2 the *TS* of plane 1–2–3 is required. Sketch a solution noting similarities to the auxiliary view procedure. What alternate layouts are practical? What is the minimum number of views essential to a solution? Name and orient each view in the same manner as done with auxiliary views.

It is quite evident that rotation about normal axes is at best an impractical device for obtaining views for inclined and oblique directions of sight in comparison with the auxiliary view techniques we have previously mastered. However, a familiarity with this method does give considerable additional insight into the theory of orthographic projection which will gain especial significance when we explore some particular situations in which revolutions about inclined and oblique axes will prove to be very powerful tools. The latter will be taken up in Lesson 36.

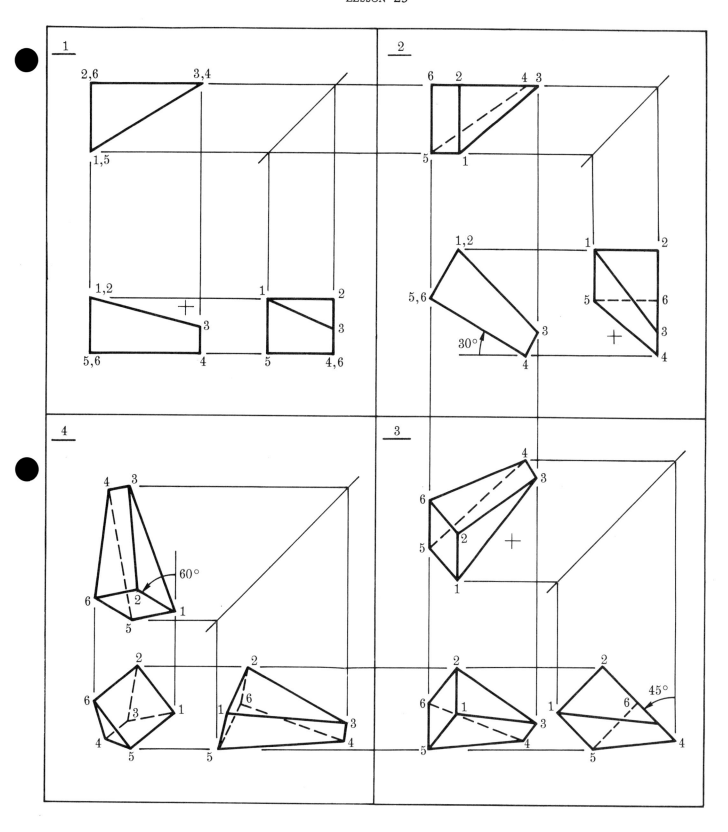

Figure 25-1

SUPPLEMENTARY NOTES

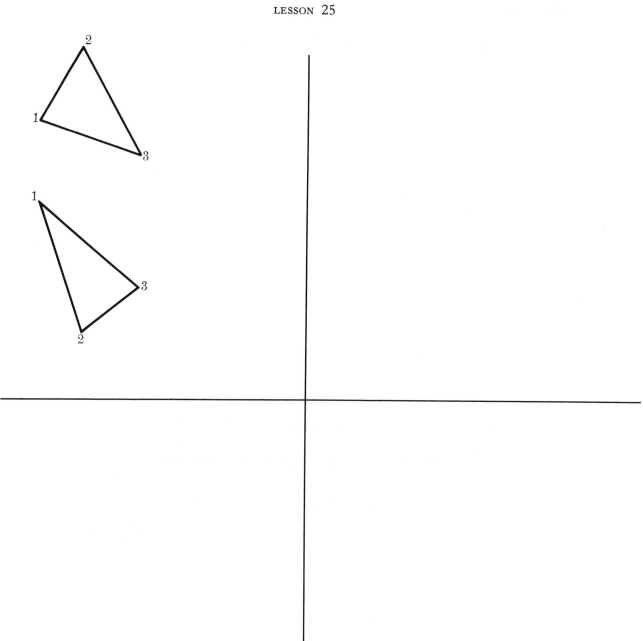

Figure 25–2

SUPPLEMENTARY NOTES

SUPPLEMENTARY NOTES

Exercises

Ex. 25.1 Quarter the sheet through $(3\frac{1}{2},4\frac{1}{2})$. Draw the three principal views of pyramid $V(0\frac{3}{4},6,8)$ $A(0,5,7\frac{1}{2})$ $B(0\frac{3}{4},5,7)$ $C(1\frac{1}{2},5,7\frac{1}{2})$ in the upper left space. Rotate 30° clockwise (cw) about a HF axis in going to the lower left space. From lower left go to lower right, rotating 45° counterclockwise (ccw) about a FP axis. Finally go into the upper right quarter rotating 15° ccw about a HP axis. Show the three principal views of the object in each position.

Ex. 25.2 $A(1\frac{1}{4},2,4)$ $B(1\frac{1}{4},2,7)$ is the axis of a right prism. The bases are regular hexagons $1\frac{1}{4}''$ on a side with one diagonal horizontal. The prism is truncated by an OH plane through line $C(0,1,4)$ $D(3,0,6\frac{1}{2})$. Rotate about an FP axis to obtain the view of the entire object which shows the cut face in true shape.

Ex. 25.3 By successive rotations of the entire pyramid $V(0\frac{1}{2},5\frac{3}{4},7\frac{1}{2})$ $A(0,5,7)$ $B(1,5\frac{1}{2},6\frac{3}{4})$ $C(0\frac{1}{2},5\frac{1}{4},8)$ obtain a view in which surface VAB appears visible and true shape. Draw a minimum of views.

Ex. 25.4 Obtain the UBL isometric projection of pyramid $V(0,6\frac{1}{4},7\frac{1}{4})$ $A(1\frac{1}{4},6\frac{1}{2},7)$ $B(1\frac{1}{4},5\frac{1}{2},7)$ $C(1\frac{1}{4},5\frac{1}{2},8)$ $D(1\frac{1}{4},6\frac{1}{2},8)$ by successive rotations. Draw a minimum number of views.

Ex. 25.5 Solve the problems of Ex. 21.8 by the method of successive rotations.

Lesson 26

Oblique Projection

In making orthographic projections, the projectors are drawn parallel and toward the observer stationed at an infinite distance from the object. The view is traced on a transparent plane of projection, or picture plane, at right angles to the projectors. The observer's direction of sight appears as a point in the view, but the view is a true representation only so long as the reader satisfies the original conditions of projection: He must theoretically be located at infinity and his direction of sight must be normal to the plane of the drawing. To illustrate, place your eye close to the center of a sheet of graph paper and observe the distortion of the outer squares. As you back away from the sheet, the distortion disappears. Next incline the sheet to your line of vision as in turning a page and note the foreshortening of the horizontal distances.

Imagine, now, that an observer is looking at an object and we interpose a picture plane inclined to his direction of sight. The parallel projectors intersect the picture plane and the view is traced upon it in the usual way. If the observer remains at his original station he sees a foreshortened image of the view which is identical to the orthographic projection for that direction of sight. If, however, he shifts his position to look squarely at the image on the picture plane, the view appears elongated and the sight line used in making the view is no longer seen as a point. The concept is illustrated in Figure 26–1. Study it carefully and then reread this paragraph.

If a picture plane were oriented oblique to the line of sight, a similar effect would result. So long as the view obtained is seen from the original station of the observer, it will appear identical to the corresponding orthographic view, but when the observer shifts to a natural reading position and looks directly at the view, he sees a distorted image. Such views are called oblique projections because the projectors are oblique to the picture plane. Unfortunately the same term is commonly used to describe higher order auxiliaries because the direction of sight for these orthographic views is oblique to the principal planes of projection. Recognizing that oblique views are not true representations, we will find that they are of great practical value as easily drawn and quite descriptive pictorials.

Figure 26–2 illustrates the technique of oblique projection. The principal views of the object, the direction of sight AB, and the picture plane are given. Oblique projectors are drawn to the picture plane in the top and side views. Because a frontal picture plane was used, the resulting pictorial is a pseudo front view.

> Number a few of the corners in all views and verify the construction.
> Notice that surfaces parallel to the picture plane appear in true shape.
> Also note that the receding edges are parallel to $A_F B_F$ and project from the front view (from which it follows that the construction can be made with any one of the three principal views omitted.)
> Place the tip of a pencil at B_F and incline the pencil in the direction of AB. With the paper at arm's length sight along the pencil to see the pictorial as the corresponding orthographic view (the point view of AB).

With colored pencil draw a new picture plane through the front face of the object and sketch the pictorial. This choice of picture plane is much more convenient than the one used for illustration.

Notice that by changing the direction of the sight line AB, any degree of inclination and any amount of foreshortening can be obtained for the receding edges. To visualize this imagine AB approaching a horizontal position. What is the effect on the pictorial? What happens if AB is made to approach a profile position?

In Figure 26–3 an oblique projection is made for an object so oriented that none of its faces is parallel to the picture plane. Depth and width dimensions are distorted. Only the vertical lines being parallel to the picture plane are seen in true length.

Does this figure represent the general case? How would it have to be changed to do so?

View the pictorial from the position giving the point view of the sight line as you did for the previous example and note the natural appearance.

Test the effect of shifting the picture plane by sketching the oblique obtained on a picture plane through the front edge of the object.

Oblique Drawing

In the discussion of Figure 26–2 it was pointed out that the faces of the object parallel to the picture plane appear in true shape on the pictorial and that by shifting the direction of sight the *HP* edges can be made to have any desired slope and any degree of foreshortening. This being the case we can dispense with projection and readily make oblique drawings of any object in any orientation by the simple expedient of enclosing the object in a rectangular box with one pair of faces parallel to the picture plane, drawing the oblique of the box and measuring offsets parallel to the edges in much the same manner that we constructed isometric drawings.

Oblique drawings made with the scale of the receding axis full size are called *cavalier drawings* and those drawn with the receding axis foreshortened to half size, *cabinet drawings*. Cabinet drawings usually have the more natural appearance but are a little more trouble to construct.

For representing objects having curved or irregular features appearing in contour in only one principal view, oblique drawings are considerably more convenient than the orthographic pictorial forms (isometric, dimetric, and trimetric). Placing the contour face parallel to the picture plane results in a minimum of construction and greatly simplifies freehand sketching. Curves in the receding planes may be plotted by offsets. For the special case of circles in the receding surfaces of cavalier drawings, the enclosing quadrilateral is a rhombus and the same four-center approximate ellipse used for isometric drawings can be applied. The enclosing rhombus is first constructed. The perpendicular bisectors of the sides intersect at the centers of the circular arcs which approximate the true ellipse. The arcs are tangent to one another at the midpoints of the sides of the rhombus. If the angle of the receding axis is 30° one pair of centers will coincide with the corners on the rhombus on the short diagonal. Sketch the construction on the surfaces of the cavalier cubes in Figure 26–4 to find the location of the centers for angles greater than and less than 30°.

The effect of various choices of scale and orientation of the receding axis is explored in Figure 26–5. Complete the oblique sketches as indicated.

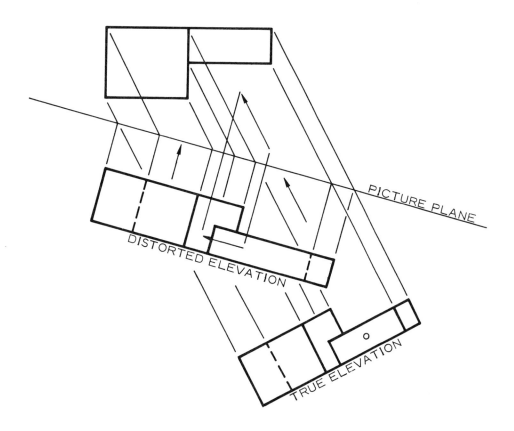

PICTURE PLANE

DISTORTED ELEVATION

TRUE ELEVATION

Figure 26–1

SUPPLEMENTARY NOTES

SUPPLEMENTARY NOTES

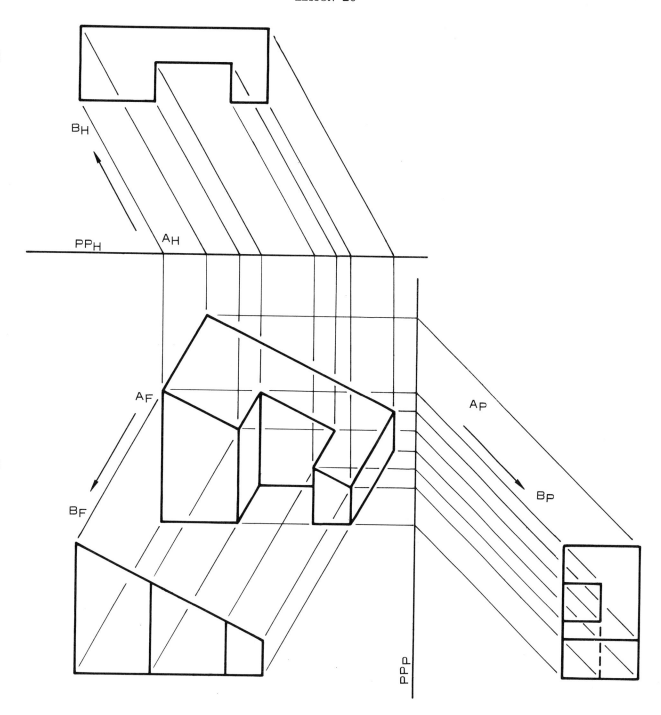

Figure 26–2

FIGURE 26–2

SUPPLEMENTARY NOTES

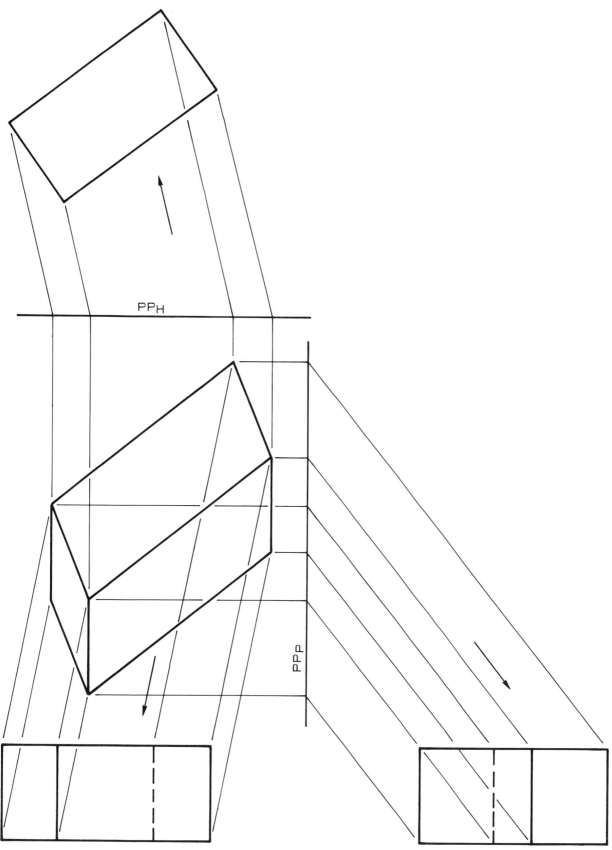

Figure 26-3

SUPPLEMENTARY NOTES

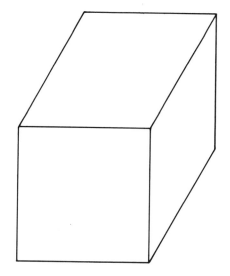

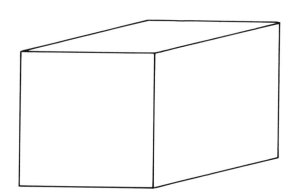

Figure 26–4

SUPPLEMENTARY NOTES

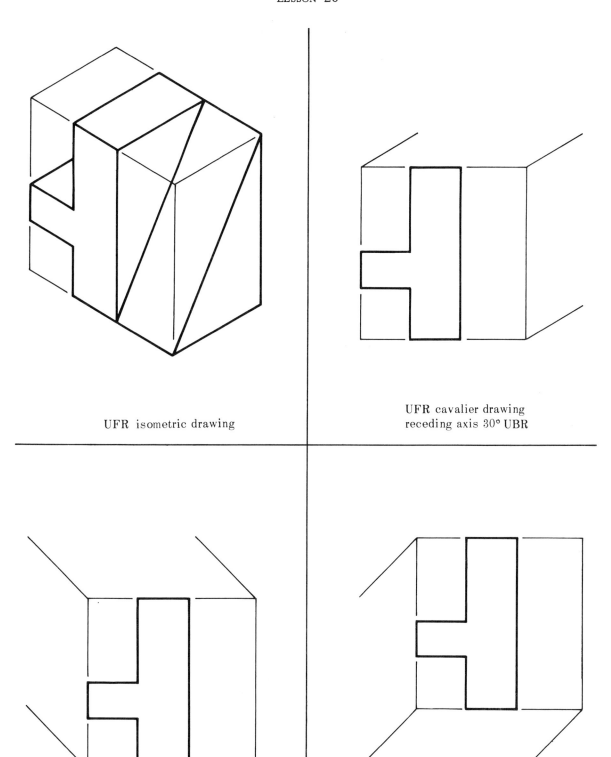

UFR isometric drawing

UFR cavalier drawing
receding axis 30° UBR

UFL cabinet drawing
receding axis 45° UBL

LFL cavalier drawing
receding axis 45° DBL

Figure 26–5

FIGURE 26–5

SUPPLEMENTARY NOTES

Exercises

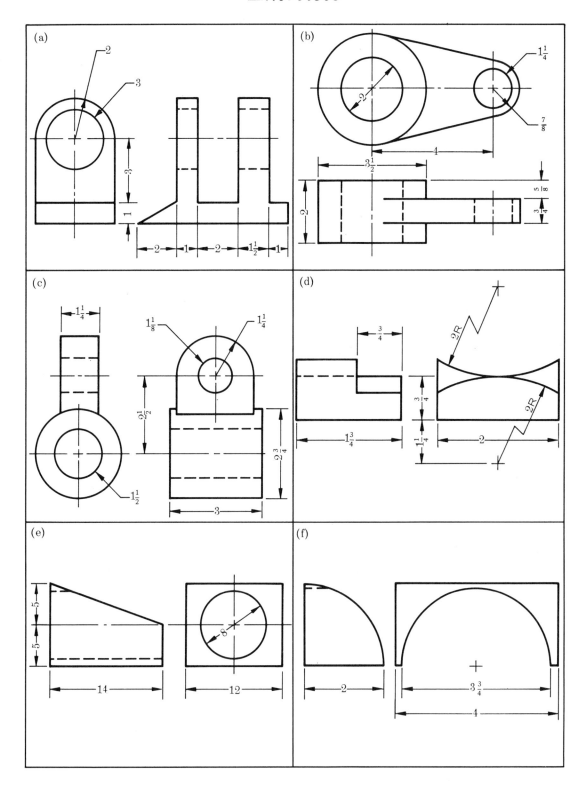

Ex. 26.1 Construct cabinet or cavalier drawings of the objects above to convenient scale as assigned. Select angle of receding axis for greatest clarity. Use a full sheet for each problem.

Lesson 27

Theory of Perspective Projection

In perspective projection we attempt to obtain more realistic pictorials by removing the restriction of oblique drawing that the observer be stationed at an infinite distance. The observer, in perspective, is stationed at some arbitrarily chosen point. All projectors, or visual rays, converge to that point, passing through a picture plane which may have any desired orientation with respect to the object and the rays. The view traced out on the picture plane is the perspective projection.

Parallel or One-Point Perspective

Review Figure 26–2, the construction of an oblique projection, then examine the perspective projection of Figure 27–1. You should discover at once that the two procedures are really identical; that the oblique is the special case of the perspective for which the station point (SP) is taken at infinity. Both pictorials are shown constructed by means of visual rays drawn toward the station point in the top and side views. All the observations previously made concerning the oblique apply equally to the perspective. Note the following particularly:

The receding edges of the pictorial converge to the station point as seen in the front view (SP_F). Their inclination and foreshortening would be modified by a change in station point.

The construction can be performed using any two of the three principal views.

Surfaces parallel to the picture plane are geometrically similar on both pictorial and object.

The purpose in constructing the perspective was ostensibly to obtain a natural appearance. The resulting drawing is anything but natural. Can you explain why?

The only "true" viewing position for a perspective is from the station point. For Figure 27–1 this is a point 3″ from the paper at SP_F. Put one eye at this point and note the effect. In planning a perspective the draftsman must select the scale and station point to be reasonably compatible with the normal reading or viewing position for the drawing, about 12″ to 16″ for a page of this size.

Observe the effect of shifting the picture plane by sketching in color the perspective obtained using a picture plane through the front face of the object, and then, in a second color, that resulting when the picture plane is taken through the back face.

It is important to notice that any family of parallel horizontal lines converges to a particular point along the horizon, a horizontal line through SP_F. The SP_F is itself the vanishing point for one such family of lines, the receding edges of the rectangular solids. To illustrate other vanishing points, draw the diagonals of the top and bottom surfaces of the large cube. The long diagonals converge to a point in the horizon to the right of SP_F, and the short diagonals to the left. Parallel diagonals in the vertical receding faces converge to points on a vertical line through SP_F. Would you expect parallel oblique lines to converge?

[266]

The convergence of horizontal lines is easily visualized if one imagines that he is standing at a highway junction on a level plain. Each road with its curbs and telephone poles appears to vanish in the horizon at eye level. Parallel roads, even if widely separated, vanish in the same point.

Figure 27–2 is a sketching exercise to bring out the effect of shifting the eye level of the observer. Sketch the perspectives as indicated. In Space 4 sketch the interior of a room. Add a door at the end, windows at the sides, a skylight in the ceiling, and tile on the floor.

Angular or Two-Point Perspective

Figure 27–3 shows the oblique of Figure 26–3 redrawn as a perspective. Again, note the similarity of the construction. Both appear highly distorted because of the choice of station point. Where should your eye be placed to view the perspective? Does it appear natural when seen from there? Note the manner in which the horizontal lines in the receding planes converge in the two vanishing points from which the method takes its name.

Three-Point Perspective

In one-point perspective one surface of the basic rectangular solid is oriented parallel to the picture plane. In two-point, one set of edges was placed parallel. In the general case all three sets of edges are inclined to the picture plane, producing three vanishing points. Such views are readily obtained by the visual ray procedure but are of limited usefulness and are usually drawn only for special effects.

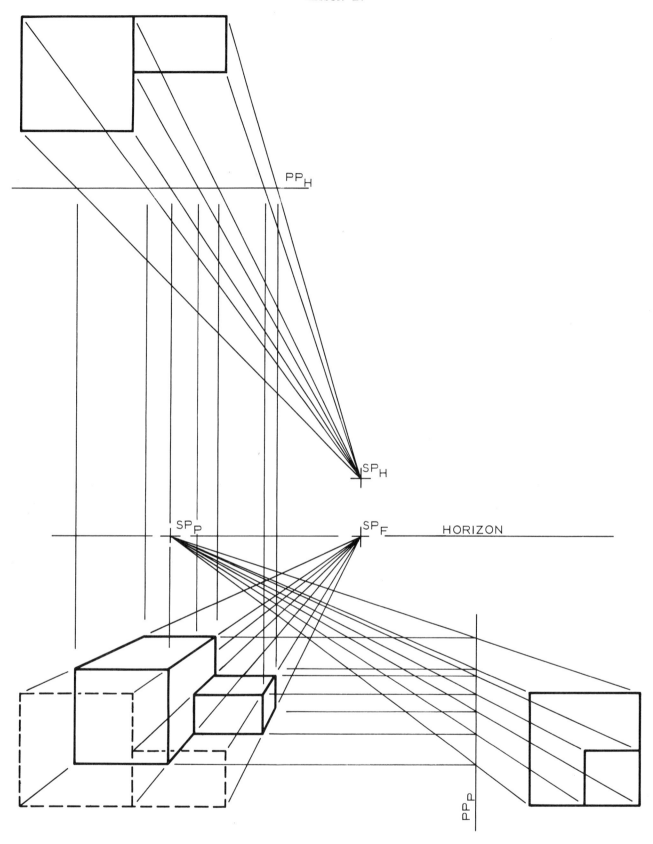

Figure 27–1

[269]

SUPPLEMENTARY NOTES

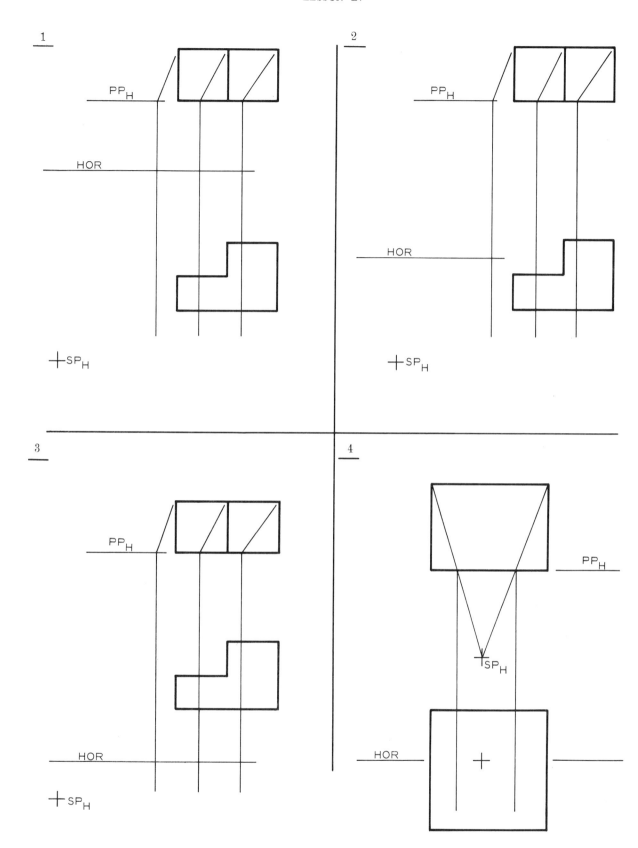

Figure 27–2

SUPPLEMENTARY NOTES

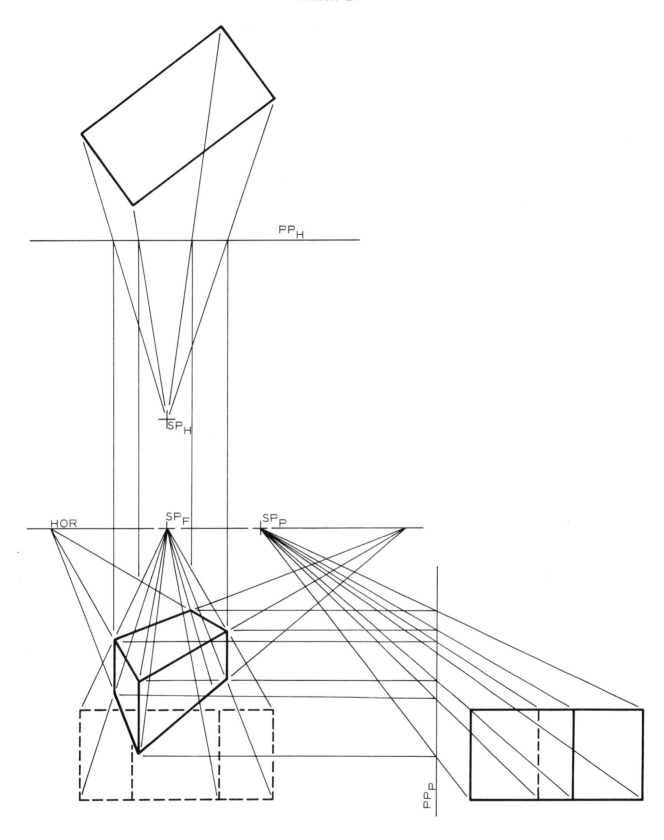

Figure 27–3

SUPPLEMENTARY NOTES

Exercises

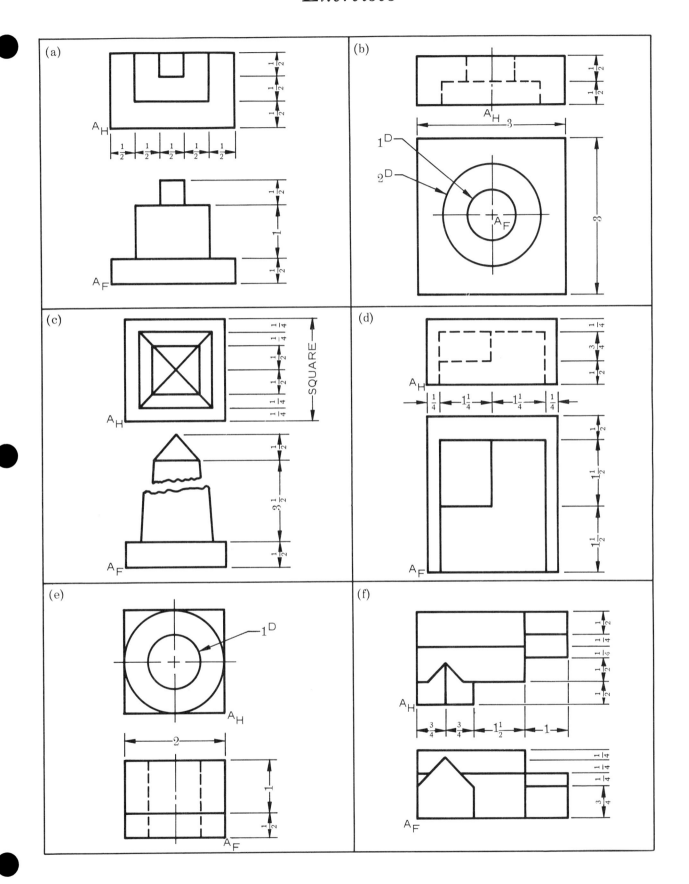

Ex. 27.1 Construct the parallel perspective of the stepped blocks of (a) as viewed from the station point $\overline{SP}(7,5\frac{1}{2},0)$. Assume the picture plane through the frontal face containing point $A(0,2,6\frac{1}{2})$.

Ex. 27.2 Construct the angular perspective of the stepped blocks of (a) as viewed from the station point $\overline{SP}(2,5\frac{1}{2},1)$. Assume the picture plane through the FP line containing point $A(1\frac{1}{2},2,6\frac{1}{2})$. The frontal face is to be inclined at 30° to the picture plane.

Ex. 27.3 Construct the parallel perspective of the object shown in (b) as viewed from the station point $\overline{SP}(1\frac{1}{2},1,1\frac{1}{2})$. Assume the picture plane through the frontal face containing point $A(5,3\frac{1}{2},7)$.

Ex. 27.4 Construct the parallel perspective of the monument given in (c) as viewed from the station point $\overline{SP}(2\frac{1}{2},3\frac{1}{2},2)$. Assume the picture plane through the frontal face containing point $A(4,1,7)$.

Ex. 27.5 Construct the angular perspective of the monument given in (c) as viewed from the station point $\overline{SP}(3\frac{1}{2},4,2\frac{1}{2})$. Assume the picture plane through the FP line containing point $A(5,1\frac{1}{2},6\frac{1}{2})$. The frontal and profile faces are to be inclined at 45° to the picture plane.

Ex. 27.6 Construct the parallel perspective of the object given in (d) as viewed from the station point $\overline{SP}(7,0\frac{1}{2},2)$. Assume the picture plane through the frontal face containing point $A(2,2\frac{1}{2},7\frac{1}{2})$.

Ex. 27.7 Construct the parallel perspective of the object of (e) as viewed from the station point $\overline{SP}(5\frac{1}{2},6,2\frac{1}{2})$. Assume the picture plane through the frontal face containing point $A(2,0\frac{1}{2},7)$.

Ex. 27.8 The base of a right pyramid of 4″ altitude is a regular hexagon, $1\frac{1}{2}$″ on a side. Two sides of the base are frontal. Construct the parallel perspective of the pyramid as viewed from the station point $\overline{SP}(2,5\frac{1}{2},1\frac{1}{2})$. Assume the picture plane $1\frac{1}{2}$″ in front of the vertex $V(1\frac{1}{2},5,7\frac{1}{2})$. Show all hidden lines. Finally, pass an OP cutting plane through point $P(1\frac{1}{2},5,8)$ sloping forward and down at 60° to the horizontal. Shade the intersection of this plane with the pyramid in the perspective view.

Ex. 27.9 Construct parallel perspective drawings of the objects given for Ex. 12.1(a),(b); 13.3; 11.2. Construct angular perspectives of the objects given for Ex. 19.1(a),(c),(d),(f). Choose orientation and station point to produce best shape description.

[276]

Lesson 28

Perspectives by the Vanishing Point Method

The construction of the perspective can be simplified if the vanishing points for the edges of the basic rectangular solid are predetermined.

In the case of one-point perspectives, as in Figure 27–1, the vanishing point is known at the outset. Rays from the front view to SP_F are intersected by the projectors from the picture plane in the top view and also the side. Either set of projectors can be used in conjunction with the rays to locate all required points. One of the given principal views could be omitted entirely. Exactly the same procedure could be followed in the case of angular perspectives, illustrated in Figure 27–3, but it is much more convenient to locate the vanishing points for the horizontal edges as described in the next paragraph.

The plan and end elevation (not side view) of an open front shed are given in Figure 28–1(a) along with the station point and picture plane. To locate the vanishing points of the horizontal edges, sight lines are drawn through SP_H in the top view parallel to the edges of the building. Since each family of horizontal lines on the shed converges at infinity with the corresponding sight line, the points at which the sight lines pierce the picture plane are the required vanishing points, VPR and VPL. These points are projected into the perspective view at the horizon.

Turn back to Figure 27–3 and add the construction for the vanishing points, verifying those found in the visual ray solution.

In Figure 28–1(b) the visual rays from the top view are used in conjunction with the vanishing point VPL to construct the pictorial. Horizontal lines drawn toward VPR provide a check on the accuracy of the work. Because true height measurements can be made only in the picture plane, the construction is begun by extending the shed to intersect the picture plane, giving the dashed outline or "phantom image" in the perspective. This outline and the rays from it to VPL represent a structure of infinite length. The actual shed is the portion cut off by the projectors from the top view.

Check the solution by sketching appropriate rays to VPR.

Where are the vanishing points for the inclined roof lines? What types of lines would vanish to points along a vertical line through VPL?

How would the appearance of the pictorial be modified if the picture plane were taken through the front edge of the shed? The rear edge? In front of the station point?

Where would you locate the SP to obtain a more realistic pictorial? What effect would this have on the location of the vanishing points?

What purpose did the given end view serve in the construction? Could it have been omitted?

In Figure 28–1(b) the length of the shed was extended into the picture plane to provide the height coordinates. We could just as readily extend the depth to accomplish the same purpose. The construction is given in Figure 28–1(c). Sketch the perspective and check your result with rays drawn to VPL.

Highly refined techniques have been developed for constructing all types of perspectives. We have explored only the more elementary. If you are intrigued, consult the library.

[277]

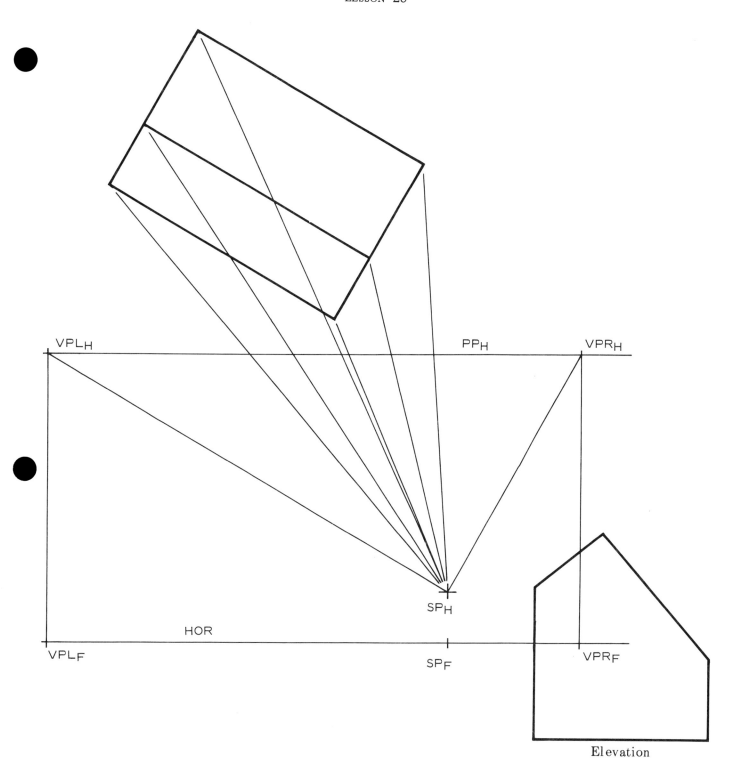

Elevation

(a)

Figure 28–1

[279]

SUPPLEMENTARY NOTES

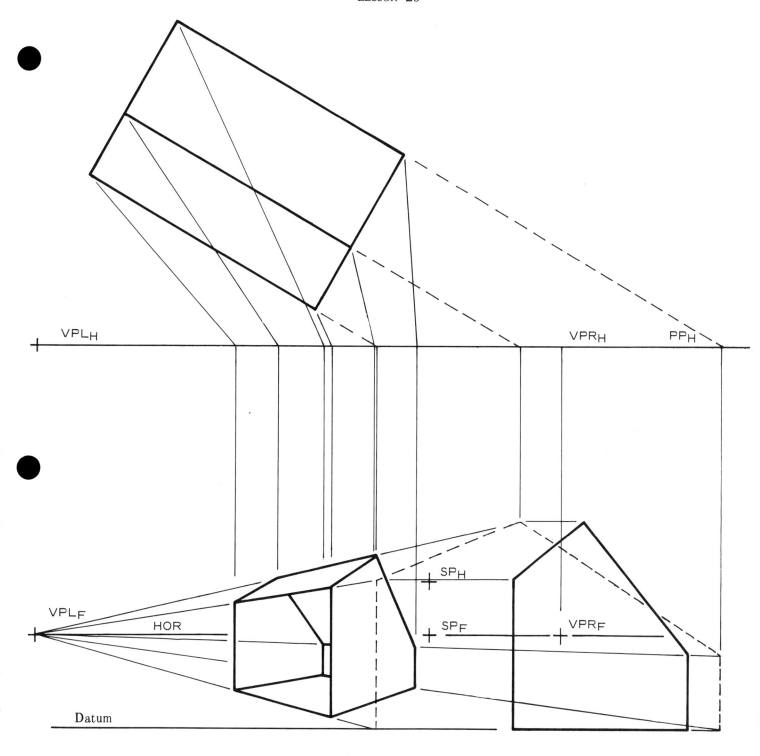

VPL$_H$ VPR$_H$ PP$_H$

VPL$_F$ HOR   SP$_H$ SP$_F$ VPR$_F$

Datum

(b)

Figure 28−1

[281]

SUPPLEMENTARY NOTES

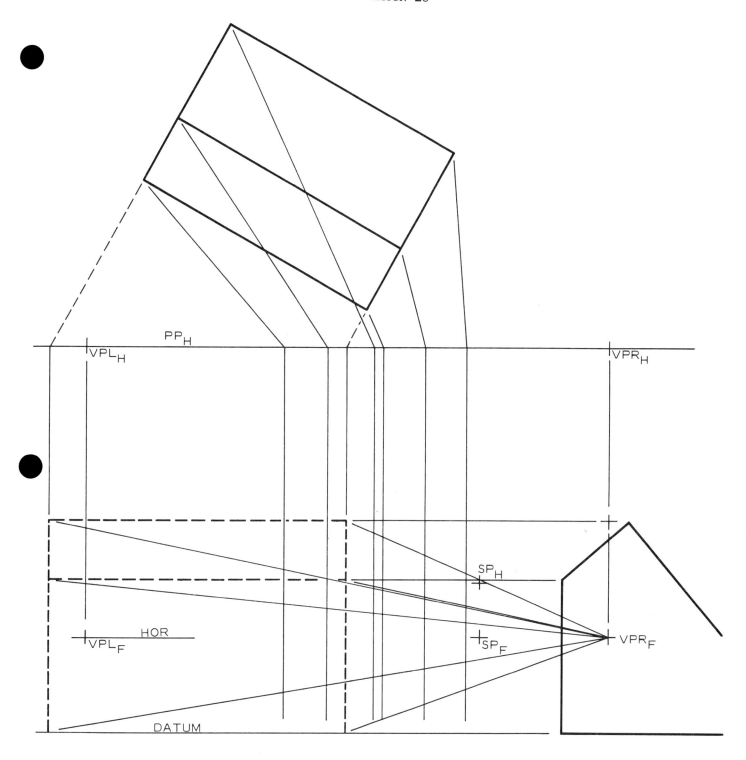

(c)

Figure 28–1

SUPPLEMENTARY NOTES

Exercises

All problems of this lesson are to be solved using visual rays from the plan view and projectors to one or more vanishing points.

For those problems designated "alternate layout" the drawing paper is to be mounted cross-ways on the grid, the bottom edge of the paper along line (X,O,X), and the left edge aligned with the edge of the grid sheet.

Ex. 28.1   Same as Ex. 27.1, except use $\overline{SP}(7,7,0)$.

Ex. 28.2   Alternate layout. Similar to Ex. 27.2, except use $A(2,0\frac{1}{2},5)$ and $\overline{SP}(2\frac{1}{2},1\frac{1}{2},1)$.

Ex. 28.3   Same as Ex. 27.3.

Ex. 28.4   Same as Ex. 27.4.

Ex. 28.5   Same as Ex. 27.5, except use $A(4\frac{1}{2},1\frac{1}{2},6\frac{1}{2})$ and $\overline{SP}(3,4,2\frac{1}{2})$.

Ex. 28.6   Same as Ex. 27.6.

Ex. 28.7   Same as Ex. 27.7.

Ex. 28.8   Construct the angular perspective of the gabled farmhouse shown in (f) for lesson 27. Incline the frontal face containing point $A(3\frac{1}{2},1\frac{1}{2},6\frac{1}{2})$ at 30° to the picture plane which is to be taken $1\frac{1}{4}''$ in front of A. Place the station point at $\overline{SP}(6\frac{1}{2},2,1)$. Add doors, windows, chimneys, etc. as desired.

Ex. 28.9   Make parallel perspective drawings of the objects given for Ex. 12.1(b),(c); 13.2; 26.1(a),(b),(c),(f). Construct angular perspectives of the objects given for Ex. 19.1(a),(c),(d),(f); 26.1(c),(e),(f). Choose orientation and station point to produce best shape description.

Lesson 29

Intersection of a Line and a Plane

First Method: The point at which a line pierces a plane is seen in any edge view of the plane. Since the point is known to lie in the line, it may be projected directly into adjacent views.

Sketch the procedure to locate the point of intersection between line AB and plane 1–2–3 in Figure 29–1. Consider the triangle to be opaque and show the visibility of the line. Note: The piercing point need not lie within the limits of either the line segment or the triangle. Both lines and planes are of indefinite extent.

The visibility is found by the familiar procedure. In the front view, for example, lines AB and 1–3 appear to cross. A projector to the top view reveals that at this position AB lies behind 1–3. Therefore, in the front view the line from A is hidden behind the plane of 1–2–3 to the piercing point and visible beyond to B. Show the visibility of AB in color.

Second Method: The piercing point can be easily located without recourse to the auxiliary view. In Figure 29–2 an orthofrontal plane is imagined through AB, cutting plane 1–2–3 in line XY. XY is the locus of the intersection of all lines in the OF plane with the given plane. The intersection of AB with XY is therefore the piercing point.

Note again that the piercing point need not fall within the confines of the triangle, but could as easily fall somewhere on XY extended.

With a colored pencil locate the piercing point in the front view, and show the proper visibility of AB.

Could we add a third method—that the piercing point can be found by obtaining a point view of AB? Would such a procedure be advantageous?

Intersection of a Line and a Solid of Plane Surfaces

The intersection of a line AB and a solid is found by the second method above. The inclined cutting plane through the line cuts a polygon from the solid. The intersections of AB and the polygon are the piercing points. It is customary to encircle the piercing points and to omit the portion of the line lying within the solid. The part outside the object is, of course, shown in proper visibility.

Line Piercing a Cone

In Figure 29–3 the points at which the line AB pierces the cone VO are required. A vertical cutting plane through AB would intersect the cone in a hyperbola, and an OF cutting plane would give an ellipse, necessitating the plotting of one of these curves to obtain the piercing points if one of these cutting planes was used.

Any plane passed through the vertex of a cone and intersecting the cone will cut straight line elements from its surface. Suppose, then, that we choose a cutting plane VAB. The line AB in the plane will then intersect the two elements of surface cut from the cone in the required piercing points.

[286]

In order to locate the elements cut from the cone, the cutting plane *VAB* is extended into the plane of the base of the cone, intersecting it in line 1–2. Line 1–2 meets the base of the cone at 3 and 4. Lines *V*–3 and *V*–4 are therefore elements of the cone lying in the cutting plane, which also contains *AB*, and their intersections with *AB* are the required piercing points.

Had the line *AB* been excessively long for a convenient construction, a short segment of it could have been used, or point 5, the piercing point of line *AB* in the plane of the base, could have been used for one point along 1–2.

What would it have meant if the line 1–2 had not touched the circle? Been tangent to the circle? Sketch the auxiliary elevation showing *VAB* as an edge.

Could this construction be used for oblique cones? Truncated cones? Pyramids? Cylinders?

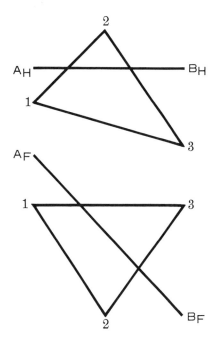

Figure 29–1

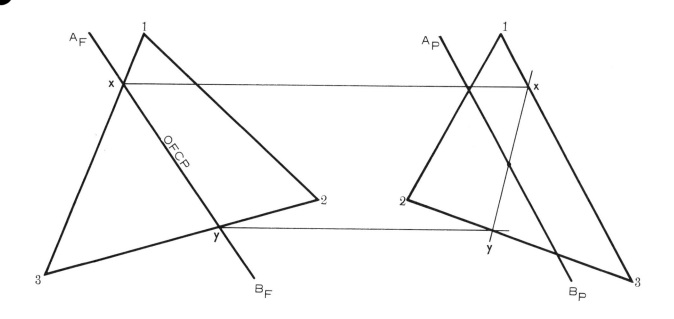

Figure 29–2

SUPPLEMENTARY NOTES

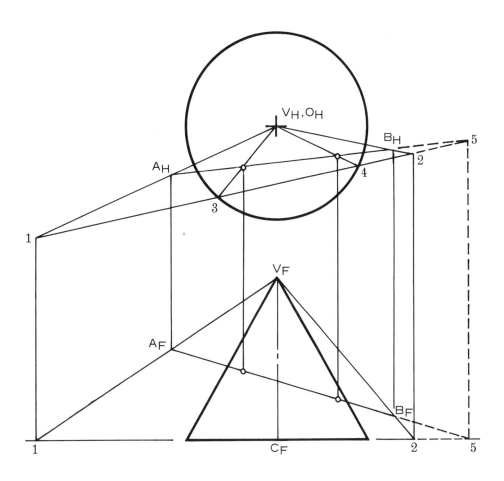

Figure 29–3

SUPPLEMENTARY NOTES

Exercises

Ex. 29.1 Given plane $A(1,1,7)$ $B(3,3,8)$ $C(3,0,5)$ and point $P(5,1\frac{1}{2},6)$. Without using additional views, find the following: (a) the point X at which an HF line from P pierces plane ABC; (b) the point Y at which a FP line from P pierces plane ABC; (c) the point Z at which an HP line from P pierces plane ABC.

Ex. 29.2 Complete the given views of tetrahedron $A(1\frac{1}{2},1,4)$ $B(2\frac{1}{2},2\frac{1}{2},7)$ $C(4\frac{1}{2},3,6)$ $D(5,1,4\frac{1}{2})$ with correct visibility. Find where the line $L(1,1,6)$ $M(6,3,4\frac{1}{2})$ pierces the solid and draw the line in proper visibility omitting the portion inside the tetrahedron.

Ex. 29.3 $V(3,2\frac{1}{2},5\frac{1}{2})$ is the vertex and $O(3,2\frac{1}{2},8\frac{1}{2})$ is the center of the base of a right circular cone. The diameter of the base is $5''$. Show in the specified color that portion of each of the following lines that lies within the cone. (a) A red HF line, $L(0,1\frac{1}{2},7\frac{1}{2})M$. (b) A blue HP line, $R(2,4,5)S$. (c) A green FP line, $E(3,1,8)F$. (d) A black line, $A(2,3,6)$ $B(4\frac{1}{2},3\frac{1}{2},9)$.

Ex. 29.4 Construct plane $V(2,3,6\frac{1}{2})$ $P(4,2\frac{1}{2},7\frac{1}{2})M$ tangent to the right circular cone with vertex V whose base is a frontal circle $3''$ in diameter and whose altitude is $1\frac{1}{2}''$. Let M be a point on the base circle. Find all possible solutions.

Ex. 29.5 $O(2,2,7\frac{1}{2})$ is the center of a $3''$ diameter sphere. $A(3,2,X)$ is a point on the rear hemisphere as is $C(2\frac{1}{2},1,X)$. $B(2,X,6\frac{1}{2})$ is on the upper surface. (a) Determine the true length of line AB. (b) Through C establish a plane tangent to the sphere. Show the plane as an area bounded by inclined lines in the given views. Shade the area with red.

Ex. 29.6 $V(0,1,6)$ is the vertex and $O(3\frac{1}{2},0\frac{1}{2},3)$ is the center of the base of an oblique cone whose base is a frontal circle of $2''$ diameter. (a) Show in red the portion of the line $A(0\frac{1}{2},0,4\frac{1}{2})$ $B(5,2,3\frac{1}{2})$ which lies inside the cone and measure its true length. Show AB in proper visibility. (b) Show in blue a plane VBM tangent to the cone. Make BM frontal and show all possible planes.

Ex. 29.7 The traiangle $A(0\frac{1}{2},0,8\frac{1}{2})$ $B(1\frac{3}{4},1\frac{1}{4},6\frac{1}{4})$ $C(0,2,6\frac{1}{2})$ is the base of a pyramid whose lateral surfaces form a solid right angle at the vertex V. The vertex lies below the base. Complete the top, front, and necessary auxiliary views of the pyramid.

Lesson 30

Intersection of Plane Surfaces

Edge View Method: The line of intersection between two planes may be found directly in a view showing one of the planes as an edge.

Figure 30–1 gives the top and auxiliary elevation views of two triangles, the elevation being the edge view of *ABC*. Sketch *ABC* extended in the elevation to intersect *QRS* in line *XY* and project *XY* into the top view. *XY* is a segment of the required line of intersection.

Piercing Point Method: By use of the piercing point method the intersection between planes may be found in any two adjacent views. Any two points known to lie in both planes will serve to establish the line. The attack is demonstrated in Figure 30–2.

The triangles *ABC* and *QRS* are given in the top and front views. The line of intersection of their planes is required. The point *X* at which line *QR* pierces the plane of *ABC* has been found in both views by the use of an orthohorizontal cutting plane (*OHCP*) through *QR*. *X* is therefore one point lying in both planes. Verify its position by sketching in color the construction for the piercing point using a horizontal cutting plane through *QR*.

The necessary second point on the intersection can be located by finding the point at which any other line in either plane pierces the other. Since none of the given lines aside from *QR* is convenient for this purpose (Why?), a random cutting plane showing as an edge in one of the views is used. In the figure a horizontal cutting plane (*HCP*) through *A* has been arbitrarily selected. It cuts plane *ABC* in line *A*–5 and *QRS* in 3–4. Since these lines both lie in the same cutting plane, they must intersect. Because one lies in each of the given planes, the point of intersection *Y* is common to both planes. *XY*, therefore, is a segment of the line of intersection. In the same manner a third point on the line of intersection should always be found to provide a check.

(The foregoing construction could be described in terms of piercing point: The horizontal line *A*–5 was established in *ABC* and the point *Y* at which it pierces *QRS* was then found through the use of an *HCP*. We could also say that horizontal line 3–4 in *QRS* was arbitrarily chosen, and then its piercing point with plane *ABC* established by use of the *HCP*. The three viewpoints are equivalent and the constructions identical.)

Exercises involving the intersection of bounded plane areas are solved by the same procedure. The line of intersection, however, is of definite length, extending only as it lies within the boundaries of both areas. If the areas are considered opaque, visibility is determined in the usual manner at the apparent intersections of the edges. Note that for two plane figures the line of intersection must always be visible.

Intersection of a Plane and a Solid

The intersection is found by the repeated application of the piercing point technique if it is not convenient to construct a view showing the plane as an edge. It may prove helpful to draw the various cutting planes and projectors in different colors to avoid confusing the different steps. The intersection of the solid and plane will be visible or hidden depending upon the visibility of the surface in question on the solid.

[294]

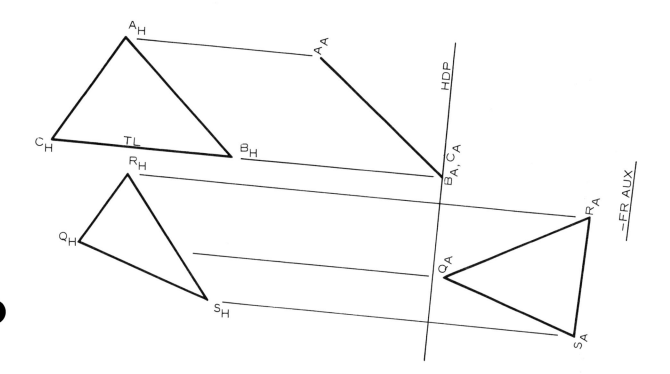

Figure 30–1

[295]

FIGURE 30–1

SUPPLEMENTARY NOTES

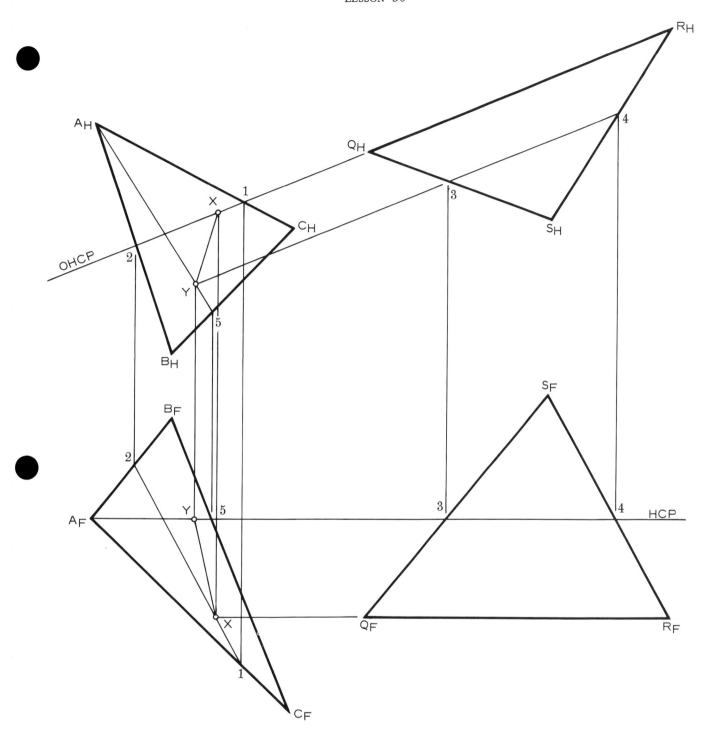

Figure 30–2

SUPPLEMENTARY NOTES

Exercises

Ex. 30.1 Find the line of intersection of the planes of the angles $A(6,0,9)$ $B(1,3,6)$ $C(3,3,5)$ and $D(2,0,8)$ $E(6,2,6)$ $F(4,4,5)$. Locate the point X at which this line pierces the plane ADF, and the point Y at which it intersects plane BCD.

Ex. 30.2 Find the intersection of the opaque triangles $A(1,2,7)$ $B(7,1,8\frac{1}{2})$ $C(5,4\frac{1}{2},5)$ and $D(2,4,8\frac{1}{2})$ $E(6\frac{1}{2},4,X)$ $F(2,1,5)$. DEF lies in an orthoprofile plane. Show all edges in proper visibility. Solve without the use of additional views.

Ex. 30.3 Locate in the top, front, and side view, the point X which is common to the OH plane $A(1,X,8)$ $B(3,X,6)C$, the OF plane $QR(1,3,X)$ $S(3,4,X)$, and the OP plane $D(2,3,7\frac{1}{2})$ $E(4,2,7)F$.

Ex. 30.4 The tetrahedron $A(0,1,7)$ $B(2,3,8)$ $C(5,1,6)$ $D(3,3,5)$ is cut by plane $Q(4,2\frac{1}{2},7)$ $R(7,4,8\frac{1}{2})$ $S(5\frac{1}{2},1\frac{1}{2},6\frac{1}{2})$ and the front portion removed. Show the remainder of the object with the cut surface shaded.

Ex. 30.5 $O(5,4,5\frac{1}{2})$ $O'(2,1,7\frac{1}{2})$ is the axis of an oblique cylinder whose bases are horizontal circles $2''$ in diameter. Without using additional views, find the intersection of the cylinder with the plane of the triangle $A(0,4,8)$ $B(3,4,5)$ $C(7,0,8)$. Remove the upper portion and shade the cut surface. Locate the exact points at which the extreme elements of the cylinder in each view are tangent to the cut surface.

Ex. 30.6 Given the opaque intersecting triangles $A(1,6\frac{1}{2},8\frac{1}{2})$ $B(2\frac{1}{2},4\frac{1}{2},7)$ $C(3,6,9)$ and $D(1\frac{1}{2},5,9)$ $E(2\frac{3}{4},6\frac{1}{4},6\frac{3}{4})$ $F(3\frac{1}{4},5,8)$. Construct the UFR isometric drawing of the triangles. Place the lower front corner of the enclosing box at $O(3\frac{1}{2},0,X)$. In the isometric pass the necessary cutting planes and determine the line of intersection. Complete the figure in correct visibility and shade the triangles.

Ex. 30.7 $C(0,1\frac{1}{2},7)$ is the center of a $2\frac{1}{2}''$ diameter sphere. Pass a plane through the line $A(0\frac{3}{4},1\frac{1}{2},5)$ $B(2\frac{1}{2},3\frac{1}{2},7\frac{1}{2})$ cutting the sphere in a circle of $2''$ diameter with the center of the circle lying below that of the sphere. Show the intersection with proper visibility in all views.

Lesson 31

Intersection of Solids

The line of intersection of the surfaces of any two solids can be established by the repeated application of the cutting plane concept. The work involved in such a solution can be minimized by a judicious choice of cutting planes and the use of a methodical procedure.

Intersection of Pyramids

Figure 31–1 illustrates the attack on problems dealing with the intersection of surfaces of nonprismatic objects having plane faces.

From the front view it is at once evident that the base of each pyramid lies entirely outside the other solid and cannot figure in the solution. This observation so simplifies the problem that we need only examine the three lateral edges of each pyramid for piercing points. In the solution shown, OF cutting planes have been used as a matter of convenience, but it should be noted at OH planes would have led to the same result.

The intersection of $CP1$, drawn through VB, with the pyramid $ODEF$ is the triangle abc. Points 1 and 2 are the intersections of VB with surfaces ODF and OEF, respectively. The piercing points along VC, VA, and OE are found in like manner. To avoid cluttering the figure, the intersections of $CP5$ and $CP6$ with pyramid $VABC$ have been omitted. They show only that no piercing points exist along edges OF and OD.

All piercing points having been located, they must next be connected in the proper order and visibility.

It is self-evident that, if two intersecting surfaces both appear visible in a particular view, their line of intersection must be visible in that view. If, however, either or both of the surfaces are hidden, the line of intersection will appear hidden.

From the construction it is seen that surface ODF is intersected by surface VBC in line 1–3, by VAB in 1–5, and by VAC in 5–3. ODF is visible in both top and front views. Since VAB and VBC are both visible in the top view, 1–3 and 1–5 are solid in that view. Since VAC is a hidden surface in the top view, 3–5 is a hidden line. In the front view by the same argument 1–3–2 is visible and 1–5 is hidden. For the right portion of the top view 4–2–7–6 is visible and 6–8–4 is hidden. Add each of these lines to the figure with colored pencil, complete the intersection in the front view, and finally, extend all lateral edges to their piercing points in proper visibility. Where a portion of an edge lies inside the other pyramid, it should be omitted. The intersecting objects are thus represented as a single solid.

Intersection of Prisms

The line of intersection of the surfaces of solids, one or both of which are prisms, can of course be obtained by the method demonstrated for pyramids. The work is greatly facilitated, however, if one prism is shown in end view as is the prism EFG in the front view given in Figure 31–2. In this view one can at once set down the numbering sequence for the entire line of intersection.

Beginning at the intersection of *AA′* with surface *FG*, and progressing around the near surfaces, the lines 1–2–3–4–5–6 are defined. Passing then to the rear surfaces, the intersection is readily identified as 6–7–8–1. Points 1, 2, 5, and 6 are known. 3, 4, 7, and 8 are found by use of a single *OF* cutting plane through surface *EF* which intersects the prism *ABC* in triangle *qrs*.

Join the points in order and determine the visibility of the lateral edges and the line of intersection to complete the top view.

Intersection of Cylinders

Cutting planes chosen parallel to the axes of intersecting cylinders contain straight line elements of the surfaces. For the cylinders given in Figure 31–3, frontal cutting planes satisfy this requirement. The elements of the inclined cylinder contained by the various cutting planes are found in the partial auxiliary view.

*CP*4, a typical cutting plane, contains two elements of each cylinder which intersect one another to locate the four points "4" on the line of intersection of the two surfaces. Each of the other cutting planes illustrated is used to locate so-called "critical points" at which tangencies, changes in visibility, and/or limiting conditions are attained.

Horizontal cutting planes are utilized in the alternate construction illustrated in Figure 31–4. Each *HCP* intersects the *FP* cylinder in the circle seen in the top view, and cuts the inclined cylinder in an ellipse. The ellipse need be plotted only once— by trammel, on tracing paper—since the same ellipse is produced by all *HCP*. For a particular *HCP* selected in the front view, the center of the ellipse is found and projected into the top view. The ellipse is slid into position; the intersections with the circle cut from the other cylinder are noted and projected back into the cutting plane in the front view.

In the top view several points on the circle are indicated by radial tic marks. These correspond to critical points on the intersection. To locate such a point, the ellipse is positioned to pass through the point. The center of the ellipse is then projected to the centerline of the cylinder in the front view, thus establishing the elevation of the corresponding *HCP*.

Intersection of a Cone and a Cylinder

Cutting planes taken through the vertex of the cone and parallel to the axis of the cylinder contain straight line surface elements of both. In Figure 31–5 orthoprofile cutting planes meet these conditions. The solution shown is self-explanatory. The labeled cutting planes locate the various critical points. Between *Va* and *Vb* sketch another cutting plane. Locate the corresponding points on the required line of intersection.

This particular problem could also have been conveniently solved by the use of horizontal cutting planes except that certain of the critical points would have to be located by trial and error. A combination of the two procedures would be expeditious.

Using colored pencil, sketch an *HCP* and locate the corresponding points on the line of intersection. What rules are used for determining the visibility of the intersection?

How would the attack on the problem be modified if the given figures were changed as follows.

[301]

1. The cone is oblique with a circular horizontal base.
2. The cylinder contains the vertex of the right cone.
3. The cylinder intersects the base of the right cone.
4. The cylinder is inclined.
5. The cylinder is inclined and partially intersects the base of the cone.
6. The centerline of the cylinder intersects that of the cone.
7. The cylinder is replaced by a normally oriented rectangular prism.

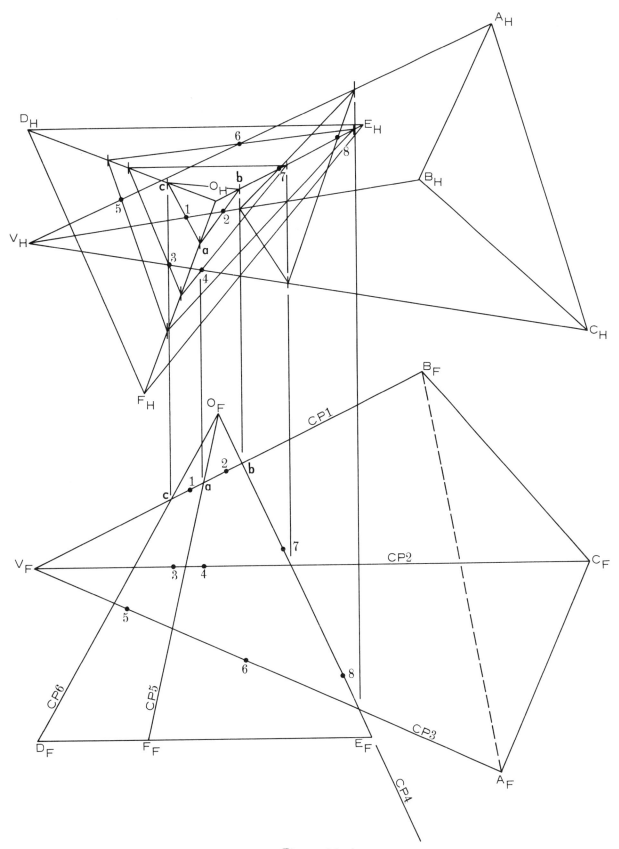

Figure 31–1

SUPPLEMENTARY NOTES

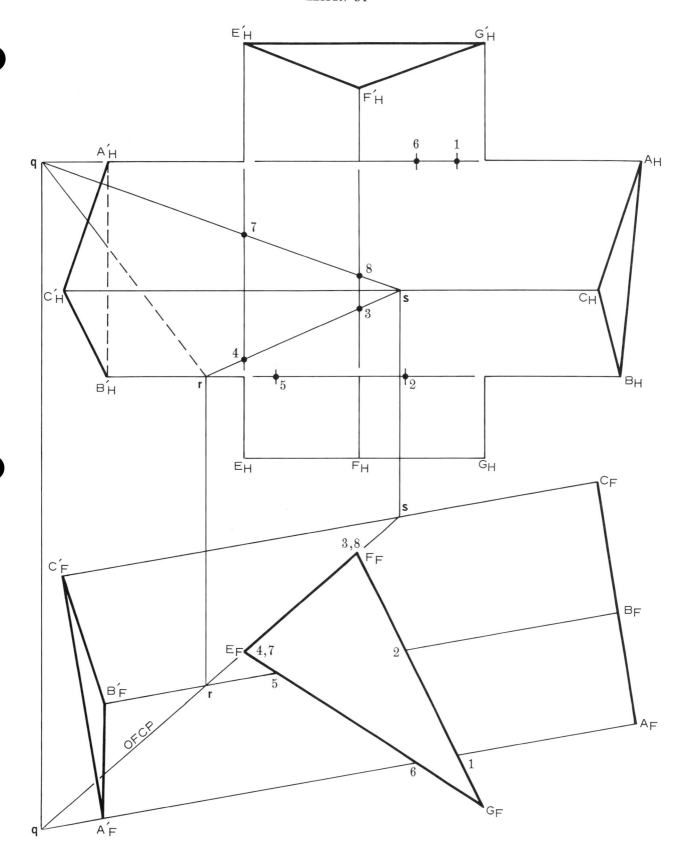

Figure 31–2

SUPPLEMENTARY NOTES

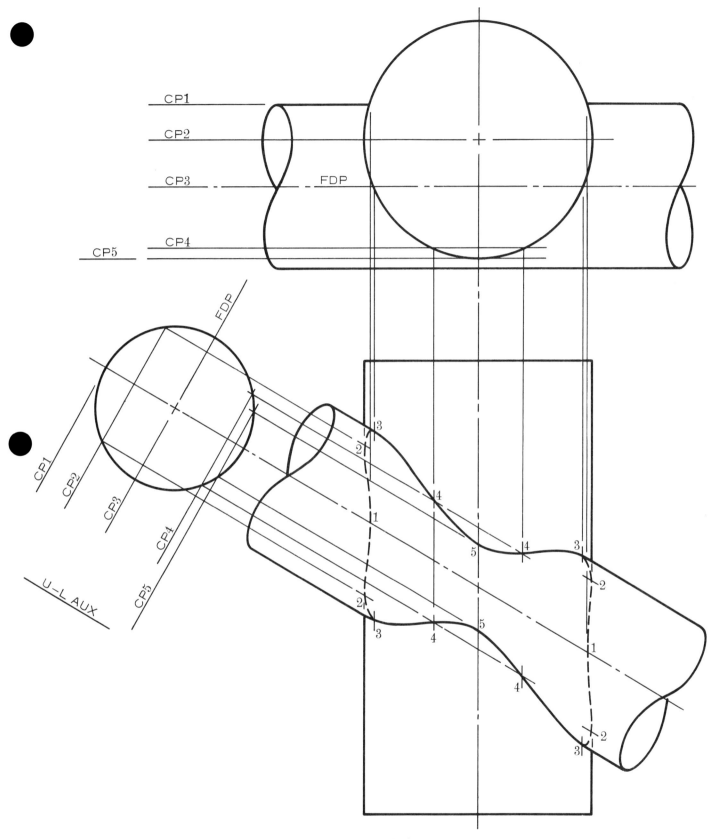

Figure 31-3

SUPPLEMENTARY NOTES

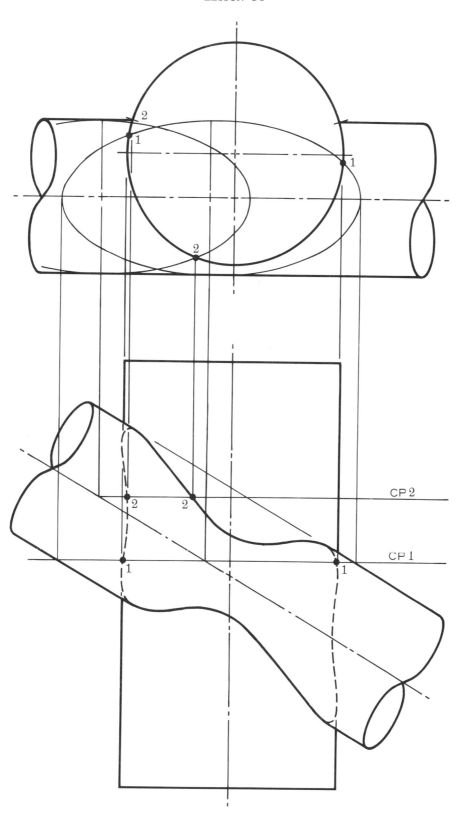

Figure 31-4

SUPPLEMENTARY NOTES

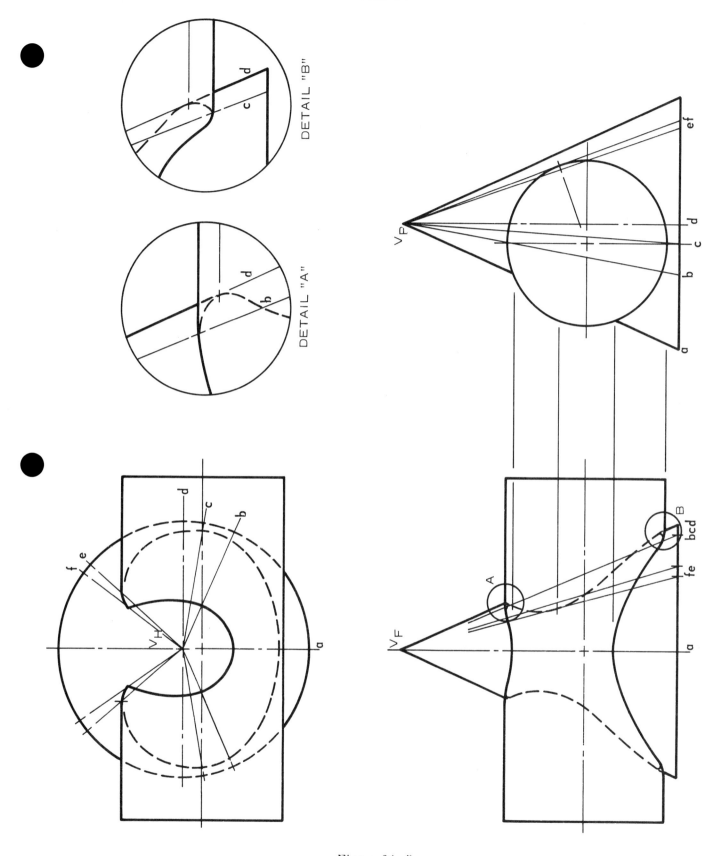

Figure 31-5

SUPPLEMENTARY NOTES

Exercises

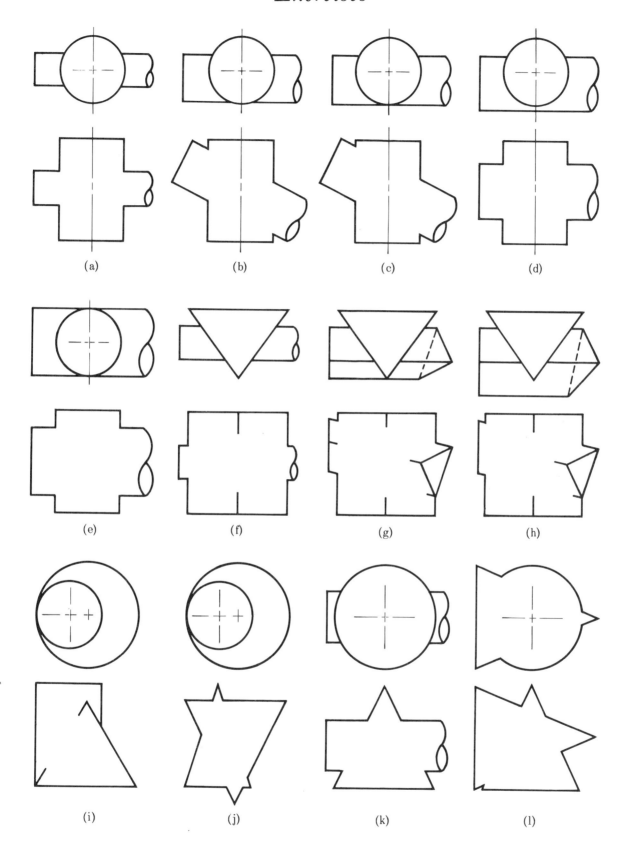

(a)   (b)   (c)   (d)

(e)   (f)   (g)   (h)

(i)   (j)   (k)   (l)

Ex. 31.1 Visualize and sketch each intersection.

Ex. 31.2 Given the top and front views of a normally oriented $3\frac{1}{4}''$ cube whose *UFL* corner is $Q(3,3\frac{1}{2},6)$. The cube is intersected by a triangular prism, one of whose bases is $A(1,4\frac{1}{2},5\frac{1}{2})$ $B(3\frac{1}{2},2\frac{1}{2},5\frac{1}{2})$ $C(4\frac{1}{2},5,5\frac{1}{2})$. The lateral edges of the prism are parallel to the *DBR* diagonal of the cube. The rear base of the prism is frontal and is $2\frac{1}{4}''$ behind A. Show the prism and cube as a single object.

Ex. 31.3 $V(4\frac{1}{2},3\frac{1}{2},6\frac{1}{2})$ is the vertex and $O(4\frac{1}{2},0,6\frac{1}{2})$ is the center of the $5''$ diameter horizontal base of a right circular cone. $P(2\frac{1}{2},4,6\frac{1}{2})$ is the vertex of a right pyramid. The base of the pyramid is an equilateral triangle in the same horizontal plane as the base of the cone. The altitude of the base is $4\frac{1}{2}''$. The left edge of the base of the pyramid is *HP*. Find the intersection and show the cone and pyramid as a single object.

Ex. 31.4 $V(6,3\frac{1}{2},8)$ $O(2\frac{1}{2},0\frac{1}{2},6)$ is the axis of an oblique cone whose base is a horizontal circle of $5''$ diameter. The cone is intersected by a $4''$ diameter sphere with center at O. Show the complete intersection with proper visibility.

Ex. 31.5 Establish the intersection of the two tetrahedrons $A(1,3,7)$ $B(4,0,9)$ $C(6,4,5\frac{1}{2})$ $D(2,1,5)$ and $J(2,0,8)$ $K(4,4,8)$ $L(6,0,8)$ $M(4,1\frac{1}{2},6)$ and show them with proper visibility as a single object.

Ex. 31.6 The tetrahedron $A(0,1,5)$ $B(1,2\frac{1}{4},7)$ $C(3,3,6)$ $D(4,0\frac{1}{2},8)$ is intersected by a right circular cylinder of $1\frac{1}{2}''$ diameter whose axis is $L(0,2,8)$ $M(4,2,5)$. Show the intersection with proper visibility. (a) Solve with horizontal cutting planes, utilizing the auxiliary view showing *ML* as a point. (b) Solve on a separate sheet using frontal cutting planes and a sliding ellipse.

Ex. 31.7 $V(3,3\frac{1}{2},6\frac{1}{2})$ $O(3,0,6\frac{1}{2})$ is the axis of a cone whose base is a $5''$ diameter horizontal circle. $A(0,0\frac{1}{2},7)$ $B(6,3,4)$ is the axis of a $2''$ diameter circular hole to be drilled through the cone. Complete the views of the drilled cone. Show all hidden lines.

Lesson 32

True Angle between Lines

The true angle between intersecting lines is seen in the true shape view of the plane defined by the lines. The angle between nonintersecting lines is, by definition, that angle seen in the view in which both lines appear in true length. This is the same view which would show the true shape of a plane parallel to the given lines.

Perpendicular Lines

If one of two perpendicular lines appears true length in a view, the angle between the lines must appear as a right angle. This is easily verified if one recalls that a plane perpendicular to a line shows as an edge perpendicular to the line in a true length view of the line. The foreshortened line lies in such a plane and any line in the plane must appear perpendicular to the true length line.

Note that lines need not intersect to be perpendicular. *Any* line lying in the perpendicular plane is perpendicular to the true length line.

Angle between a Line and a Plane

The angle a line makes with a plane is defined as the angle which it makes with its own projection in the plane. In Sketch 32–1 *AC* is the projection of *AB* on the plane *QRST*. Angle *BAC* is the true angle between the line and the plane and so can be measured in the view showing the true shape of plane *ABC*. Since *BC* was constructed perpendicular to the given plane, *ABC* and *QRST* are mutually perpendicular planes. In the view showing *ABC* true shape, therefore, plane *QRST* must appear as an edge.

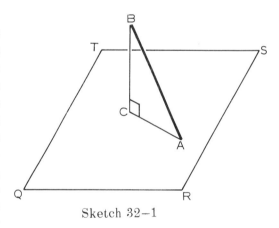

Sketch 32–1

A simple rule follows from the foregoing: The true angle between a line and a plane is measured in a view in which the line is shown true length and the plane shown as an edge. The distortion of the angle when the line does not appear in true length is demonstrated in Figure 32–1.

In this problem the front and top views of line *AB* are given. The angle with the horizontal is required. Since an edge view of a horizontal plane is needed, an auxiliary elevation (*HDP*) must be used, and it must be projected normal to *AB* so that the *TL* of the line will appear in the same view. Note that a view can be drawn in which the apparent angle is as much as 90°. The true angle is a minimal value.

On the same figure, sketch in red the auxiliary you would use to find the angle which *AB* makes with a frontal plane.

[315]

How might you find the angle between *AB* and some inclined plane? An oblique plane?

Suppose that you were given only the top view of an oblique line, but told that it sloped forward and down making a given angle with the horizontal. Could you draw the front view of the line?

Angle between Two Planes

A dihedral angle, that is, the angle between two planes, is found in the view showing both planes as edges. Note that in this view the line of intersection between the planes appears as a point.

The angle between an oblique plane and one of the principal planes is readily obtained in a first auxiliary in which the principal plane is a datum and the oblique plane shows as an edge. In Figure 17–4 the angle which oblique plane *ABC* makes with all frontal planes may be measured in the auxiliary view.

How would you find the angles which an inclined plane makes with the three principal planes?

What steps would be necessary to find the angle between two inclined planes? Between one inclined and one oblique? How many auxiliary views would be required in each case?

Can you prove that the angle between two planes is the same as the angle between two lines, one in each of the planes, constructed perpendicular to the line of intersection of the planes?

LESSON 32

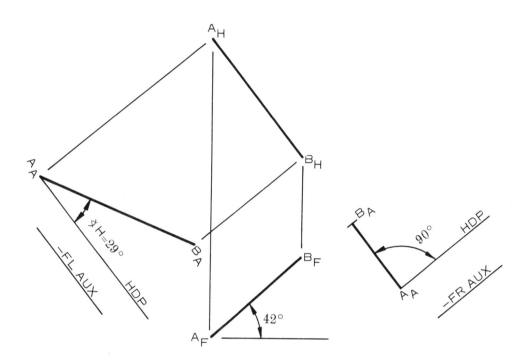

Figure 32–1

[317]

FIGURE 32–1

SUPPLEMENTARY NOTES

SUPPLEMENTARY NOTES

Exercises

Ex. 32.1 Measure the true angle between each of the following pairs of noninter-secting lines (Both problems fit on same sheet): (a) $A(1,5,7)$ $B(1,6,8)$ and $C(1\frac{1}{2},5\frac{1}{2},8)$ $D(2\frac{1}{2},5\frac{1}{2},7)$. (b) $E(0,1,3)$ $F(1,0,3)$ and $G(1,1,3)$ $H(2,0,4)$.

Ex. 32.2 $V(0,2,7)$ $O(2,3,7)$ is the axis of a right pyramid whose base is an equilateral triangle $2''$ on a side with center at O. The upper edge of the base lies in a profile plane. Find the angle which each lateral edge makes with the plane of the base and record the angles where measured.

Ex. 32.3 Point $P(2,2\frac{1}{2},7)$ is $1''$ from the plane of points $A(0,2,8)$ $B(2,1,9)$ $C(1,X,7)$. (a) Locate all possible positions of C in the front view. (b) If D is a point in the plane ABC and PD is perpendicular to the plane, locate the possible positions of D in the top and front views.

Ex. 32.4 Line $A(2,3,6)B$ is $1''$ long, lies in an orthoprofile plane which contains the line $C(1,1,5)$ $D(3,2,X)$, and makes an angle of $30°$ with all profile planes. Locate all possible positions for B in the top and front views. Measure the distance from A to CD.

Ex. 32.5 Given the principal views of the triangle $A(1,0\frac{1}{4},7)$ $B(0,1,6)$ $C(1\frac{1}{2},1\frac{1}{2},7)$. BCD is an equilateral triangle which forms an angle of $60°$ with the plane of triangle ABC. D lies below and behind point C. Consider the triangles opaque and show them in proper visibility in all views. Project initially from the side view.

Ex. 32.6 D is a point on the circumference of a circle which circumscribes tri-angle $A(0,2,7)$ $B(1\frac{1}{2},0\frac{1}{2},8)$ $C(1,2,6)$. Find and measure the shortest possible distance $P(2\frac{1}{2},0\frac{1}{2},8)D$. Locate D in the given views.

Ex. 32.7 Find a $1''$ line segment $A(0,3,7)D$ perpendicular to line $E(0,1,6\frac{1}{2})$ $F(2,2,6)$ and lying in the plane of the triangle $AB(1,3\frac{1}{2},6\frac{1}{2})$ $C(2,2\frac{1}{2},8)$. Show all possible locations of D in the given views.

Ex. 32.8 Through $E(1\frac{1}{4},4\frac{3}{4},7)$ construct a line EM which makes equal angles with the planes of the triangles $A(0,3\frac{1}{4},5\frac{3}{4})$ $B(0\frac{1}{2},4\frac{1}{2},8)$ $C(1\frac{1}{2},2\frac{1}{2},6\frac{1}{4})$ and $D(0\frac{1}{2},3\frac{1}{2},5\frac{1}{2})$ $EF(2,2\frac{3}{4},6\frac{1}{4})$. Let M lie in plane ABC. Measure the true angle which EM makes with the planes, find its true length, and show the line in the given views.

Ex. 32.9 Given the angle $A(2,3\frac{1}{2},8)$ $B(0,3,7\frac{1}{2})$ $C(1,2\frac{1}{4},7)$. On separate sheets of paper obtain each of the following, avoiding trial and error solutions. (a) A view which shows the true size of the angle and also one in which the angle appears to be $0°$ or $180°$. (b) A view in which the angle appears to be a right angle. (c) A view in which the angle appears to be $30°$. (d) A view in which the angle appears to be $20°$ larger than its actual size.

[319]

Lesson 33

Slope, Bearing, and Grade of a Line

Lines are frequently described by their bearing and slope or grade. A *bearing* is a map direction read in the top view. North is always considered to lie at the top of the sheet unless otherwise specified. The bearing is expressed as angular deviation to the east or west from the north–south line, as, for example, N60°E. In referring to a specific line *AB*, the bearing is the direction of *B* from *A*, the first named point being considered the origin.

The *slope* of a line is nothing more than the angle it makes with the horizontal, which is, as we have seen, always obtainable in an auxiliary elevation. In calling the slope it is necessary to specify "up" or "down." For example, if we are told that line *ML* slopes up 30°, we should understand this to mean that the line goes upward from *M* towards *L* while making an angle of 30° with the horizontal plane of projection.

Grade is used to express the slope in terms of the rise in a horizontal run of 100 units. It is equivalent to the tangent of the slope expressed as a percent. A 10% grade means a rise of 10 feet in a run of 100 feet. What slope corresponds to a 100% grade? What grade to a slope of 30°?

Figure 33–1 illustrates the usual manner of recording bearing and slope on a drawing.

Would a line be fully established if its bearing and true length were given?

Would a line be fully established if its bearing, slope, and one point on the line were given? If not, what additional information would be required?

Consider the significance of slope and bearing as applied to normal and inclined lines.

Given the front view of an oblique line, its true length, and a point on the line in the side view, could you find its bearing and slope? How many solutions are possible?

Strike and Dip of a Plane

The terms strike and dip offer a convenient way of describing a plane. The *strike* of a plane is the bearing of the horizontal lines in the plane. (They are parallel, you recall.) *Dip* is the angle of depression of the plane from the horizontal and is measured between the *HDP* and the edge view of the plane in an auxiliary elevation.

Let a plane through point *A* in Figure 33–2 have a strike of S70°E and a dip of 40°NE.

The strike line is horizontal through *A* and is drawn to its bearing in the top view. The strike shows a point in the auxiliary elevation, hence the required plane as an edge and the dip angle true size. The dip angle is given as 40°, but the edge view of the plane could be drawn as either the solid or the dashed line in the elevation unless further information were given. This is provided by the notation NE which follows the 40° in the statement of the problem.

In the required plane a line drawn perpendicular to the strike line is the steepest possible line in the plane and would appear true length in the auxiliary. Therefore, this line has a slope equal to the dip of the plane. It is usually shown as an arrow in the top view and is called the dip line or dip arrow. The dip line is always drawn pointing downward in the plane. It can be thought of as the path followed by a marble released on the plane at a point on the strike line. All points on the same side of the strike as the dip arrow lie below the elevation of the strike line.

The statement of the problem gives the dip as "40°NE." Note first that this is not a bearing. The 40° is simply angle H. The NE is to indicate that the dip arrow lies in the northeast quadrant in the top view. A little thought will show that this is equivalent to saying that the dip line slopes DBR. When the term *slope* is applied to a plane, it is actually the slope of the dip line that is referred to.

The dip line having been drawn in the top view and its significance kept in mind, it becomes obvious that the plane described by the problem is the one shown solid in the auxiliary.

The customary notation for strike and dip is shown in the top view. Actually the dip arrow and the NE convey the same information, and one could be omitted; but the inclusion of the NE to indicate the dip quadrant is essential in a verbal description of the plane.

On the figure in colored pencil sketch the procedure by which you would locate points B and C in the plane such that AC is profile, C being $\frac{1}{2}''$ above A, and that B is $2''$ to the right of A and that BC is frontal. Show triangle ABC in the top, front, and auxiliary views.

On the back of the preceding page sketch the top and front views of an oblique triangle. Sketch the necessary construction and properly record the estimated strike and dip of the plane on the top view.

Consider the significance of strike and dip for the special cases of normal and inclined planes. Sketches will help.

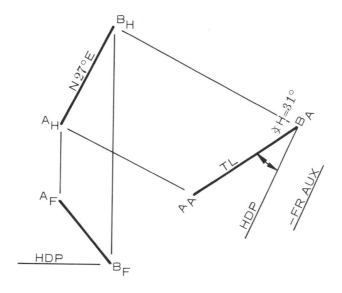

Figure 33—1

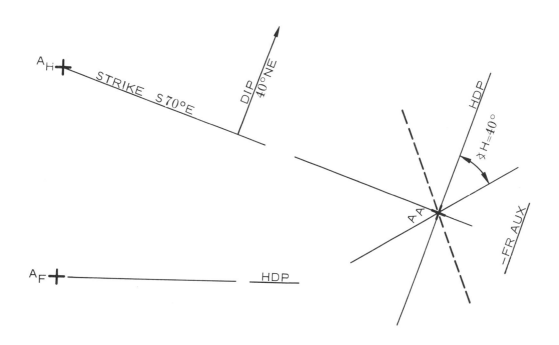

Figure 33—2

SUPPLEMENTARY NOTES

Exercises

Ex. 33.1 $L(3\frac{1}{2},1\frac{1}{2},X)$ $M(4,0\frac{1}{2},4)$ $N(3,X,3\frac{1}{2})$ $O(2,X,3\frac{1}{2})$ $P(1,1,5)$ is a plane with a strike of S80°W. Complete the top and front views. Find the dip of the plane and record in accepted notation.

Ex. 33.2 $A(0,2,6)$ $B(1,1,6\frac{3}{4})$ is a line in an equilateral triangle ABC which strikes N60°W. Point C lies to the right of B. Show the triangle in the principal views, find and record the dip of the plane and, finally, measure and tabulate the bearing and grade of all inclined (H,F,P) lines in the plane.

Ex. 33.3 $P(1\frac{1}{2},X,7)$ is a point in a plane ABP which is perpendicular to a given plane $A(0,2,7\frac{1}{2})$ $B(2,1\frac{1}{2},8\frac{1}{2})$ $C(1,0\frac{1}{2},6\frac{1}{2})$. Find and record where measured the angle which ABP makes with each of the principal planes of projection.

Ex. 33.4 In all principal views of the triangle $A(1,1\frac{1}{2},6\frac{1}{2})$ $B(2,3\frac{1}{2},5)$ $C(0,2\frac{1}{2},4\frac{1}{2})$ show the lines BH, BF, and BP which lie in the plane and which make the maximum possible acute angle with the horizontal, frontal, and profile planes of projection, respectively. Find these angles and record where measured. The required lines may be drawn any convenient length.

Ex. 33.5 A cutting plane through corner A of the tetrahedron $A(0,3,7)$, $B(0\frac{1}{2},2,8)$ $C(2,4,8)$ $D(1\frac{1}{2},2,5\frac{1}{2})$ strikes N60°W and dips 30°NE. The upper portion of the object as cut by the plane is discarded. Show the remaining portion with proper visibility in the top, front, and necessary auxiliary views.

Ex. 33.6 Find the strike and dip of a plane which contains the point $P(3,X,6\frac{1}{2})$ and is perpendicular to line $A(1\frac{1}{2},X,5)B$. Line AB has a bearing of N40°E and is 2″ long. Points A and P are above point B, $\frac{3}{4}″$ and 1″, respectively. Record the required strike and dip in the accepted notation.

Ex. 33.7 The tetra hedron $A(0,1\frac{1}{2},6)$ $B(2,1,7)$ $C(3,3\frac{1}{2},5\frac{1}{2})$ $D(1,3,4\frac{1}{2})$ is intersected by a plane through point $R(1,3\frac{1}{2},5\frac{1}{4})$ which strikes S75°E and dips 60°NE. Show the line of intersection on the surface of the object in proper visibility in all views drawn, and obtain the true shape of the intersection.

Ex. 33.8 Line $A(2\frac{1}{2},2\frac{1}{2},5\frac{1}{2})B$ has a bearing of N30°E, has the direction DBR, and a slope of 40°. Plane ABC strikes N45°W. Determine and record in proper notation the dip of plane ABC and measure the angle which it makes with the profile plane of projection.

Ex. 33.9 A plane through point $A(0,2,7\frac{1}{2})$ strikes S60°E and dips 45°SW. A second plane is defined by parallel horizontal lines through points $B(3,2,7)$ and $C(4,1\frac{1}{2},6\frac{1}{2})$ having a bearing of N60°E. Find and record where measured the slope of the line of intersection of the two planes.

Ex. 33.10 Construct a plane $A(0,3,7)BC$ such that it makes equal angles with the three principal planes of projection. Measure that angle and verify the result mathematically. What is the relationship between plane ABC and a *line* which makes equal angles with the principal planes. Prove your conclusion.

Ex. 33.11 What is the greatest possible value (in degrees) of the *sum* of the angles which a plane makes with the principal planes of projection? The least possible value? The greatest and least which could be made by a line? Prove.

Lesson 34

Perpendicular from a Point to a Plane

The shortest distance from a point to a plane is measured on a perpendicular from the point to the plane and will appear *TL* in a view showing the plane as an edge.

In Figure 34–1 a perpendicular has been dropped from *P* to the plane 1–2–3 in the auxiliary elevation. Since it is *TL* in this view, *PO* must appear in the top view at right angles to the projectors for the auxiliary, hence perpendicular to the *TL* (horizontal) lines in the plane. A construction from the front view would obviously yield a similar result. We may then conclude that a line perpendicular to a plane shows perpendicular to *TL* lines in the plane in all views.

This concept permits us to drop a perpendicular from a point to a plane without using an auxiliary view. A *TL* line is drawn in the plane in each of the principal views. The required line from *P* is constructed perpendicular to these lines. The usual constructions for piercing point and visibility may then be made, if desired.

Plane through a Point and Perpendicular to a Line

In Figure 34–2 we are given the point *A* and the line *BC*. A plane through *A* and perpendicular to *BC* is required.

An obvious method of solution would be to obtain *BC* in true length. In that view the required plane would show as an edge through *A*.

An equally valid solution can be obtained in the principal views alone. Two lines through *A* are necessary to establish the plane. If these lines are chosen so that each appears true length in one of the principal views, they must be drawn perpendicular to *BC* in their true length views. Why?

In the figure *AX* has been drawn frontal and *AY*, profile. *XAY* is the required plane. Locate the piercing point in colored pencil and then sketch an auxiliary view to prove the correctness of the solution.

Plane through a Line and Perpendicular to a Given Plane

Two planes are perpendicular if one plane contains a line which is perpendicular to the other plane. (Actually in each plane a family of lines exists each of which is perpendicular to the other plane.)

To construct a plane through a given line *AB* perpendicular to a given plane 1–2–3 (no figure given), it is only necessary to construct a line from any point on *AB* perpendicular to the plane. *AB* and the perpendicular define the required plane.

Plane through a Point and Perpendicular to Two Given Planes

The required plane is determined by two lines constructed through the given point. Each line is made perpendicular to one of the given planes. Hence, the plane formed by the lines is perpendicular to the given planes. For proof imagine the construction as seen in the view showing the line of intersection of the given planes as a point.

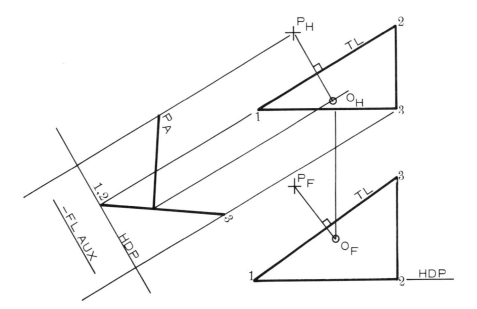

Figure 34-1

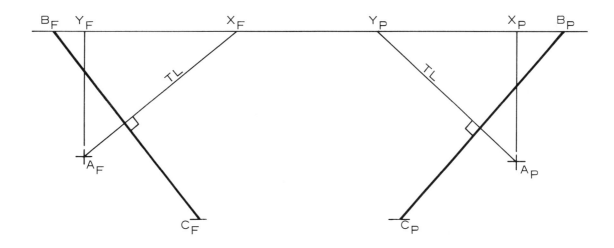

Figure 34-2

SUPPLEMENTARY NOTES

Exercises

Ex. 34.1 $A(6,2,7)$ $B(4\frac{1}{2},4,8)$ is a line in a plane striking S45°W. Without using auxiliary views, construct the perpendicular from point $P(4,1\frac{1}{2},7)$ to the plane. Find and circle the piercing point. Finally, using such auxiliary views as may be necessary, measure and record the true length, slope, and bearing of the perpendicular.

Ex. 34.2   Construct triangle $A(1,2,5)$ $B(4,X,8)$ $C(1,3,X)$ perpendicular to line $L(0,0,8)$ $M(6,3,4)$ without the use of auxiliary views.

Ex. 34.3   Through point $P(4,4,5)$ construct a perpendicular to plane $A(0,2,5)$ $B(6,1,6)$ $C(4\frac{1}{2},4,8)$, one surface of tetrahedron $ABCD(2,0,9)$. Show the line piercing the tetrahedron in proper visibility, omitting the portion inside the solid.

Ex. 34.4   Through point $P(3,4\frac{1}{2},8)$ construct plane PQR perpendicular to the planes $A(0,4,6)$ $B(2,1,8)$ $C(4\frac{1}{2},1,6)$ and $ABD(3,4,6)$. Locate Q in plane ABC, and R in plane ABD.

Ex. 34.5   A plane $A(5,0\frac{1}{2},5)$ $B(4,1,4)C$ is perpendicular to the plane of triangle $Q(6,1,6)$ $R(4,2,5)$ $S(4,3,7)$. Without using auxiliary views, establish the line of intersection of the two planes. Show the required line in color. Prove the validity of the solution by adding the appropriate auxiliary views.

Ex. 34.6   Plane $A(0,3,6)$ $B(0\frac{1}{2},1\frac{1}{2},5)C$ strikes S45°W. AC is a frontal line. Plane $D(5,3,7)EF$ is perpendicular to line AB. Establish a plane $Q(3,3\frac{1}{2},7)RS$ perpendicular to both planes ABC and DEF. Locate point W which is common to both line AC and the plane of QRS.

Ex. 34.7   Given the tetrahedron $A(0,3,4)$ $B(2,0\frac{1}{2},9)$ $C(7,5,8)$ $D(5,0,5)$. A plane containing point D is perpendicular to plane ABC and intersects it in a frontal line. In proper visibility show the intersection of this plane with the entire solid.

Ex. 34.8   Through point $A(4,3,7)$ establish a plane ABC which is perpendicular to a second plane which strikes N45°W and dips 30°NE. The required plane contains a profile line which slopes DF- at 60° with the horizontal. Find the strike and dip of plane ABC.

Lesson 35

Line Parallel to a Plane

An infinite number of lines can be drawn through a given point parallel to a given plane. In a view showing the given plane as an edge, all of these lines coincide and appear parallel to the plane.

In Figure 35–1 point A and plane KLM are given. Point B is given in the front view only. It is required to establish B in the top view such that AB will be parallel to KLM. In the auxiliary elevation sketch AB parallel to the plane. The horizontal locus of B is known from the front view. Project B into the top view. Sketch the solution again using an auxiliary projected from the front view.

A second and even more direct procedure does not require the use of any auxiliary view. With colored pencil sketch a line through K in the front view parallel to AB and intersecting ML at N. KN is one of the family of parallel lines in the plane, each of which is parallel to AB. Carry KN into the top view and draw $A_H B_H$ parallel to it.

Plane through a Point and Parallel to a Given Plane

As demonstrated above, a plane through a given point may be established parallel to a given plane in any view showing the given plane as an edge. In the auxiliary elevation of Figure 35–1, AB is the edge view of an oblique plane parallel to the given plane KLM.

A solution may be obtained without recourse to the auxiliary view, however, if the required plane is established by means of two lines, each of which is parallel to a known line in the given plane. For example, in the same figure sketch a line AC parallel to KM in both given views, and a second line AD parallel to LM. The plane CAD is the required plane. Verify by projecting C and D into the auxiliary elevation.

Plane through a Point and Parallel to Two Non-Intersecting Lines

A plane parallel to two non-intersecting lines can be drawn through the given point in the view showing one of the given lines as a point. Make a sketch of such a view in the margin.

This problem may also be solved directly in the given views. Two lines are constructed through the given point, each parallel to one of the given lines. These lines define a plane which is parallel to both given lines, fulfilling the specifications of the problem. Suppose one were to construct an auxiliary showing the plane as an edge. How would the given lines appear in that view? Sketch.

Shortest Distance between Two Lines

The perpendicular distance between two lines can be found by either of the following two procedures.

The first method is illustrated in Figure 35–2. The true length of CD is obtained in a

[330]

first auxiliary and its point view in a second. In the secondary auxiliary sketch the perpendicular from the point CD to line AB. Prove that this perpendicular is true length and that it is the shortest distance between the lines. Without making additional views, locate the intersection of the perpendicular with CD and carry the perpendicular back into both principal views.

The second method is discussed with reference to Figure 35–3. Through point C plane CDa is constructed parallel to the given oblique lines. The edge view of this plane is drawn in the first auxiliary. The given lines appear parallel in this view and the shortest distance between them can be measured along any perpendicular line. Why?

If the problem requires that the *location* of the shortest connecting line be found, the true shape of CDa is found in a second auxiliary. The apparent intersection of the given lines in that view is the point view of the required connecting line. Sketch the true shape view, locate the connecting line and carry it back into the principal views.

Shortest Line Connecting Two Given Lines and Having a Specified Slope

Again referring to Figure 35–3, it is now required to find the shortest line on a 30° slope connecting the given lines AB and CD. The first auxiliary is obtained as in the previous case. Next the second auxiliary is drawn whose direction of sight is the true length arrow inclined at 30° to the HDP. Sketch the view. The apparent intersection of the given lines is the point view of the required line. Carry the solution back into the given views.

To demonstrate the validity of this construction, consider the pair of parallel planes which may be drawn through AB and CD so as to appear in edge view in the auxiliary elevation of Figure 35–3. From any point E in the plane through line CD, sketch a cone having a horizontal base and a base angle equal to the specified slope. The surface of this cone is the locus of all lines from E having the specified slope. The required line is not constrained to pass through E, but it must necessarily be parallel to some surface element of the locus cone. It is evident that the true-length element of the locus cone is the shortest line segment on the required slope between the parallel planes. It follows that the required line must be parallel to that TL element and that the apparent intersection of AB and CD established in the second auxiliary is indeed the point view of the shortest connecting line on the given slope.

Could one apply this same procedure to find the shortest line connecting the given lines and making a specified angle with a frontal or a profile plane? With an inclined plane? An oblique plane? Does more than one solution exist to each of these problems? If the word "shortest" were omitted from the problem statement, how many solutions might be found?

Suppose the problem were worded, "Find the shortest line on a specified slope, through a given point, and connecting two given skew lines." Would a solution be possible? If so, under what conditions? (Don't jump to a conclusion.)

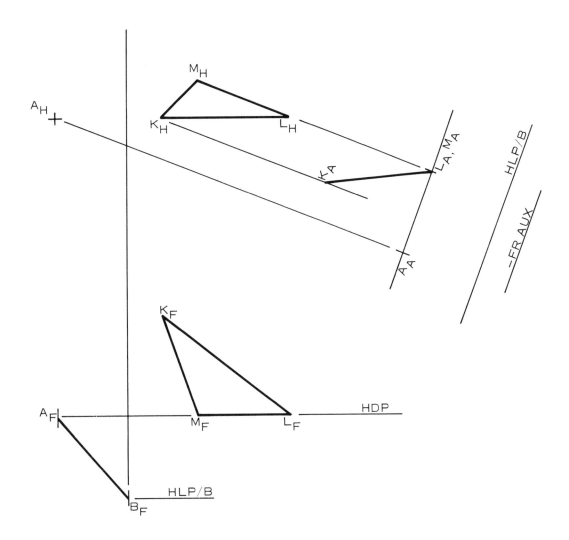

Figure 35–1

SUPPLEMENTARY NOTES

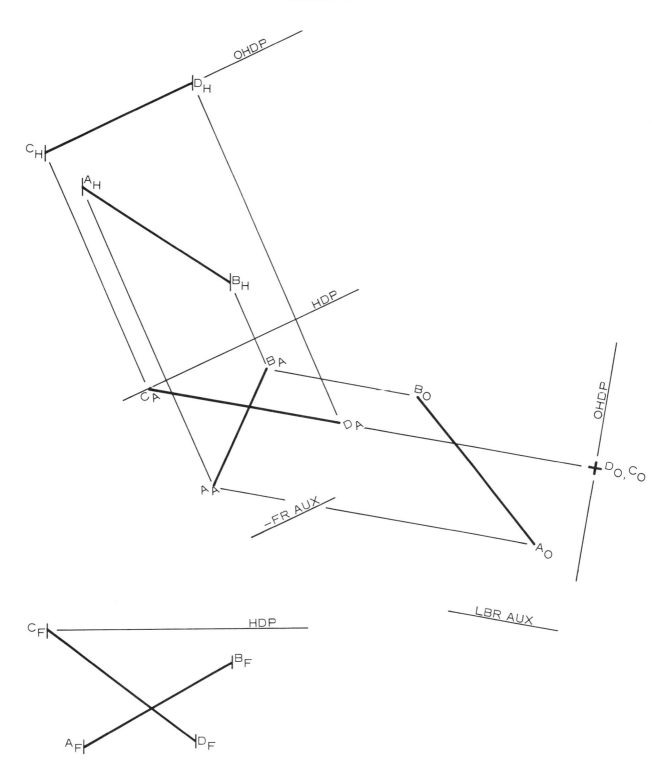

Figure 35–2

SUPPLEMENTARY NOTES

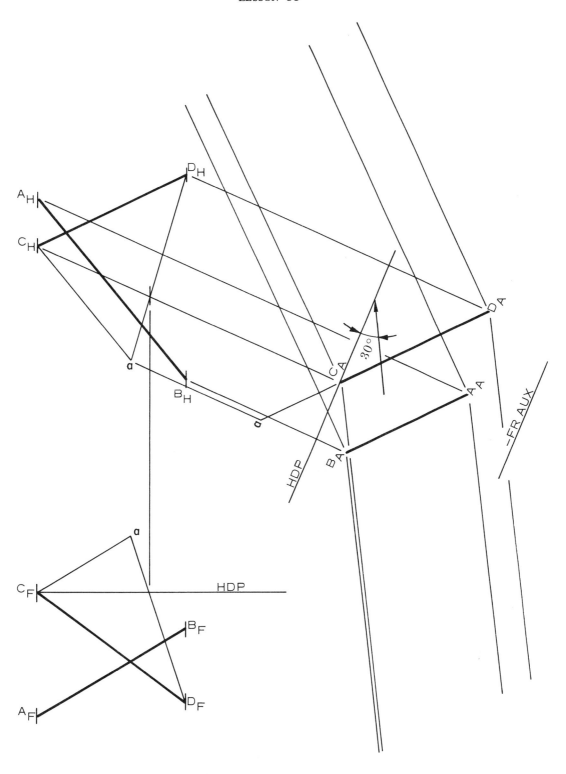

Figure 35—3

SUPPLEMENTARY NOTES

Exercises

Ex. 35.1   Line $A(3,2,7)B$ has a bearing of N60°E and is parallel to the plane of triangle $Q(0,2,6)$ $R(3,4,5)$ $S(1,0,8)$. Find the slope of AB and record where measured. How many solutions are possible?

Ex. 35.2   Through $P(3\frac{1}{2},X,6\frac{1}{2})$ establish a line parallel to the plane of triangle $D(0,3,6)$ $E(3,1,6)$ $F(2,3,4)$ and lying in the plane of triangle $A(4,4,5)$ $B(5,1,8)$ $C(7,3,7)$.

Ex. 35.3   Planes $A(6,4,8)BC$ and $D(7,4,7)EF$ both strike S60°W and dip 45°NW. Find and record where measured: (a) the shortest distance between them; (b) the shortest horizontal distance between them; (c) the shortest frontal distance between them.

Ex. 35.4   Using only one additional view, measure the angle made by a plane parallel to lines $A(0,1,6\frac{1}{2})$ $B(2,2,7\frac{1}{2})$ and $C(0,3,8)$ $D(1\frac{1}{2},2\frac{1}{2},6)$ with a frontal plane. Also, find the shortest distance between the given lines.

Ex. 35.5   Measure the angle which a plane through point $P(1,4,5)$ parallel to lines $A(0,3,7)$ $B(1\frac{1}{2},3,7)$ and $C(0,3\frac{1}{2},5\frac{1}{2})$ $D(1\frac{1}{2},2,7\frac{1}{2})$ makes with each of the principal planes.

Ex. 35.6   Given the skew lines $A(0,1,7\frac{1}{2})$ $B(1,1,6\frac{1}{2})$ and $C(0,0,7)$ $D(1,1\frac{1}{2},8)$. (a) Show in red the shortest normal line connecting the given lines. (b) Show in blue the shortest frontal line connecting the given lines. (c) Show in green the shortest line parallel to the plane of points $Q(2,X,6)$ $R(2\frac{1}{2},X,8)$ $S(2,X,6)$ that can be drawn connecting the given lines. Show each of the required lines in the given views.

Ex. 35.7   Find a line $P(0,3,5)C$ which is parallel to the plane of triangle $L(3\frac{1}{2},4,5)$ $M(5,1,8)$ $N(7,3,6)$ and which intersects the line $A(1,3\frac{1}{2},9)$ $B(3,1\frac{1}{2},5)$ at C. Solve without the use of additional views.

Ex. 35.8   Find the length of the shortest line which can be drawn connecting lines $A(5\frac{1}{2},2,8)$ $B(7,3,7)$ and $C(5\frac{1}{2},3\frac{1}{2},6)$ $D(7,2,6\frac{1}{2})$ and making an angle of 45° with a frontal plane. Show the required line in the given views.

Ex. 35.9 $A(5,4,6)$ $B(6\frac{1}{2},2,5\frac{1}{2})$ is the centerline of a $1''$ square bar having two sides vertical. $C(5\frac{1}{2},2,6\frac{1}{2})$ $D(6,4,8)$ is the centerline of a $\frac{1}{2}''$ diameter pipe. Find and record where measured the clearance between the pipe and the bar. Do not complete more views than necessary to obtain the answer.

Ex. 35.10   Construct the isosceles triangle $Q(0\frac{1}{2},2\frac{1}{2},5)RS$ parallel to lines $A(0,2,5\frac{1}{2})$ $B(1,1,6\frac{1}{2})$ and $C(1,2,5)$ $D(2,2\frac{1}{2},5)$. Legs QR and QS are equal. QR is a frontal line $1\frac{1}{2}''$ long and has the direction U–R. RS is a profile line. Show QRS in the given views.

Ex. 35.11   Pass a plane through tetrahedron $A(1\frac{1}{2},2,5\frac{1}{2})$ $B(0,4,6)$ $C(0\frac{1}{2},1\frac{1}{2},7)$ $D(2,3,7\frac{1}{2})$ parallel to lines AB and CD and cutting BC $1''$ from C. Show the intersection of the plane with the solid in proper visibility in the given views. What kind of polygon is the intersection? Why?

Ex. 35.12   Construct triangle $B(2,1\frac{1}{2},4\frac{1}{2})XY$. BX is a $2''$ line parallel to the shortest horizontal line connecting lines $A(0,1,5\frac{1}{2})B$ and $C(0,3,6\frac{1}{2})$ $D(1\frac{1}{2},2\frac{1}{2},8)$. Line BY is perpendicular to plane $CDE(1,1\frac{1}{2},5\frac{1}{2})$ and Y lies in the plane of CDE. Show the required triangle in the top and front views.

Lesson 36

Revolution of a Line

The solution of problems requiring the true length of a line or the angle between a line and a plane are facilitated if certain auxiliary views are replaced by revolutions of the line about appropriate axes.

Length of a Line and its Angles with Principal Planes

In Figure 36–1(a) the oblique line AB is given in top, front, and side views. Required are the angles H, F, and P and the true length of the line. We will revolve the line about a FP axis, AO, thus generating the surface of a right cone having its vertex at A with B a point on the circumference of the circular base. Since AB is a surface element of the cone, its apparent length in the top view is the radius of the base. Recognizing this, we now complete the top and front views of the cone. Because the base of the cone is horizontal, we will refer to the cone as an H *cone* and similarly, F *cone* and P *cone* for those having frontal or profile bases, respectively.

The two frontal elements AB' of the H cone are true length in the front view, and the angle they make with the plane of the base is a true angle. Since all surface elements of the cone are of equal length and make the same angle with the plane of the base, the true length of AB' and the angle between AB' and the horizontal base are also the true length and true angle H of the original line AB.

The vertex of the H cone could have been as readily taken at B. In space (b) sketch this cone, and compare with the one just discussed.

An F cone has been constructed in space (c). The axis is a horizontal-profile line, the base is frontal, and the true length elements are horizontal. Note that the true length of AB must be the same as that previously found.

Sketch a P cone in space (d). Label the TL of AB and the angle P it makes with the profile base.

Figure 36–2 shows the three constructions superimposed. Only the necessary portions of the cones have been drawn, but it is essential that each be completely visualized as the construction is made. Label the base and sketch the axis of each cone. Note that we have actually solved for the true length of AB three separate times. This should suggest the further simplification illustrated in Figure 36–3. The true length and angle H have been found in an H cone with vertex at A. This TL has been transferred with a compass into a P cone in the front view and into an F cone in the top view. The original point B must be made to lie in the base of each cone. It is now seen that the circular views of the F and P cones in Figure 36–2 were unnecessary.

The three revolutions are the equivalent of three first auxiliary views. Note that no projections of the revolved line into auxiliaries can be permitted, since it does not bear the same relation to the principal planes as the original line. (One would have to project the entire cone into the auxiliary to avoid error—obviously not a worthwhile effort). A revolution can frequently be conveniently used to replace the last view in a sequence of auxiliaries. In fact, as will be seen in the next lesson, the last two or three may sometimes be profitably replaced by a like number of revolutions.

Dip of a Plane by Revolution of Dip Line

The dip line of a plane, being perpendicular to the strike, is true length in the auxiliary showing the plane as an edge, and so it has a slope equal to the dip of the plane.

In Figure 36–4 a dip line has been drawn in the top and front views of plane ABC (C is seen to be the lowest corner in the front view) and then rotated on an H cone to determine its slope. Angle H is the dip of the plane.

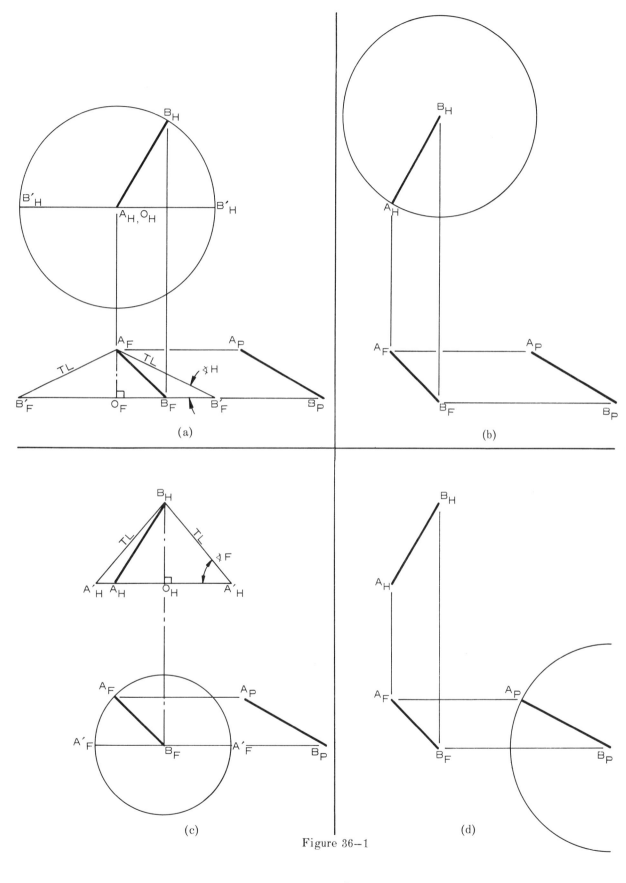

(a)

(b)

(c)

(d)

Figure 36–1

SUPPLEMENTARY NOTES

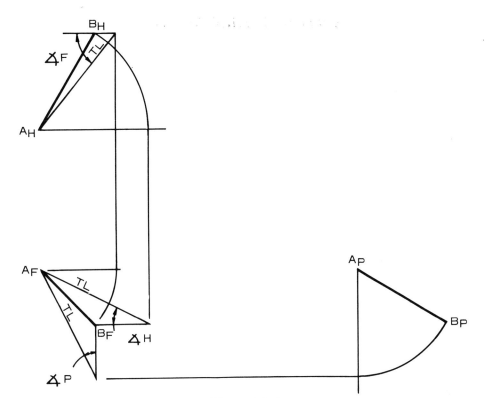

Figure 36–2

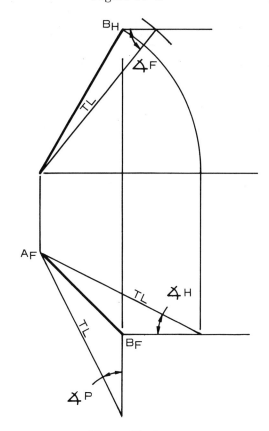

Figure 36–3

SUPPLEMENTARY NOTES

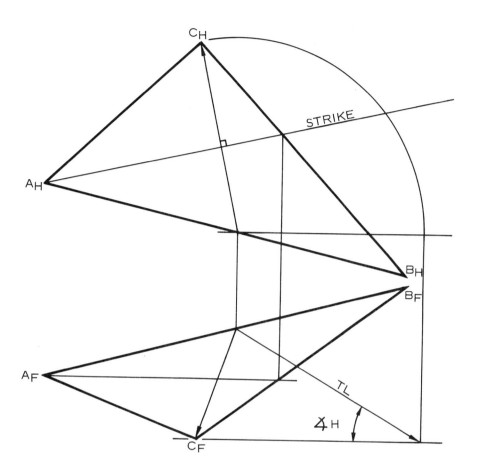

Figure 36–4

SUPPLEMENTARY NOTES

Exercises

Ex. 36.1 $A(3,3,4)$ $B(5,3,6)$ is the upper edge of the OH square base of a right pyramid whose altitude is $4''$. The vertex of the pyramid is to the left of the base. Find the true length of each lateral edge and the angles which each makes with the three principal planes. Solve for $\measuredangle H$ in red, $\measuredangle F$ in blue, and $\measuredangle P$ in green. Use revolution in the given views.

Ex. 36.2. Complete the top and front views of the tetrahedron $A(3,3,6)$ $B(2,2,X)$ $C(5,4,X)$ $D(X,1,X)$. Line AB is directed DBL and is inclined to the horizontal at $30°$. AC, directed UBR, forms a $45°$ angle with the frontal plane of projection. AD is $3''$ long, is directed DFR, and is inclined at $30°$ to the frontal plane of projection. Solve by revolution without using additional views.

Ex. 36.3 By revolution find the true length of each side of triangle $A(2,2,7)$ $B(4\frac{1}{2},0,6\frac{1}{2})$ $C(2,4,5)$ and the angles which each side makes with the frontal and profile planes. Use revolution in the given views. Solve for $\measuredangle F$ in red and for $\measuredangle P$ in blue.

Ex. 36.4 Without using auxiliary views, construct through point $C(3,3,8)$ a line intersecting a given line $A(1,3,5)$ $B(4,1\frac{1}{2},7)$ at D such that CD has the same slope as AB. Measure the length of CD.

Ex. 36.5 $A(1,2,4\frac{1}{2})B$ is a line bearing N45°W and sloping down at an angle of $30°$ with the horizontal. Line $C(5,0,X)$ $D(3\frac{1}{2},1,X)$ intersects AB, is directed UFL, and makes an angle of $45°$ with the frontal plane of projection. Without the use of additional views find the strike and dip of plane $ABCD$ and record the values in the accepted form.

Ex. 36.6 Using revolution in the principal views, find the angles that surface $A(0,2,6)$ $B(1,3\frac{1}{2},7\frac{1}{2})$ $C(3,2\frac{1}{2},7\frac{1}{2})$ $D(2,1,6)$ makes with each principal plane. Solve for $\angle H$ in red, for $\angle F$ in blue, and for $\angle P$ in green.

Ex. 36.7 Triangle $A(1,2,7)$ $B(2,4,7\frac{1}{2})$ $C(4,1\frac{1}{2},8\frac{1}{2})$ is the base of a pyramid whose vertex is in front of B. VB is perpendicular to ABC and is $3''$ long. Complete the given views of the pyramid, and by revolution find the following angles, recording them where measured. (a) $\angle H$, $\angle F$, and $\angle P$ for VB; (b) $\angle H$ and $\angle P$ for VA; (c) $\angle F$ and the angle the line makes with plane ABC for VC.

Ex. 36.8 Line $A(4,2,7)$ $B(3,X,X)$ is $3''$ long, is directed UFL, and makes an angle of $45°$ with the frontal plane of projection. Construct an equilateral triangle ABC having side AC frontal. Solve by revolution using no additional views. Show all possible solutions.

Lesson 37

Angle between a Line and an Oblique Plane

Method 1. Three Successive Auxiliary Views: It should be recalled that the angle between a line and a plane can be measured only in a view showing the true length of the line and the edge view of the plane (page 315). The procedure for obtaining such a view by the auxiliary view method is shown in Figure 37–1. Line *AB* and plane *RST* are given in top and front views. The edge view of the plane is obtained in the first auxiliary and its true shape in the second. In the third auxiliary, projected normal to *AB*, the line is true length and plane *RST* is an edge so the true angle may be measured. Notice that since the *ODP* coincides with the edge view of *RST*, it is unnecessary to plot the true shape of the plane in the second auxiliary, nor to project points in the plane into the third.

A second legitimate solution (not illustrated) can be found by obtaining the true length of *AB* in a first auxiliary, its point view in a second, and its true length along with an edge view of the plane in a third.

Method 2. Two Successive Auxiliary Views and One Revolution: Figure 37–2 shows the previous solution modified. The third auxiliary has been replaced by revolution between the first and second. The axis of the cone of revolution has been taken through *B*. Since the angle with the plane is required, the base of the cone is made parallel to the edge view of *RST*. The circular base is then true shape in the second auxiliary and elements $B_oA'_o$ are true length in the first auxiliary where they make the required angle with *RST* and also with the base of the cone.

Method 3. One Auxiliary View and Two Revolutions: In Method 2 the only purpose of the second auxiliary was for it to participate in the revolution for the true length used in the first. The true length can be found just as readily between two given or existing views and then transferred into the required cone in the first auxiliary.

On Figure 37–3 sketch a revolution of *AB* on an *F* cone in the top and front views to obtain its true length. You may now transfer this length into the auxiliary showing the plane as an edge, and measure the angle with the plane, providing the base of the cone contains the end point of the line and is parallel to *RST*.

In the figure the first revolution was made on an *H* cone, giving the true length *BA'* in the auxiliary. Note, however, that even though *BA'* is true length and *RST* is an edge, the angle between them is *not* true since *RST* was not the base of the cone. *AB'* is therefore transferred to *BA''* in the required cone and the angle measured.

True Shape of a Plane by Revolution

By the auxiliary view method the true shape of an inclined plane is found in a first auxiliary projected normal to the edge view of the plane and that of an oblique plane in a second auxiliary. The revolution concept will permit us to dispense with the last auxiliary in each case.

A vertical plane *ABC* is given in Figure 37–4. If the plane is revolved about a vertical axis through *B*, a solid will be generated as shown in the sketch. Frontal sections through the solid show the plane in true shape. It is convenient to choose the axis and section so that the true shape falls in a clear area.

The given views can be imagined in any orientation. The construction is valid between any adjacent views so long as one is the edge view of the plane.

Angle between Oblique Planes

We have previously recognized that the angle between two planes can be measured only in a view showing both as edges. Obviously this would also be the point view of the line of intersection. Several procedures are available for obtaining the necessary view.

Method I: The line of intersection is given or found by a preliminary construction. Its true length is obtained in a first auxiliary, and its point view in a second.

Method II: The line of intersection is found in a first auxiliary showing one of the planes as an edge. Its true length is obtained in a second auxiliary and its point view in a third.

Method III: The edge view of one of the planes is found in a first auxiliary and its true shape in a second. The projection into a third auxiliary is made parallel to a true length line in the other plane so that both appear as edges in the third auxiliary. Since the first plane coincides with the *ODP* in the first and third auxiliaries, it is not necessary to construct its true shape.

Prove that Methods II and III are actually identical.

Method IV: A modification of Method I, replacing the second auxiliary by a revolution, is convenient when the line of intersection is given. In Figure 37–5, the elevation showing the true length of *BC*, the intersection of planes *ABC* and *BCD* is given. A plane *D*–1–2, perpendicular to the line of intersection, is established in the two views, and then revolved to appear true shape in the top view where the required angle *D*–1′–2′ is measured.

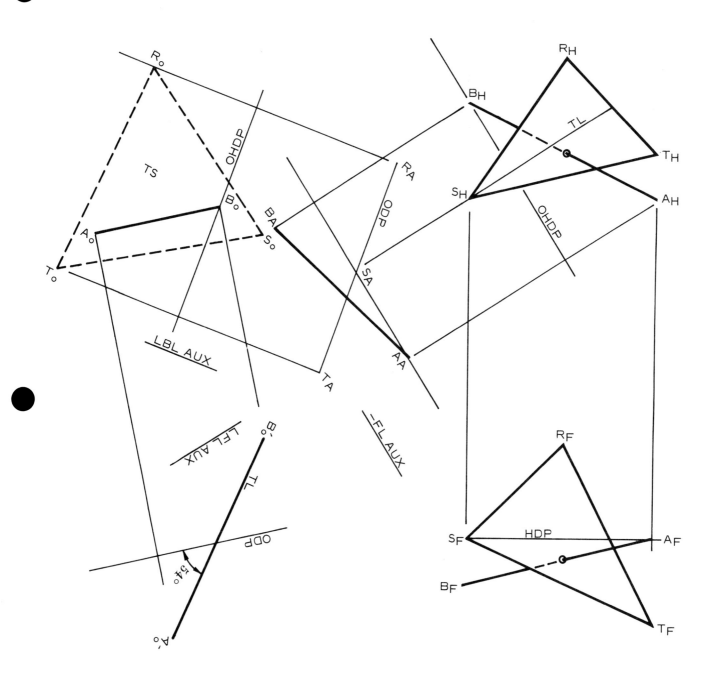

Figure 37–1

[353]

SUPPLEMENTARY NOTES

SUPPLEMENTARY NOTES

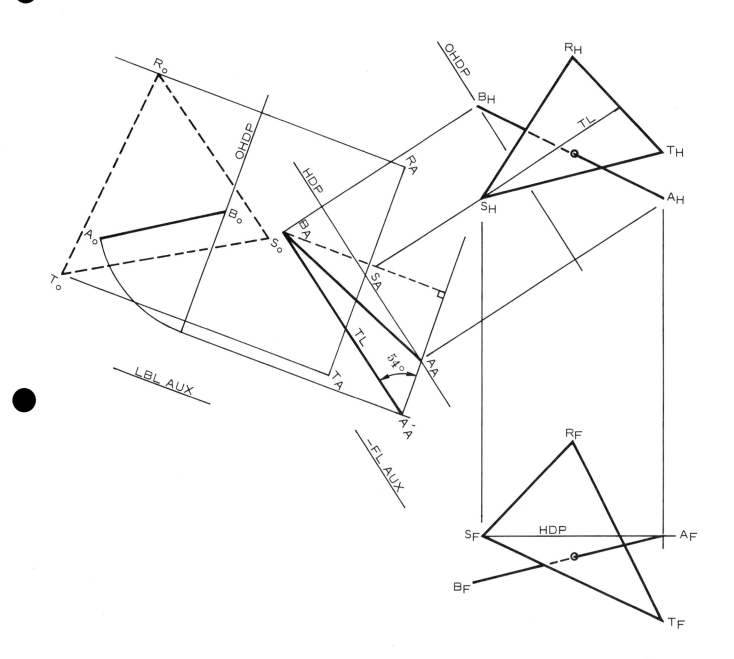

Figure 37–2

SUPPLEMENTARY NOTES

SUPPLEMENTARY NOTES

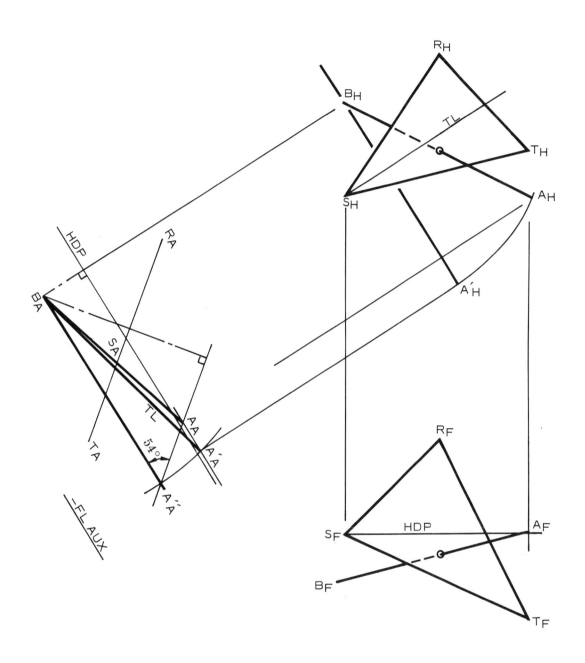

Figure 37–3

FIGURE 37–3

SUPPLEMENTARY NOTES

SUPPLEMENTARY NOTES

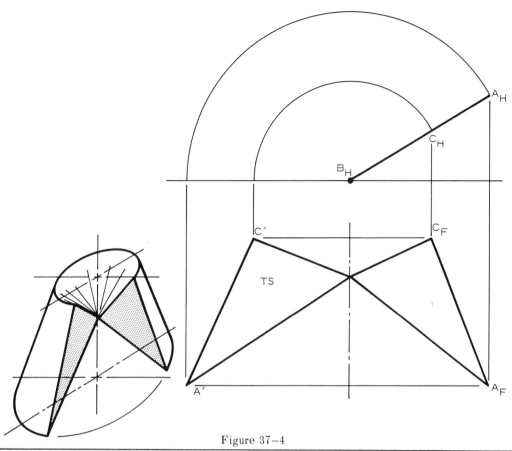

Figure 37–4

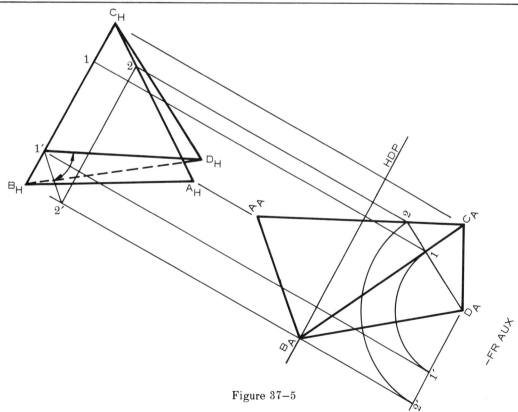

Figure 37–5

SUPPLEMENTARY NOTES

SUPPLEMENTARY NOTES

Exercises

Ex. 37.1 $V(1,2,8\frac{1}{2})$ is the vertex of pyramid $VA(0,1,8)$ $B(1\frac{1}{2},2,6\frac{1}{2})$ $C(2,1,7)$. Find and record where measured the angle which each lateral edge makes with the plane of the base. Solve: (a) by the auxiliary view method; (b) by revolution in the edge and true shape views of the base; (c) by revolution in the top view and auxiliary elevation.

Ex. 37.2 The true size of angle $B(0,1\frac{1}{2},8)$ $A(3,3,7)$ $C(1,2,X)$ is 60°. Line CA is directed UBR. By revolution solve for the bearing and grade of CA, recording where measured.

Ex. 37.3 The triangle $A(0,1,8)$ $B(2,3,9)$ $C(2\frac{1}{2},X,7\frac{1}{2})$ is orthoprofile. Locate in the top and front views the point P which is equidistant from the sides of the triangle. Solve by revolution.

Ex. 37.4 $V(3,3,5\frac{1}{2})$ is the vertex of a pyramid whose base is triangle $A(0,1,7)$ $B(1\frac{1}{2},0,5\frac{1}{2})$ $C(3,3,8)$. Using revolution and one auxiliary, find the angle which each lateral edge makes with the plane of the base.

Ex. 37.5 Triangle $A(2,2\frac{1}{2},7)$ $B(3,2\frac{1}{2},5\frac{1}{2})$ $C(1\frac{1}{2},2\frac{1}{2},5\frac{1}{2})$ is the base of a pyramid with vertex at $V(0,0\frac{1}{2},7)$. Find and record where measured the angle which each lateral face makes with the plane of the base. Solve: (a) by the auxiliary view procedure; (b) by revolution in the given views. Identify the angles clearly.

Ex. 37.6 Line $A(2,X,8)$ $B(2,1,6)$ is directed DF- on a 45° slope. Line $BC(5,X,6)$, directed U-R, is on a 50% grade. Using revolution and a minimum of auxiliary views, measure the size of angle ABC.

Ex. 37.7 Using revolution and only one auxiliary view, measure the angles between a FP, a HF, and a HP line with the plane of the triangle $A(0,2,8)$ $B(2,3,8)$ $C(3,0,5)$.

Ex. 37.8 Measure the angle between the planes of triangle $A(3,5\frac{1}{2},9)$ $B(5,5,9)$ $C(5,6,7\frac{1}{2})$ and triangle $AD(3,3\frac{1}{2},7\frac{1}{2})$ $E(4\frac{1}{2},4,7\frac{1}{2})$ using revolution and a minimum of auxiliary views. Record the size of the angle where measured.

Ex. 37.9 From $A(3,1,6)$ draw all horizontal lines to the plane of triangle $Q(0,2,7)$ $R(1\frac{1}{2},0,8)$ $S(2\frac{1}{2},3,6)$ which form an angle of 50° with QRS. Show the required lines in the given views.

Ex. 37.10 By revolution construct line $A(2,3,7)$ $B(4,1,X)$ 4″ long. Measure the angle between AB and an OH plane containing $AC(1,3,5\frac{1}{2})$.

Ex. 37.11 From point $P(0\frac{1}{2},3,6)$ construct a line PO which makes an angle of 45° with the plane of triangle $A(1,3,8)$ $B(0,2,7)$ $C(2,2,6)$ and is perpendicular to the line AC. O is to lie in the plane of ABC.

[361]

Lesson 38

Development of a Surface

Many objects such as bins, chutes, and pipe sections are formed by bending sheet metal or other flat material. The pattern used to lay out the surface on the flat stock is called the development of the surface. Objects composed of plane faces or singly curved surfaces can be developed exactly. More complex surfaces can be approximated.

A development is visualized as the unfolding or unrolling of the surface into a plane. Each face of the object, every line on the surface, appears in its true size in the development.

Usually developments are drawn showing the inside surfaces so that scribe marks will be concealed inside the final product.

Development of a Prism

The surface of a prism is developed in Figure 38–1. The lateral edges have been given in true length in the front view. These lengths are carried directly into the development by perpendicular projectors. The true lengths intersected by a right section through the prism are seen in the top view. These are laid out sequentially along one of the projectors from the front view. The order is established by visualization. The object is considered to be cut along its shortest lateral edge (in this case the edge at A) to minimize the required length of seam. In the top view the surface is then imagined "opened out" into the frontal plane containing face AB to expose the entire interior surface. This in effect converts the top view into a line $A'D'C'B'A'$. The corresponding front view is the required development.

Verify that each face of the prism is in true shape in the development. Make a freehand tracing of the development and fold it to form a model of the object. Compare the model to the given views.

The method shown in Figure 38–2 for the development of a prism given in an oblique orientation is essentially the same as that described above. The auxiliary elevation is necessary to find the true lengths of the parallel edges. The lengths of the sides of the right section are found in the second auxiliary view. The development is derived from these two views in exactly the same manner as from the given views in the previous illustration.

Satisfy yourself that the development is an inside development.

Development of a Pyramid

The surface of a truncated oblique pyramid is developed in Figure 38–3. The true lengths of the sides of the base are given in the top view. The lengths of the lateral edges, VA, VB, etc., are found by revolution. The intercepts of these edges with the truncating plane are conveyed to the true lengths directly from the front view. All necessary lengths now having been found, the triangles VAB, VBC, and so on, are laid out successively in true size. The intercepts of the edges with the truncating plane are transferred from the revolved lengths and the faces are then completed. The true shape of the cut surface is found in an auxiliary view or by revolution of the cutting plane. This view represents the outer surface. Therefore it is traced, then inverted and transferred to the development, being joined along its longest edge. The true shape of the base is transferred similarly.

Visualize the "opening out" of the surface to verify that this is an inside development.

This problem would have been somewhat simplified had the object been a right or "regular" pyramid. A truncated square based right pyramid is shown in Figure 38–4 with the development partially indicated. Sketch the necessary construction and the inside development.

Development by Triangulation

The surface of any object whose faces are planar can be developed by the triangulation procedure illustrated in Figure 38–5.

The given object is a sheet metal transition piece designed to connect a rectangular duct at *ABCD* to one of triangular cross section at 123. The true lengths of the oblique edges are found by revolution. Because face *23CD* is a quadrilateral, it is necessary to draw a diagonal to break the face into triangular portions. This diagonal is also revolved into true length. Construction of adjacent true shape triangles from the true lengths of the sides produces the required development.

The solution in the illustration is shown lettered as an inside development. Could the same figure be relettered as a legitimate outside development of the same object? Is the same conclusion valid for the developments shown in the other illustrative problems? Make a conclusion as to what conditions must obtain for the inside and outside developments of a surface to be identical.

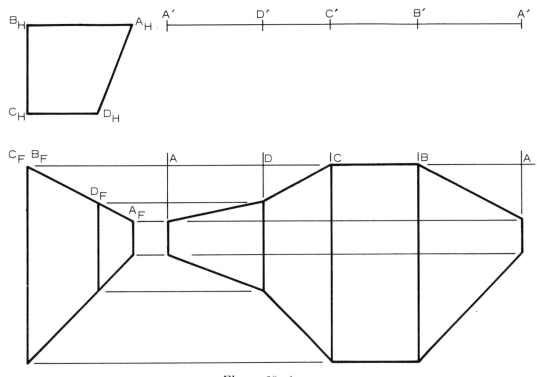

Figure 38—1

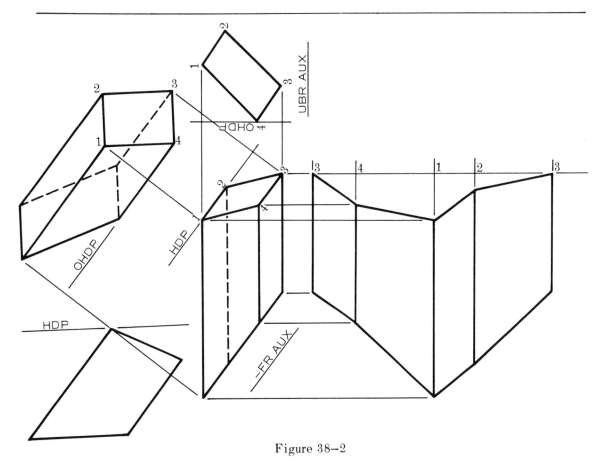

Figure 38—2

SUPPLEMENTARY NOTES

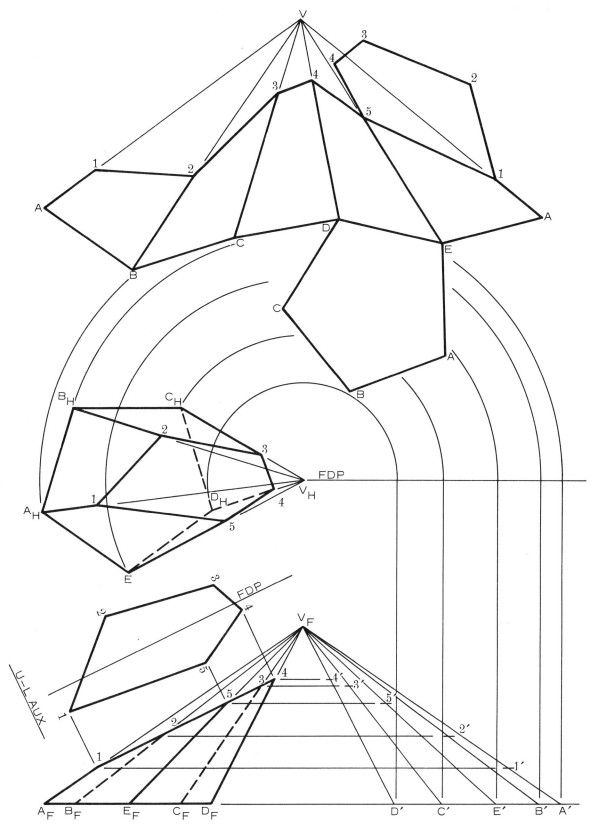

Figure 38—3

SUPPLEMENTARY NOTES

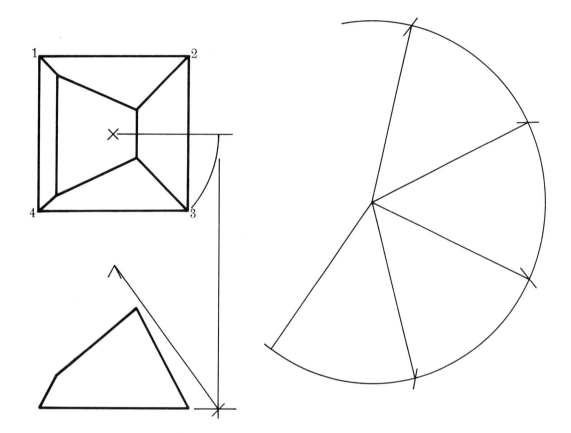

Figure 38–4

SUPPLEMENTARY NOTES

SUPPLEMENTARY NOTES

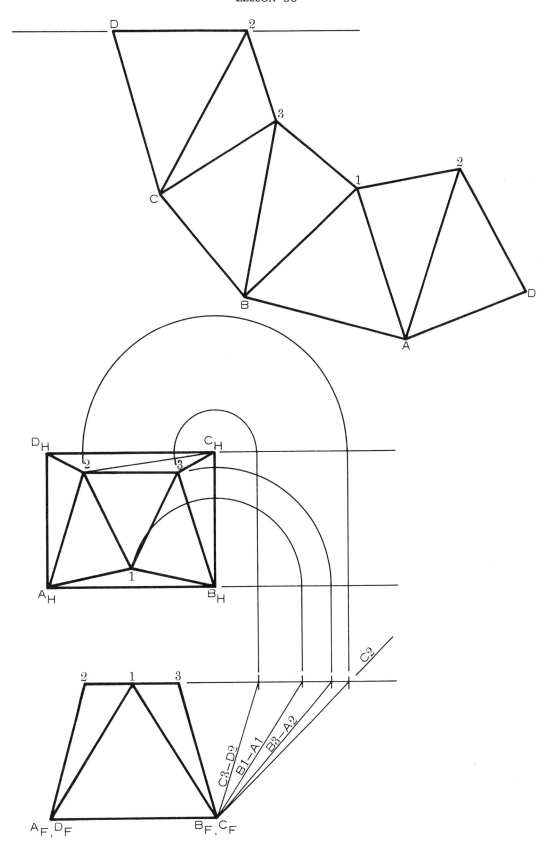

Figure 38–5

SUPPLEMENTARY NOTES

Exercises

Ex. 38.1 Make an inside development of the entire pyramid $V(4,6,9)$ $A(5\frac{1}{2},6,7)$ $B(7,5\frac{1}{2},7)$ $C(5\frac{1}{2},4\frac{1}{2},7)$ $D(4,5,7)$. Open the surface along line VD and begin the development with VD along $(X,4,X)$.

Ex. 38.2 $AA'(1,1,8)$ is one lateral edge of a prism, one of whose bases is $A(0,3,8)$ $B(0,4,9)$ $C(1,5,9)$ $D(1,4,8)$. The two bases are parallel. Make an inside development of the lateral surfaces.

Ex. 38.3 Make inside developments of the objects of Ex. 16.1(b),(c); 17.1(b); 19.1(b),(c),(d),(f); and 20.4(b),(c),(d) as assigned. Cut out the developments and make paper models of the objects.

Ex. 38.4 $V(0,5,9)$ is the vertex and $O(2,5,7\frac{1}{2})$ is the center of the hexagonal base of a right pyramid. Each side of the base is $1\frac{1}{2}''$ long and the lowest side of the base is horizontal. The pyramid is truncated by a profile plane $(1,X,X)$ and the vertex portion is discarded. Make an inside development of the entire frustrum including the base and the cut surface.

Ex. 38.5 The pyramid $V(1,6\frac{1}{2},8)$ $A(2,4\frac{1}{2},7)$ $B(0,4\frac{1}{2},7)$ $C(0,4\frac{1}{2},9)$ $D(2,4\frac{1}{2},9)$ is cut by an oblique plane $L(0,5\frac{1}{2},8)$ $M(2,6,8)$ $N(1,5,7)$ and the upper portion is discarded. Make an inside development of the resulting frustrum. Open along edge VB and begin the development with VB along line $(X,2\frac{1}{2},X)$.

Ex. 38.6 Make inside developments of the objects of Ex. 6.3; 12.1; 12.2; and 17.7(b).

Ex. 38.7 Construct models of the intersecting objects of Ex. 32.1, and 32.4.

Lesson 39

Development of a Right Cylinder

The development of the surface of a normally oriented right cylinder is illustrated in Figure 39–1. The procedure followed is virtually identical to that for a right prism as was shown in Figure 38–1. The right section which appears in the top view is divided into an arbitrary number of equal arcs. The true lengths of the corresponding elements are projected from the front view into the development. Chords of the numbered arcs are laid off in sequence along one of the projectors.

Because the development is symmetrical, only the rear half has been constructed.

Development of a Right Cone

Because all elements of a right circular cone are equal, the development of the surface is a sector of a circle. In Figure 39–2 the basic cone is cut by a horizontal plane which removes a small sector from the development, and by an orthofrontal plane which intersects each numbered element. The true distance from the vertex to each of these intersections is measured along the true length element $V7$ in the front view, and is then transferred to the development.

Development of an Oblique Cylinder

The surface of the oblique cylinder in Figure 39–3 is developed in the same manner as that of the oblique prism in Figure 38–2. An auxiliary elevation is constructed to provide the true lengths of the elements which are then projected directly into the development. The right section, obtained in a second auxiliary, is divided into equal parts which are then laid out in sequence along one of the projectors.

Because this particular object is symmetrical about the $OHDP$, it would have been sufficient to develop either half.

Development of an Oblique Cone

The surface of an oblique cone is developed in Figure 39–4. Each numbered element and its intersection with the given orthofrontal cutting plane is revolved into true length. This provides all information necessary for the construction of the development by triangulation.

In this instance would it be permissible to develop only half of the surface?

Development of a Transition Piece

The transition piece shown in Figure 39–5 contains both planar and conical surfaces. Only one half is developed since the piece is symmetrical about a frontal plane.

The development is constructed by triangulation after the elements of the oblique cones from A and B have been found by revolution.

[374]

Approximate Developments

The surface shown in Figure 39–6, not being singly curved, cannot be exactly developed. However, when broken into a large number of triangles, it can be approximated with reasonable accuracy.

The upper and lower curves are first divided into the same number of equal spaces. Corresponding points are joined by "elements," 1–1′, 2–2′, etc., and "diagonals," 1–2′, 2–3′, etc., are added. From the true lengths of the elements and diagonals, and of the chords of the segments of the bases, the development is constructed by triangulation.

The true lengths of the elements and diagonals have been found by means of *true length diagrams* in the illustration to avoid the confusion of lines which would accompany the use of revolution in this case. The construction of the true length diagram is exactly equivalent to the revolution process. For a given line, say 3–3′ for example, the height y, taken from the front view, is laid out as one leg of a right triangle. Along the other leg is laid out the distance x, the length of the line as measured in the top view. The hypotenuse of the triangle is the required true length.

Note that only one quarter of the development has been constructed in this case. Is this sufficient for a solution?

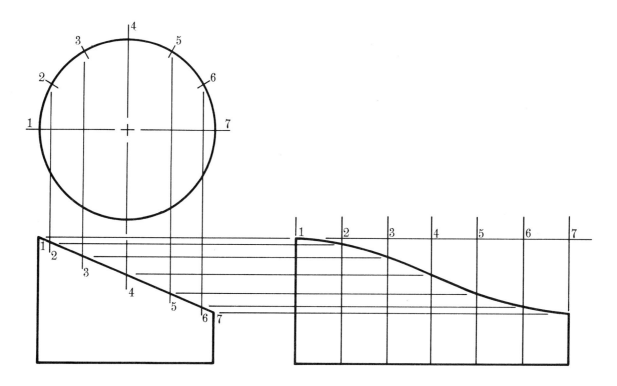

Figure 39—1

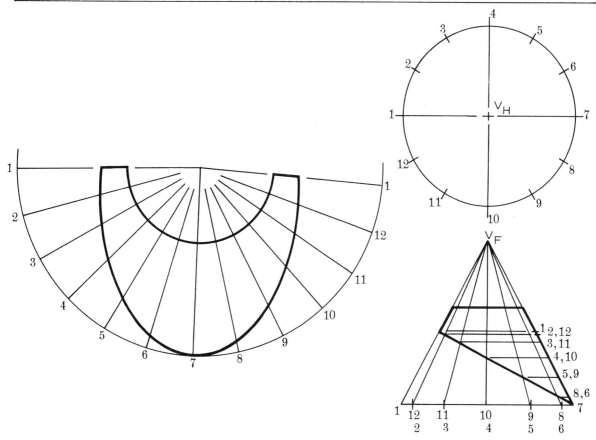

Figure 39—2

SUPPLEMENTARY NOTES

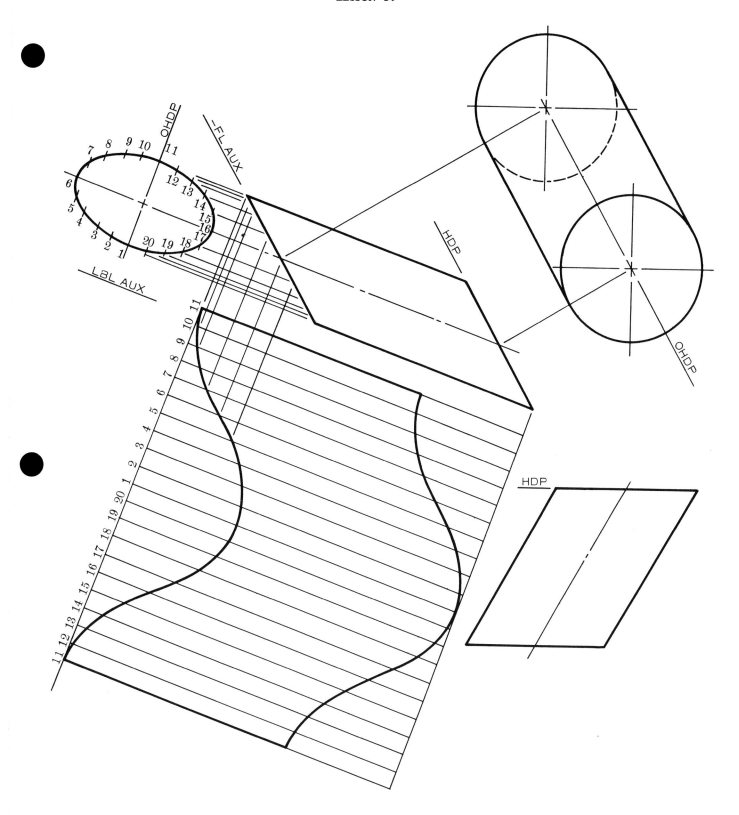

Figure 39–3

SUPPLEMENTARY NOTES

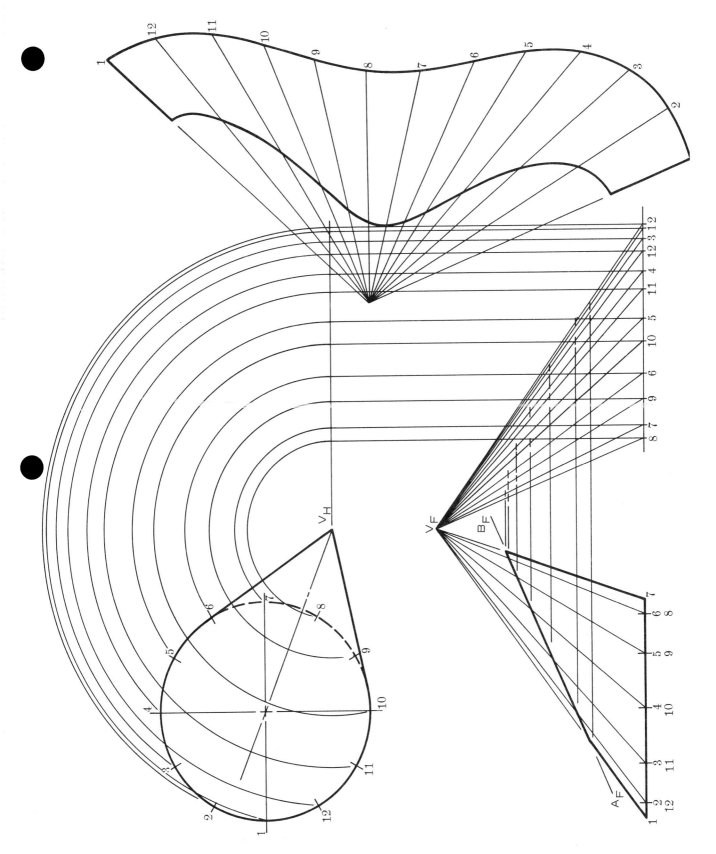

Figure 39–4

SUPPLEMENTARY NOTES

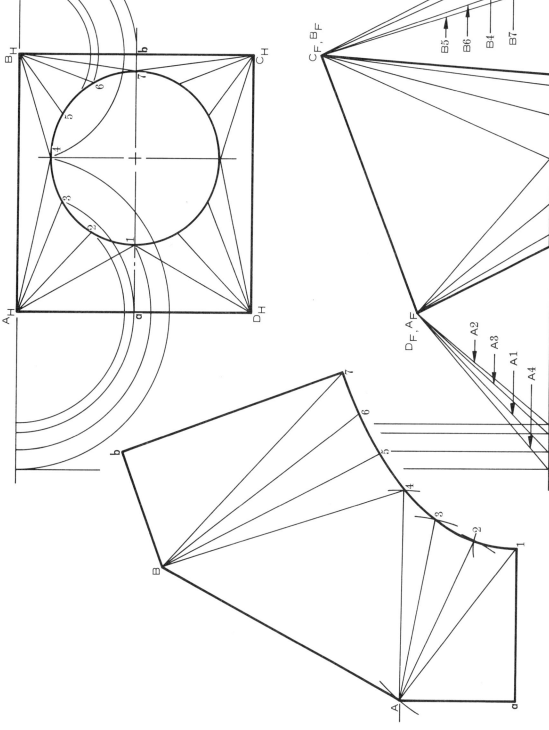

Figure 39—5

SUPPLEMENTARY NOTES

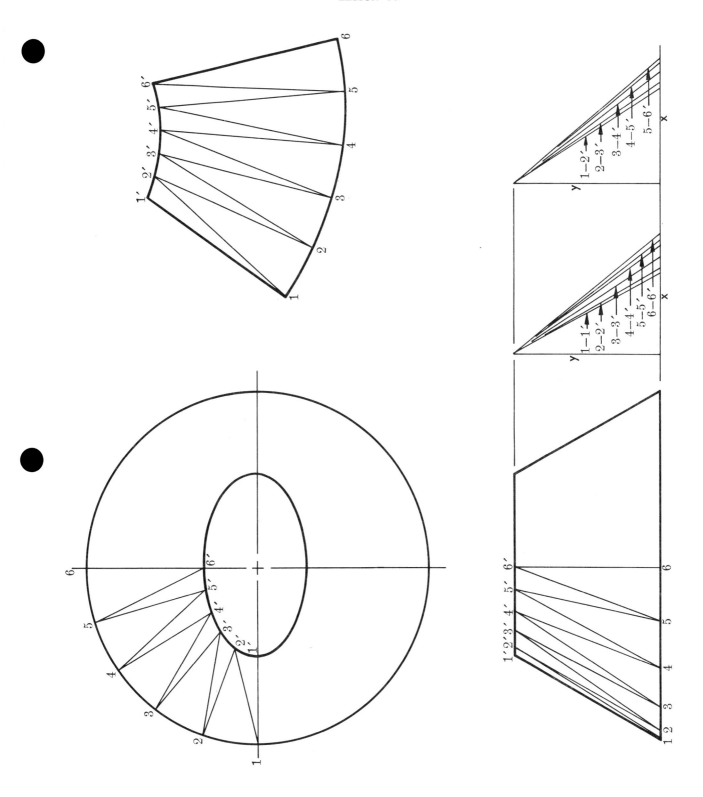

Figure 39–6

SUPPLEMENTARY NOTES

Exercises

Ex. 39.1 $A(0,2,7)$ $B(1\frac{1}{2},0,9)$ is the axis of a right circular cylinder. The end of the cylinder at A is horizontal. That at B is a $1\frac{1}{2}''$ diameter circle cut perpendicular to the axis. Make an inside development of the surface of the cylinder. It is not necessary that the given views be completed.

Ex. 39.2 $A(0,1\frac{1}{2},7)$ $B(0\frac{1}{2},0,9)$ is the axis of a right circular cylinder $1\frac{1}{4}''$ in diameter. Both ends of the cylinder are frontal. Make an inside development of the lateral surface. The given views need not be completed.

Ex. 39.3 Make inside developments double sized of the objects of Ex. 9.1. Develop all surfaces and cut out to form models.

Ex. 39.4 Make inside developments of all surfaces of the objects of Ex. 17.1(e),(f), and 26.1(f).

Ex. 39.5 $V(1\frac{1}{2},3\frac{1}{2},7)$ $O(1\frac{1}{2},0,7)$ is the axis of a cone whose base is a horizontal circle of $3''$ diameter. The cone is cut by an OF plane through points $A(0,4,X)$ $B(3,1,X)$, by a second through $AC(2,0,X)$, and by a third through BO. The central portion of the cone is retained. Make an inside development of the surface of this remaining portion. The cut surfaces need not be included in the development.

Ex. 39.6 $V(1\frac{1}{2},4,7\frac{1}{2})$ is the vertex and $O(1\frac{1}{2},0,7\frac{1}{2})$ is the center of the $3''$ diameter base of a right circular cone. The portion of the cone in front of the OH plane through line $A(0,X,7)$ $B(3,X,7\frac{1}{2})$ is discarded, as is the portion below the OF plane through $C(0,2,X)$ $D(3\frac{1}{2},0,X)$. Make an inside development of the lateral surface of the remaining portion.

Ex. 39.7 $V(0,3\frac{1}{2},9)$ is the vertex and $O(2,1,7\frac{1}{2})$ is the center of the base of an oblique cone. The base is a $2''$ diameter profile circle. Make an inside development of the lateral surface.

Ex. 39.8 A transition piece is to join the triangular opening $A(0,4\frac{1}{2},6)$ $B(2,3,6)$ $C(0,1\frac{1}{2},6)$ to a frontal circular opening of $1\frac{1}{4}''$ diameter having its center at $O(0\frac{5}{8},3,8)$. Make an inside development of the transition piece.

Ex. 39.9 Make an inside development of a sheet metal transition piece joining the square opening $A(0,2,2\frac{1}{2})$ $B(0,2,4\frac{1}{2})$ $C(0,0,4\frac{1}{2})$ $D(0,0,2\frac{1}{2})$ to the end of a $1''$ diameter FP pipe at $O(1\frac{1}{2},2,3\frac{1}{2})$.

Ex. 39.10 Make full sized inside developments of the conical surfaces of the objects of Ex. 31.2 and 31.3.

Lesson 40

Lines through a Point Making Specified Angles with Two Given Planes

The locus of all lines through a given point and making some certain angle with a given plane is a right circular cone having a base angle equal to the specified angle and its base in or parallel to the given plane. Both nappes of a cone may be conveniently drawn within an enclosing sphere. In Sketch 40–1 a cone through P contains all lines 1″ long which make an angle of 45° with plane ABC. Note that all elements of both nappes are equal in length to the radius of the enclosing sphere, and that the bases are circles on the surface of the sphere.

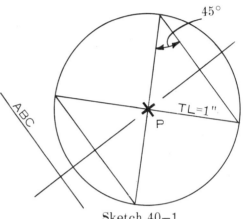

Sketch 40–1

Now suppose that we are to find all lines from point P, $1\frac{1}{2}$″ long, making angles of 45° and 30° with the planes ABC and QRS, respectively, in Figure 40–1. Fortunately, the given planes are vertical so the locus cones are easily drawn in the top view, their bases showing as edges parallel to the planes and their surface elements making the required angles with their bases. The cones are drawn inscribed in a sphere to assure that the necessary condition, all elements in both be the same length, is satisfied. By taking the radius of the sphere to be $1\frac{1}{2}$″, the solution lines will be found in the required length without additional work.

The two nappes of both cones have been shown, although one intersecting pair is actually sufficient to establish the solution lines. These lines must, to satisfy the conditions of the problem, be elements of *both* cones and are drawn through P and the intersection of the bases of the cones at points 1 and 2. To find the height coordinates of 1 and 2, it is necessary only to draw the true shape of the base of one of the cones. The points are known to lie on the circle. Now, having been found in two adjacent views, the solution lines may be projected into others as desired.

Suppose that our problem had not stated a required angle for the solution lines to make with plane ABC. Could you select one which would lead to four solution lines? Three? One? None? If the length of the required lines were not specified, would you still draw an enclosing sphere? Of what radius? Why?

Planes ABC and QRS were given vertical. Suppose they had been oblique. How would the solution need to be modified?

An interesting and important special case of the problem is the one in which the given planes are perpendicular to one another. In this circumstance the view showing the base of one locus cone in true shape shows the base of the other as an edge. The intersection of the base circles is seen and the solution line readily identified in that view. The implications of this are explored in the first problem (40–1) of the lesson in your workbook. When you have completed its solution in class, sketch over in colored pencil the *minimum* of the construction necessary to obtaining a solution without drawing a side view.

[388]

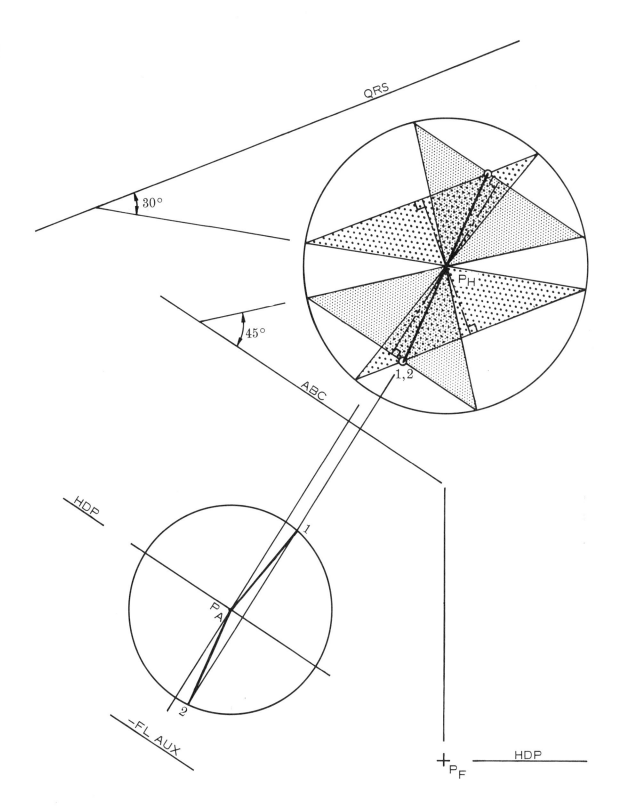

Figure 40–1

SUPPLEMENTARY NOTES

Exercises

Ex. 40.1 Find the bearing of a line $A(2,2,6)B$ which is directed *UBL*, has a slope of 45°, and lies in an *OP* plane which makes an angle of 30° with the frontal plane of projection.

Ex. 40.2 *AD* is a frontal line 2″ long which makes an angle of 30° with the plane of triangle $A(0,5,7)$ $B(2,4\frac{1}{2},8)$ $C(1,3,6)$ and is directed *D–R*. Locate *AD* in the top and front views.

Ex. 40.3 In the top, front, and right side views show each of the following $1\frac{1}{2}$″ line segments drawn from point *A* and lying in the plane of the triangle $A(0,3,7)$ $B(1,2\frac{1}{2},8)$ $C(2,2,6\frac{1}{2})$: (a) in red, a segment making a 15° angle with the *H* plane; (b) in blue, a segment making a 30° angle with the *F* plane; (c) in green, a segment making a 45° angle with the *P* plane.

Ex. 40.4 A line segment *AP* is $1\frac{1}{4}$″ long, lies in an *OF* plane containing line *AC*, and makes a 30° angle with the plane of triangle $A(4\frac{1}{2},1\frac{1}{2},7)$ $B(5,2\frac{1}{2},5)$ $C(7,2,5)$. Establish *AP* in the top and front views. Show all possible solutions.

Ex. 40.5 $X(2,3,5)$ is a point on the ceiling of a room. The floor is at $(X,0,X)$ and the *OH* rear wall contains points $L(0,X,6)$ and $M(5,X,7)$. From *X* establish the centerlines of two chutes, each making angles of 50° with the floor and 30° with the rear wall. Chute *XA* is directed *DBL*, and *XB* is *DBR*. Find the true lengths of the chutes and the angles they form with the profile plane of projection.

Ex. 40.6 $V(6\frac{1}{2},2\frac{1}{2},7)$ is the vertex and $O(5,0,5\frac{1}{2})$ is the center of the 2″ square base of a right pyramid. The diagonal of the base drawn to the lowest corner of the base is inclined to the frontal plane of projection at a 30° angle. The lowest corner is behind *O*. Complete the top, front, and necessary additional views.

Ex. 40.7 Through the point $L(2,3,6)$ construct a plane *LMN* perpendicular to the family of parallel lines in plane $A(2,1,7\frac{1}{2})$ $B(0,1,6\frac{1}{2})$ $C(0\frac{3}{4},3\frac{1}{2},5)$ which make an angle of 30° with the frontal plane of projection. Show only the most convenient solution.

Ex. 40.8 Show in the top and front views all possible lines downward from *A* which make an angle of 30° with the plane of triangle $A(0,0\frac{1}{2},7)$ $B(1\frac{1}{2},0\frac{1}{2},9)$ $C(0,2\frac{1}{2},7)$ and 45° with the plane of $Q(1\frac{1}{2},3,6)$ $R(0,0,6)$ $S(1\frac{1}{2},1\frac{1}{2},8)$.

Ex. 40.9 Construct one line $P(0\frac{1}{2},0,6\frac{3}{4})X$ (there are 4 possible lines) which makes an angle of 25° with the plane of triangle $A(0,0\frac{3}{4},7\frac{1}{2})$ $B(1\frac{1}{2},0\frac{3}{4},6\frac{3}{4})$ $C(0\frac{1}{4},1\frac{3}{4},6\frac{1}{2})$ and an angle of 50° with plane $BCD(1,0,5\frac{3}{4})$. Show *PX* in the top and front views.

Lesson 41

Through a Given Line Construct a Plane
Making a Specified Angle with a Given Plane

Because the strike and dip nomenclature is convenient for the explanation, we will restate the problem: "Through a given oblique line construct all planes having a specified angle of dip," but the student should bear in mind that the method is general and in no way restricted to this special case.

In Figure 41–1 line *AB* is given. Planes through *AB* having a dip of 45° are required.

1. A cone containing all possible dip lines is established at *B*. Its base is made to lie in a horizontal plane through *A*.
2. The tangents *AC* and *AC'* drawn in the top view are the strike lines of the required planes. *CB* and *C'B* are their respective dip lines.

The proof of the construction will be evident at once when you sketch the elevation views showing the planes as edges. Why is it absolutely essential that the base of the cone be taken in the horizontal plane through *A*? Can you discover any alternate procedures which would lead to solutions for problems of this type?

What would have been the significance of the situation had *A* fallen within the circular base of the locus cone in the top view? If it had fallen on the circle?

Suppose that you were asked to find the planes through *AB* making a stated angle with some given oblique plane. How would you proceed?

Planes through a Point Making Specified Angles with Two Given Planes

There is no direct procedure by which the required plane can be found, but by the method discussed in the preceding lesson a line perpendicular to the required plane may be obtained, and the required plane then constructed at right angles to that line.

Sketch 41–1 shows a given plane *ABC* as an edge. The required plane through *P* is to make an angle of 30° with *ABC*. A line perpendicular to the required plane is seen to make the complement of this angle with the given plane.

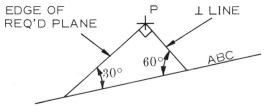

Sketch 41–1

There will, of course, be as many planes satisfying the conditions of a problem as there are solutions to the problem of the perpendicular line. If the slope of the required plane is stated (the typical direction of the dip line), the relation between it and the direction of the necessary perpendicular line must be determined. In Sketch 41–2, the plane *QRS* slopes *DBR* while the perpendicular line *ab* slopes *DFL*. It is always prudent to rough out a sketch similar to this to avoid confusion.

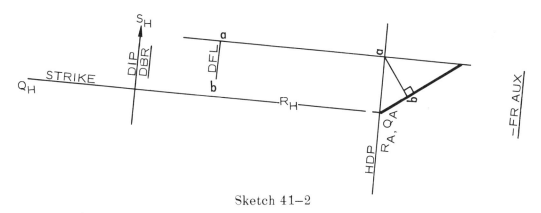

Sketch 41–2

The steps in the construction (no figure) are summarized below.

1. Determine the angles which the line perpendicular to the required plane must make with the given planes (complements of the angles specified for the required plane).

2. Determine the direction of the necessary perpendicular line from the desired properties of the required plane.

3. Draw locus cones and solve for the perpendicular line described by steps 1 and 2 above.

4. Construct the required plane perpendicular to the line found from the cones by the method given in Lesson 34.

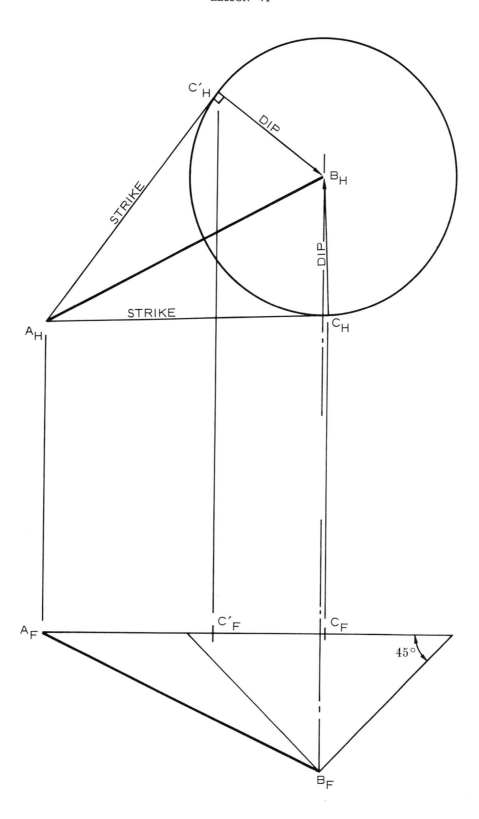

Figure 41–1

SUPPLEMENTARY NOTES

Exercises

Ex. 41.1   Establish planes $A(0,2,6)$ $B(1\frac{1}{2},0,8)C$ and ABD. Each makes an angle of $60°$ with the profile plane of projection. Measure the angle between planes ABC and ABD using revolution.

Ex. 41.2   Find the strike of plane $A(2,2,7)BC$ which dips $60°$NE and makes an angle of $40°$ with all profile planes.

Ex. 41.3   Through line $Q(0,0,4)$ $R(1\frac{1}{2},1,3)$ construct plane QRS making an angle of $45°$ with the OH plane $A(0,X,4\frac{1}{2})$ $B(3,X,4)$ $C(3,X,4)$. Show all possible solutions.

Ex. 41.4   Construct plane ABC making an angle of $75°$ with the frontal plane of projection and $60°$ with an OF plane through line $A(5,3,8)$ $D(7,1\frac{1}{2},X)$. Of the several possible solutions, show that plane which has the least dip angle and dips SW. Record the strike and dip of this plane.

Ex. 41.5   Line $A(0,3,X)$ $B(2\frac{1}{2},1,8)$ is directed DBR and makes a $45°$ angle with the profile plane of projection. Plane ABC dips $60°$SE. Find the strike and dip of plane ABC, and by revolution find the angle plane ABC makes with the frontal and profile planes.

Ex. 41.6   Angle $B(2,1,7\frac{1}{2})$ $A(0,2\frac{1}{2},6)$ $C(1\frac{1}{2},X,6\frac{1}{2})$ is $20°$. Locate the two possible positions of point C. Solve first by projection from the top view, then analyze the procedure for solution by projection from the front view.

Ex. 41.7   A plane $A(0\frac{1}{2},1\frac{1}{2},6\frac{1}{2})$ $B(1\frac{1}{2},1,8)E$ forms a $60°$ dihedral angle with the plane of points $X(0\frac{1}{2},2\frac{1}{2},6)$ $Y(1\frac{1}{2},1\frac{1}{2},7)$ and $Z(2\frac{1}{2},3,5\frac{1}{2})$. E is a point on line segment $C(0,0,6\frac{1}{2})$ $D(2\frac{1}{2},2,7)$. Locate point E in the top and front views.

Ex. 41.8   A plane through point $A(3\frac{1}{2},4,6\frac{1}{2})$ makes an angle of $60°$ with a frontal plane and is perpendicular to a plane striking N45°W and dipping 30°NE. Find the strike and dip of the required plane through A.

Ex. 41.9   Establish a plane $B(5,1,7)$ $C(4,3\frac{1}{2},6)D$ such that it makes an angle of $45°$ with line $A(6\frac{1}{2},3,8)B$. Record the strike and dip of BCD. Show all possible solutions.

Ex. 41.10   Establish an OH plane $C(1\frac{1}{2},2,6)DE$ which makes an angle of $30°$ with the given line $A(1\frac{1}{2},3,7)$ $B(0,1,5\frac{1}{2})$. Show the required plane in the top view.

Lesson 42

Lines through a Point on a Given Line Making Specified Angles with that Line and a Given Plane

The vertex of the locus cones must be placed at the given point on the line. In a view showing the true length of the given line and the edge view of the given plane, the bases will appear as edges, and the required lines can be identified as in the previous locus cone exercises. The cone whose surface contains the lines making the required angle with the given line will have the line itself as its axis and its *vertex* angle equal to twice the angle specified. The cone formed by the lines making the required angle with the given plane has its axis perpendicular to the plane, its base parallel to it, and its base angles equal to the specified angle.

Any adjacent view showing the base of one of the locus cones as a circle is used to obtain the missing coordinate of the ends of the solution lines so that they can then be projected into any desired views. Remember that you are looking for elements common to both of the locus cones so these elements must initially be the same length. Hence, it is always advisable to draw the sphere enclosing the cones.

Surely you have made several rough sketches to help you understand this explanation . . . better go back and do it right now, then.

Lines Making Specified Angles with Two Non-Intersecting Lines

The procedure is best explained with reference to Figure 42–1.

1. The true lengths of the given lines AB and CD are obtained in a view (front), adjacent to a point view of one of them (top).
2. CD is imagined translated (moved parallel to itself) to $C'D'$, intersecting AB. The locus cones are constructed with vertices at this intersection, giving the solution lines xy and $x'y'$. The top view of the cone having axis AB is used to locate the solution lines in that view.
3. In the top view xy and $x'y'$ are extended to locate points 1 and 2 on CD, and these are carried back into the front view.
4. Lines 13 and 24 are drawn parallel to xy in the front view. These are the required lines.

The construction is readily proven if line $C'D'$ is carried into an auxiliary showing plane $31CD$ or plane $42CD$ in true shape. In such a view it is seen that the solution line makes the same angle with both $C'D'$ and CD.

[398]

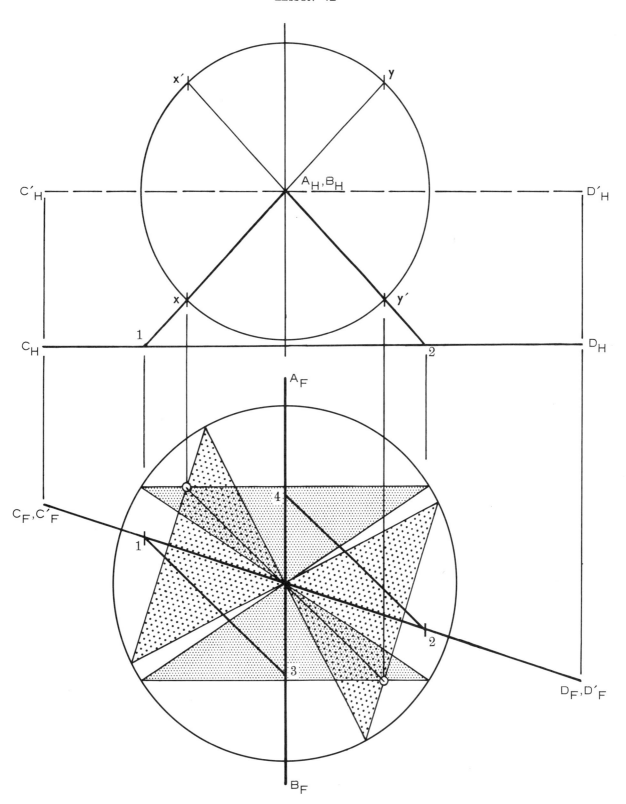

Figure 42–1

SUPPLEMENTARY NOTES

Exercises

Ex. 42.1   In the top and front views show all lines through point L which make an angle of 60° with the line $L(2,4,7\frac{1}{2})$ $M(2,2,6)$ and a 30° angle with the plane of triangle $A(0,2,8)$ $B(3,2,8)$ $C(1,4,6)$. Measure the distance from L to the plane of ABC along each of these lines.

Ex. 42.2   Connect line segments $A(4,2,5)$ $B(4,2,8)$ and $C(1,0\frac{1}{2},7\frac{1}{2})$ $D(5,0\frac{1}{2},6\frac{1}{2})$ with a line LM which makes an angle of 45° with CD and one of 60° with AB.

Ex. 42.3   Find the line or lines which make an angle of 45° with the line $E(0,3,6)$ $D(2,1,6)$ and an angle of 60° with the plane of triangle $A(0,2\frac{1}{2},5)$ $B(0\frac{1}{2},1,5\frac{1}{2})$ $C(2,2,7)$ and which originate at the point where ED pierces the plane of ABC.

Ex. 42.4   Show in the top and front views all lines which can be drawn to connect line segments $A(6,0,6)$ $B(6,2,7\frac{1}{2})$ and $C(7,0,8\frac{1}{2})$ $D(7,2\frac{1}{2},6\frac{1}{2})$, making an angle of 45° with AB and 60° with CD.

Ex. 42.5   Show in the top and front views all lines through point R which make an angle of 70° with line $R(0,2,3\frac{1}{2})$ $S(1\frac{1}{2},1\frac{1}{4},2\frac{1}{2})$, and 30° with the plane of the triangle $A(1,0,3\frac{1}{2})$ $B(0,0\frac{1}{2},2\frac{1}{2})$ $C(1\frac{1}{2},1\frac{1}{2},2)$.

Ex. 42.6   Plane $J(1,3,6)KL$ dips SE and makes angles of 30° with both line $A(0,0,8)$ $B(1\frac{1}{2},2,8)$ and line $C(0,1\frac{1}{2},6\frac{1}{2})$ $D(1\frac{1}{2},1,7\frac{1}{2})$. Find the strike and dip of JKL and the angle it makes with the frontal plane of projection.

Ex. 42.7   Find and record the strike and dip of a plane through point $P(0,0,6)$ which makes an angle of 60° with plane $C(0\frac{1}{2},X,5\frac{1}{2})$ $D(3\frac{1}{2},X,3\frac{1}{2})$ $E(3\frac{1}{2},X,3\frac{1}{2})$ and 30° with line $A(0,2,3\frac{1}{2})$ $B(3\frac{1}{2},2,5\frac{1}{2})$. The required plane dips SW.

Ex. 42.8   Find the angle which line $A(1,1\frac{1}{2},4\frac{1}{2})$ $B(2,1,4)$ makes with the plane of a triangle LMN. LMN is perpendicular to the given plane $L(0\frac{1}{2},0,6\frac{1}{2})$ $M(2,0\frac{1}{2},5)$ $P(0,1,5)$.

Ex. 42.9   The given view is the true shape view of an oblique triangle $A(1\frac{1}{2},X,6\frac{1}{2})$ $B(0,X,7)$ $C(1,X,8)$. Line AB is frontal and BC is a line making an angle of 30° with the frontal plane of projection. Obtain possible front and side views of the triangle.

Appendix

*Review Exercises**

Indicate the *best* answer to each of the following questions. Mark *only one* answer for each question.

1. Two skew lines must appear parallel in a view which shows
   - (a) both in true length.
   - (b) either one in true length.
   - (c) the shortest connecting line in true length.
   - (d) any connecting line true length.
   - (e) the true slope of both.
2. Two lines are perpendicular if, in a particular view
   - (a) both appear in true length.
   - (b) one shows as a point and the other in true length.
   - (c) the angle appears as a right angle.
   - (d) they make complementary angles with the datum plane.
   - (e) none of the above.
3. A line directed $D-R$ must appear true length in which of these views:
   - (a) *UBL Aux.*
   - (b) *U–R Aux.*
   - (c) *–BL Aux.*
   - (d) top view.
   - (e) front view.
4. Which of the following auxiliary views might give an isometric view of a normally oriented object:
   - (a) *UFL Aux.*
   - (b) *U–L Aux.*
   - (c) *–FL Aux.*
   - (d) *UF– Aux.*
   - (e) None of these.
5. A right circular cone is intersected by a sphere. The vertex of the cone is inside the sphere. The center of the sphere is on the axis of the cone. The intersection of the surfaces is
   - (a) a parabola.
   - (b) an inclined plane.
   - (c) a single-sheet hyperbola.
   - (d) an irregular space curve.
   - (e) none of these.
6. Given two planes and a point. A plane can be established through the point perpendicular to one of the given planes and parallel to the other only if
   - (a) the given planes have the same dip.
   - (b) the given planes are mutually perpendicular.

* Answers are given on page 407.

(c) the required plane is a normal plane.
(d) the given planes are parallel.
(e) no solution is possible under any circumstance.

7. An oblique plane may intersect another oblique plane in
   (a) a horizontal line.
   (b) a frontal line.
   (c) a profile line.
   (d) any of the above.
   (e) none of the above.

8. A given line is perpendicular to a given plane. Which one of the following observations is false?
   (a) In every view the line appears perpendicular to all true length lines in the plane.
   (b) The slope of the line is the complement of the dip of the plane.
   (c) The bearing of the perpendicular is the same as the bearing of the dip line.
   (d) All planes perpendicular to the given plane contain the given line.
   (e) The given line appears as a point in a view which shows the true angle between two intersecting lines lying in the given plane.

9. If the 4th and 5th auxiliary views of a triangle are given, the minimum number of additional views required to establish a true length line in the plane of the triangle in the 5th auxiliary is
   (a) 0; (b) 1; (c) 2; (d) 3.

10. The *apparent* angle between a line and a plane, in a view showing the plane as an edge, has a minimum value of
    (a) the true angle between the line and the plane.
    (b) the vertex angle of the locus cone.
    (c) 90°.
    (d) none of the above.
    (e) any of the above.

11. The angle between an oblique plane and a profile plane can be measured in a particular first auxiliary view projected from the
    (a) front view.
    (b) side view.
    (c) top view.
    (d) none of the above.
    (e) any of the above.

12. Given the principal views of a point, an inclined plane, and an oblique plane. A solution for all lines through the point to make specified angles with each of the given planes requires a minimum of how many auxiliary views if the plotting of an ellipse is to be avoided?
    (a) 0; (b) 1; (c) 2; (d) 3; (e) 4.

13. In the first auxiliary which is the true shape view of an orthofrontal plane, which of the following lines in the plane appear parallel to the projectors drawn from the front view?
    (a) all frontal lines.
    (b) all frontal and profile lines.
    (c) all profile and horizontal lines.
    (d) all normal lines.
    (e) all inclined lines.

14. The shortest line which can be drawn connecting two given lines may be measured in a view showing
    (a) one of the given lines in true length.
    (b) both given lines true length.
    (c) one of the given lines as a point.
    (d) the connecting line as a point.
    (e) none of the above.

15. If a line is perpendicular to a plane it is perpendicular to
    (a) all inclined lines in the plane.
    (b) all true length lines in the plane.
    (c) all normal lines in the plane.
    (d) all of the above.
    (e) none of the above.

16. A line is perpendicular to a plane which dips NW. The line is directed
    (a) *UBL* or *DFR*.
    (b) *UBR* or *DFL*.
    (c) *UFR* or *DBL*.
    (d) *UFL* or *DBR*.
    (e) *UBR* or *DFR*.

17. The plane of projection for a first auxiliary projected from the side view is a
    (a) *P* plane.
    (b) *OP* plane.
    (c) *O* plane.
    (d) *OF* plane.
    (e) Normal plane.

18. The datum plane for a second auxiliary whose related view is frontal is
    (a) normal.
    (b) inclined.
    (c) oblique.
    (d) any of these.
    (e) none of these.

19. The direction-of-sight arrow for a *LBL* auxiliary is
    (a) an inclined line sloping *UFR*.
    (b) an inclined line sloping *DBL*.
    (c) an oblique line sloping *UBR*.
    (d) an oblique line sloping *UFR*.
    (e) an oblique line sloping *DFR*.

20. If a pair of line segments appear separate and parallel in the top and front views,
    (a) the lines are parallel in all views.
    (b) the true distance between the lines appears in the given views.
    (c) the lines do not intersect.
    (d) the lines do not define a plane.

21. A series of profile planes intersect a given oblique plane in a family of lines. Indicate the answer which *is not* necessarily true.
    (a) The lines appear *TL* in the side view.
    (b) The lines appear parallel in an isometric drawing.
    (c) In a view showing one of the lines as a point, all of the lines appear as points.
    (d) A view showing the lines *TL* is a *TS* view of the oblique plane.

22. A rectangular block measures $2'' \times 3'' \times 4''$. Given an isometric projection of the block, which one of the following observations is false?
    (a) The faces of the block make equal angles with the plane of projection.
    (b) The edges of the block appear in true length.
    (c) The interior diagonals appear unequal in length, but intersect at their respective midpoints.
    (d) The view is orthographic.
    (e) Three edges of the block are hidden.

23. The angle between a line and a horizontal plane is termed
    (a) strike.
    (b) dip.
    (c) grade.
    (d) bearing.
    (e) slope.

24. Given an oblique line and an oblique plane in the front and side views; to find the angle between them by the auxiliary view method, the minimum number of additional views required is
    (a) 1; (b) 2; (c) 3; (d) 4; (e) 0.

25. The line of sight arrow for a fourth auxiliary appears in the third auxiliary as
    (a) a point.
    (b) a TL line perpendicular to the projectors joining the views.
    (c) a TL line parallel to the projectors joining the views.
    (d) a foreshortened line parallel to the projectors joining the views.
    (e) parallel to the plumb line.

26. The problem "Through a given point on a given line find all possible lines making specified angles with the given line and a given plane," may lead to how many solutions?
    (a) one, two, three, or four.
    (b) one.
    (c) one, two, or three.
    (d) two or four.
    (e) less than five.

27. The intersection of two inclined planes is
    (a) an oblique line or an inclined line.
    (b) a normal line or an inclined line.
    (c) an oblique line or a normal line.
    (d) an inclined line.
    (e) an oblique line.

28. A plane parallel to two given skew lines appears as an edge in an auxiliary view showing
    (a) one of the lines as a point.
    (b) the point view of the line of intersection.
    (c) both lines in TL.
    (d) the lines appearing perpendicular to each other.
    (e) none of these.

29. An OP plane strikes
    (a) due North.
    (b) due East.
    (c) N$X°$W.

(d) SX°W.

(e) any direction.

30. In a second auxiliary obtained by projection from the front view, the plumb line always appears

    (a) *TL*.

    (b) foreshortened.

    (c) perpendicular to the *OFDP*.

    (d) parallel to the *OFDP*.

Answers to Review Exercises

1. (c)
2. (b)
3. (e)
4. (a)
5. (e)
6. (b)
7. (d)
8. (d)
9. (a)
10. (a)
11. (b)
12. (c)
13. (c)
14. (c)
15. (d)
16. (a)
17. (b)
18. (b)
19. (d)
20. (c)
21. (d)
22. (b)
23. (e)
24. (c)
25. (c)
26. (e)
27. (c)
28. (a)
29. (b)
30. (b)

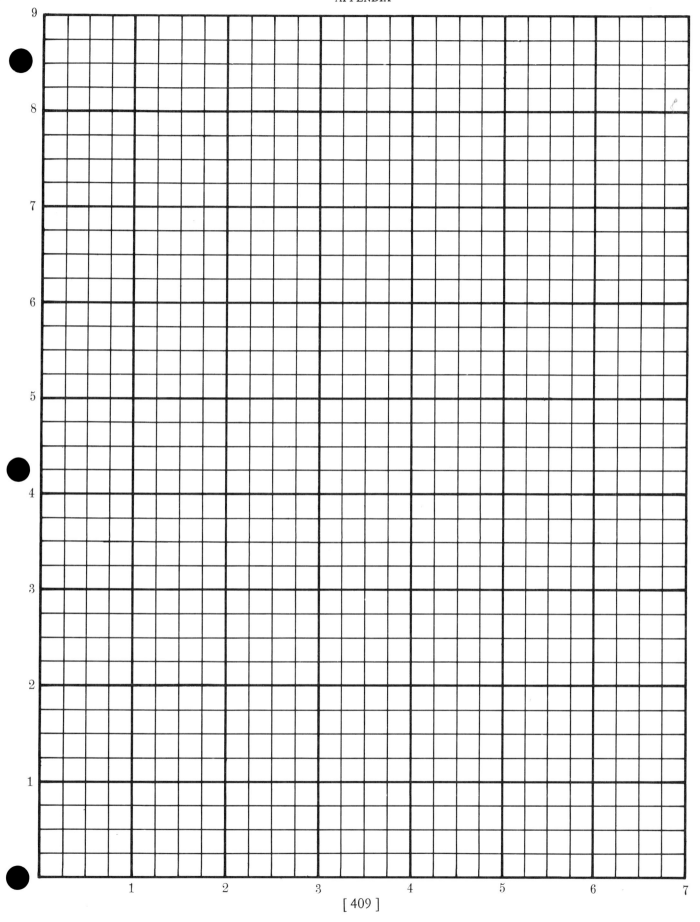

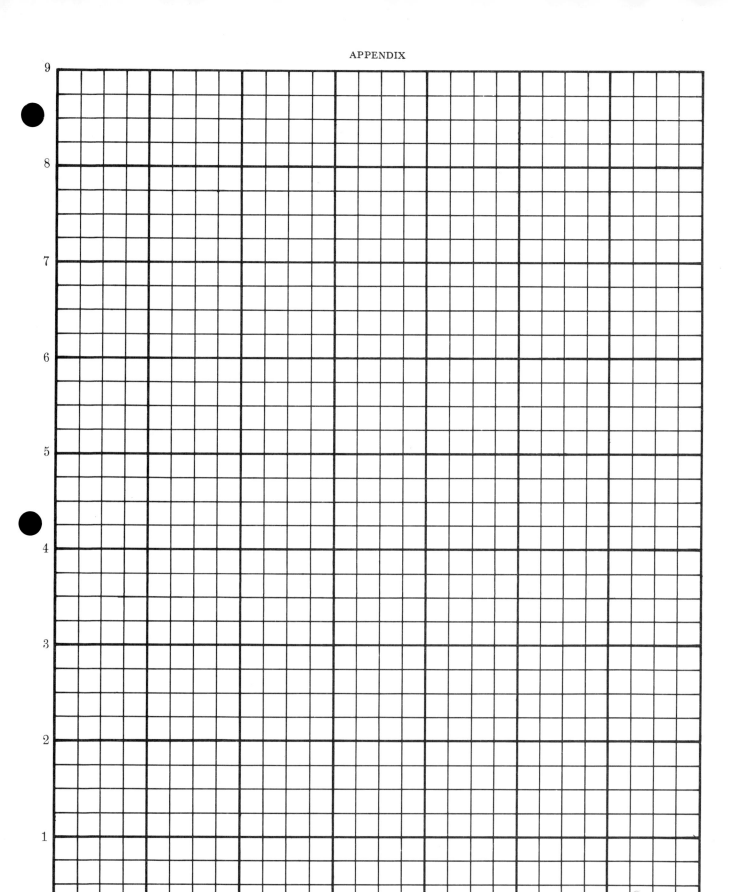